ODHAMS
Motor Manual

FINDING THE TROUBLE. *A quick glance under the bonnet will often enable the experienced motorist to diagnose the cause of engine failure without delay. Even the novice should be able to tackle fault-tracing and maintenance confidently, however, after studying this book. The emphasis throughout is on a systematic and logical approach to such problems, coupled with the avoidance of expensive repair bills by ensuring that routine maintenance and adjustments are regularly carried out. The operation of the major components of a modern car is described in simple terms, avoiding unnecessary reference to theoretical and technical detail.*

ODHAMS
Motor Manual

HOW YOUR CAR WORKS

AND HOW

TO SERVICE IT

Fourth Edition revised by
STATON ABBEY, A.J.Inst.E.

ODHAMS PRESS LIMITED · LONG ACRE · LONDON

First Published, 1949
Second Edition, 1951
Third Edition, 1952
Reprinted, 1953
Reprinted, 1954
Reprinted, 1955
Fourth Edition, 1956

Made and Printed in Great Britain by C. Tinling & Co. Ltd.,
Liverpool, London and Prescot.
S.1056.SB.

FOREWORD

THE LIFE of a motor car is not indefinite, but with proper and systematic service and maintenance it can be prolonged considerably. Also, the risks and delays on the road due to breakdown are minimized.

It is the aim of this manual, therefore, to give in non-technical language, together with specially prepared illustrations, such detailed information as will enable the owner to carry out his own servicing and maintenance, that is, without the use of special tools and equipment. Also, the principles and functions of the main components, such as engine, gearbox, differential, etc., are described so that the reader will first understand "how it works" and then "how to put it right."

Should the maintenance or repair of a part require special tools and equipment, it is advisable to place the car in the hands of a skilled motor mechanic. Another and very important point to be borne in mind is that, when it is recommended by the manufacturer to return certain parts for replacement or repair to their Works or Service Stations, it is by far the best policy to follow the recommendation and not undertake the job yourself.

The more general aspects of the motor car have not been overlooked. The beginner, in particular, will find much to interest him in the chapters given to helpful advice on matters which will confront him both before and after buying a car. By far the most important of these is the chapter on learning to drive, and every care has been taken to ensure that the reader will be familiar with those vital points which distinguish a good driver. It is appreciated, however, that no amount of reading can replace practical experience at the wheel, but it is essential that the learner understands the controls, and when and in what order they should be operated. Again, no one, experienced or otherwise, can read too much about how to drive in accordance with the Highway Code.

This is a comprehensive manual and it will be useful not only to the owner-driver, but to the prospective purchaser and persons interested in the mechanics and development of the modern motor car.

CONTENTS

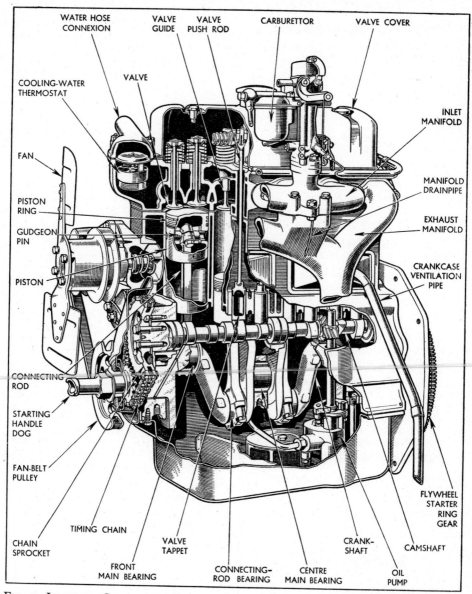

WATER HOSE CONNEXION   VALVE GUIDE   VALVE PUSH ROD   CARBURETTOR   VALVE COVER

COOLING-WATER THERMOSTAT

VALVE

INLET MANIFOLD

FAN

MANIFOLD DRAINPIPE

PISTON RING

EXHAUST MANIFOLD

GUDGEON PIN

PISTON

CRANKCASE VENTILATION PIPE

CONNECTING ROD

STARTING HANDLE DOG

FAN-BELT PULLEY

FLYWHEEL STARTER RING GEAR

TIMING CHAIN

CHAIN SPROCKET

VALVE TAPPET

CRANK-SHAFT

CAMSHAFT

FRONT MAIN BEARING

CONNECTING-ROD BEARING

CENTRE MAIN BEARING

OIL PUMP

FIG. 1. INTERNAL COMBUSTION ENGINE. *This partly cut-away view of a modern four-cylinder power unit illustrates most of the components that are referred to in the various chapters in this book. The main features can be quickly identified; the crankshaft which drives the camshaft through a double-roller chain, the pistons, valves and valve-gear, the inlet and exhaust systems, and the oil pump which forces oil under pressure through an intricate system of oil-ways in the engine. The only items not shown are the coil-ignition distributor and the sparking plugs. These are dealt with in Chapter 7.*

CHAPTER 1

THE MOTOR CAR SIMPLY EXPLAINED

THE modern car may appear at first sight to be a complicated piece of mechanism, made up of a large number of different components of intricate design. In this chapter, however, it is proposed to describe the function and principle of each part as simply as possible. More detailed information will be found in the succeeding chapters in which the maintenance and overhaul of individual assemblies is described.

Before considering the various parts, however, let us summarize briefly the general lay-out of the car. There are four essentials: an engine to provide the motive power, a transmission system to drive the wheels, a chassis or framework to carry the engine, body, transmission, steering-gear, road wheels, and the hundred-and-one other components which make up the car, and finally a body to accommodate the driver and passengers. A modern lay-out is illustrated in Fig. 2.

Until fairly recently the conventional car consisted of a separate chassis frame made from steel channel-section or box-section girders. To this were attached, by means of leaf springs, a front axle, on which the wheels could be steered, and a rear axle which incorporated a mechanism for driving the rear wheels. The engine, mounted at the front of the chassis, drove the rear wheels by means of a long, universally-jointed propeller shaft. The body, made from steel, aluminium, or fabric panels attached to a steel or hardwood framework, was bolted to the chassis side and also the cross members.

Modern Developments. Nowadays, however, this traditional construction is rapidly being replaced by more efficient designs. The body and chassis, for instance, are merging their identities, and becoming one rigid, pressed steel structure, with welded joints. Even when the body shell itself is separate from the chassis, the latter is often strengthened by incorporating a pressed steel floor with the chassis frame.

Some designers have branched out in a different direction, and have developed the so-called "backbone" chassis, in which the front and rear sections are connected by a stiff, rectangular or tubular member resembling a backbone. The integral, body-chassis design, however, is the most likely to be widely adopted in future.

Body design is already being influenced by research and experiments carried out in wind tunnels, and aerodynamic principles are likely to be applied to an increasing extent. These will result in lower wind resistance and improved fuel economy. Some designers are studying the possibility of adapting a gyro-stabilizing device to passenger cars, thus preventing the body of the car from swaying or bouncing however bad the road surface may be.

From the earliest days cars fitted with rear engines have been manufactured. These, however, have been in the minority, although they are now increasing in number. The use of a forward-mounted engine, driving the front wheels

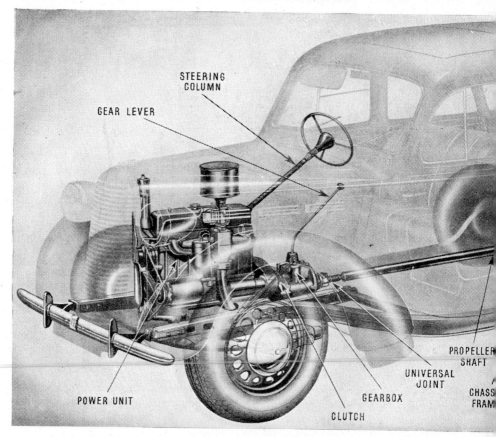

STEERING
COLUMN

GEAR LEVER

POWER UNIT

CLUTCH

GEARBOX

UNIVERSAL
JOINT

PROPELLER
SHAFT

CHASSIS
FRAME

instead of the rear, is also becoming increasingly popular with a small number of manufacturers, particularly in Europe. As forecast when dealing with the transmission system, the most likely development in the future is the four-wheel drive.

Looking well ahead, it is possible to forecast that the car as we know it today will probably undergo radical changes. The conventional piston engine will, in many cases, be replaced by the gas turbine, although it should be mentioned that the pure jet propulsion unit has no place on road vehicles.

The turbine engine, however, eliminates many sources of trouble inherent in the power unit as we know it at present, such as pistons, piston rings, cylinder bores, valves, and so on. It is true that the gas turbine lacks the most valuable property of the piston engine, flexibility, or the ability to develop a reasonable power over a wide range of speeds. Fully automatic transmission systems, however, will overcome this difficulty.

The purpose of this chapter, however, is to discuss the car of today rather than the problematical vehicle of the future. In examining the individual assemblies, therefore, it is logical to begin with the source of power, the engine.

THE POWER UNIT

The power unit of the car is a heat engine; in other words it converts the heat energy which is latent in petrol into

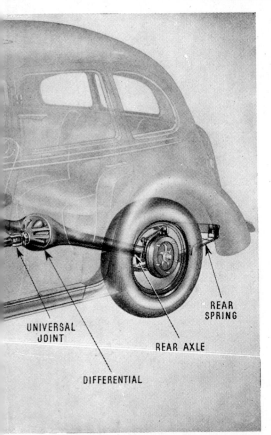

UNIVERSAL
JOINT

REAR AXLE

DIFFERENTIAL

REAR
SPRING

parts of air, although this ratio must be varied under different running conditions, as will be explained in greater detail later when describing the carburettor.

The principle of the petrol engine can best be explained by a simple experiment. Suppose we mix a few drops of petrol with the air in a tube, closed at one end. In the open end we insert a cork, through which two wires are passed. The inner ends of the wires are bared, and bent so that there is a small gap between them, as shown in Fig. 3. A mild explosion can be caused by connecting the wires to an electric battery. A spark occurs inside the tube, igniting the mixture of petrol and air, and the sudden expansion of the heated gases is sufficient to drive the cork out with considerable force. This simple experiment shows that the heat energy liberated by the burning petrol is converted into mechanical energy which forces out the tightly-fitting cork.

Single-cylinder Engine. Now, suppose the tube to be inverted and made of steel, and the cork to be replaced by a metal piston provided with sealing rings so that it forms a gas-tight, but sliding, fit in the tube. At the top of the tube two holes are cut and fitted with metal valves to allow fresh mixture to enter and the burnt gases to escape. The bent wires are replaced by a sparking plug which is screwed into the top of the tube. In its simplest form we now have the combustion chamber, cylinder and piston of an engine, as shown in Fig. 4. The burning gas above the piston will force it downwards with considerable power.

To convert the downward thrust into rotary motion, a short connecting rod is

mechanical energy which is used to drive the road wheels. It is not always realized that petrol is one of the most powerful substances known, apart from the sources of atomic power. Weight for weight, for instance, petrol contains three times the energy available in an explosive such as T.N.T., and ten times the energy which is stored up in a similar quantity of dynamite. The difference lies in the fact that this energy can be liberated progressively from petrol, providing a continuous source of power.

Only a comparatively small proportion of petrol is burnt in a car engine, compared with the amount of air which is heated by the burning fuel. An average proportion is one part of petrol to fifteen

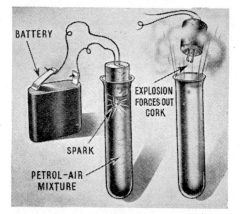

FIG. 3. *This simple experiment illustrates the heat energy or power obtained from the combustion of a mixture of air and petrol.*

fitted between the piston and crank. The downward thrust, therefore, tends to rotate the crankshaft in the same way that the pressure of a rider's foot on a bicycle pedal rotates the sprocket carrying the chain, which, in turn, rotates the rear wheel.

Four-stroke Cycle. With this basic arrangement, a succession of power impulses can be obtained. Most car engines work on the four-stroke, or Otto cycle, which is named after the German engineer who applied this system to a gas engine during the nineteenth century. Fig. 5 shows the engine with the piston descending in the cylinder, during the first half-revolution of the crankshaft. This is termed the induction stroke, since the inlet valve is open to admit the petrol-air mixture to the cylinder. Notice, incidentally, that in this case the valves are arranged in a pair, alongside the cylinder, instead of above it, as in Fig. 4.

When the piston reaches the bottom of its travel and starts to move upwards in the cylinder, the inlet valve is closed, as shown in Fig. 5. As a result, the mixture is compressed to between one-fifth and one-seventh of its original volume. This is the compression stroke, and Fig. 5 shows the piston at the beginning of this stroke. As the piston nears the top of the cylinder, an electric current passes between the points of the sparking plug and ignites the compressed gas, thus beginning the expansion or power stroke, which continues as the piston moves downwards again in the cylinder. By the time the piston has reached the bottom of its travel, the useful work of the expanding gas is expended, and the exhaust valve is opened to allow the burnt gas to be driven out by the piston as it rises once more.

This completes the four strokes of the cycle. It will be seen that only one power stroke occurs during two revolutions of the crankshaft, and that this lasts for only half a revolution. To enable the engine to keep running during the remainder of the cycle, and to compress the gas during the compression stroke, a relatively heavy flywheel is fitted to the crankshaft. This stores up part of the energy received during the power stroke, and gives it up

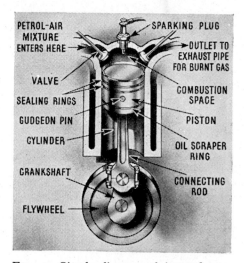

FIG. 4. *Simple diagram of internal combustion engine. Compare this with the modern design of car engine illustrated in* FIG. 1.

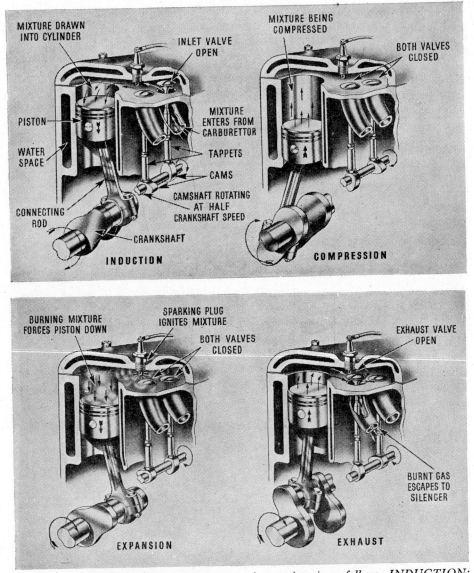

FIG. 5. FOUR-STROKE CYCLE. *The sequence of operations is as follows.* INDUCTION: *the piston descends during the first half revolution of the crankshaft and, since the inlet valve is open, sucks the petrol-air mixture into the cylinder.* COMPRESSION: *as the piston ascends during the second half revolution, the mixture is compressed; inlet and outlet valves are closed.* EXPANSION: *as the piston nears the top of its stroke, an electric current passes across the points of the sparking plug and ignites the compressed mixture, thus begins the expansion or power stroke. This is expended by the time the piston has reached the bottom of its stroke.* EXHAUST: *as the piston ascends the exhaust valve opens and the burnt gases are expelled to the silencer. This completes the four strokes of the cycle.*

during the next three strokes, i.e., exhaust, induction and compression.

Multi-cylinder Engines. A single-cylinder engine cannot produce a smooth flow of power, but by increasing the number of cylinders to two, four, six, eight or more, and coupling their pistons to a common crankshaft, the power strokes can be arranged to follow one another, or to overlap, so that smoother output is obtained. Fig. 7 illustrates some of the piston-crankshaft arrangements in general use. On a four-cylinder engine, for instance, two power strokes are obtained for one revolution; when the car is moving at between forty and forty-five miles an hour in top gear, six thousand power impulses per minute, or one hundred per second, are being transmitted to the crankshaft.

When two cylinders are used, they are generally arranged opposite one another, either horizontally or at an angle, forming a "V". The V-shaped arrangement is also adopted when more than six cylinders are used, to economize in space, although the straight-eight engine is still fairly common. V-8, V-12, and even V-16 arrangements are used when an engine of very large capacity is required; a cut-away view of a V-8 engine is shown in Fig. 6.

Future Design. Because car engines usually have even numbers of cylinders, it must not be assumed that engines with,

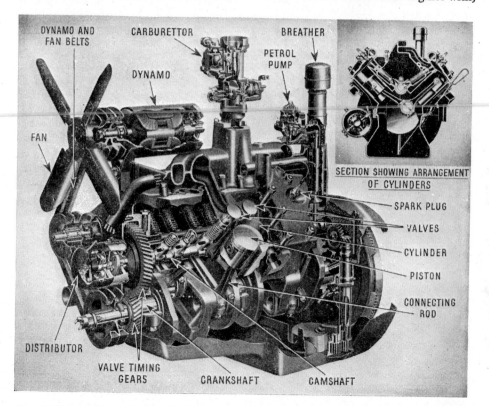

FIG. 6. V-TYPE ENGINE. *Cut-away view showing construction and disposition of the crankshaft, pistons, connecting rods and valve gear, also the layout of auxiliaries, in a modern V-type engine. The inset shows the arrangement of cylinders and valve mechanism.*

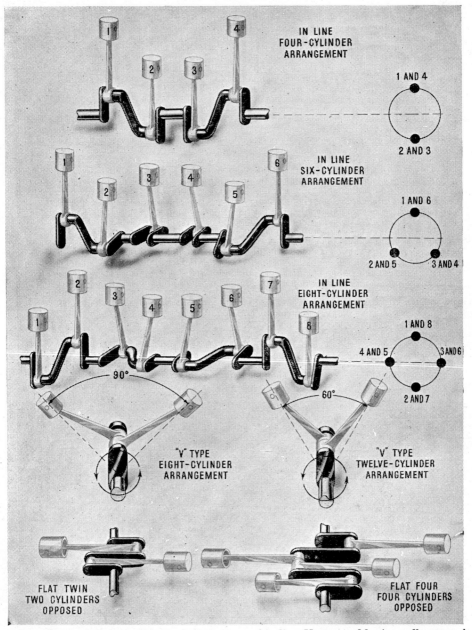

FIG. 7. CRANKSHAFT AND PISTON *arrangements of in-line, V-type and horizontally opposed designs of four-stroke cycle engine. These are designed to give a smooth transmission of power impulses to the flywheel. The greater the number of cylinders the smoother the power output, but in addition, however, the crankshaft must be perfectly balanced to prevent crankshaft vibration and its consequent damaging effect on the engine.*

say, 3, or 5 cylinders are not practicable. Three-cylinder radial or horizontally opposed engines are now being made in one or two instances, and may become popular for the economy type of car in the future. Many designers believe that the five cylinder engine provides the best balance of any in-line type, and this design is widely used in commercial and industrial diesel engines.

Two-stroke Engines. So much for the basic principles of the four-stroke engine. The method of ensuring that the valves open and close at the right moment and that the spark occurs at the beginning of the power stroke will be described later. Meanwhile, it would not be out of place to describe the two-stroke or "valveless" type of engine which is used on motor cycles, and being installed in an increasing number of light and sports cars.

As will be seen from Fig. 8, the cylinder of a two-stroke engine is provided with three openings, or ports, in its wall, and is fitted to a gas-tight crankcase. In the first illustration, the piston is rising and drawing gas into the crankcase through the inlet port. As the piston moves downwards it first closes the inlet port, so that the gas in the crankcase is compressed and forced through a passage to the transfer port. This port is in turn uncovered as the piston reaches the bottom of its stroke, so that the gas enters the cylinder and is compressed as the piston rises again.

The sparking plug ignites the charge as the piston reaches the top of its stroke, and the piston moves down until the exhaust port is uncovered, allowing the exhaust gases to escape. Simultaneously a fresh charge is entering through the

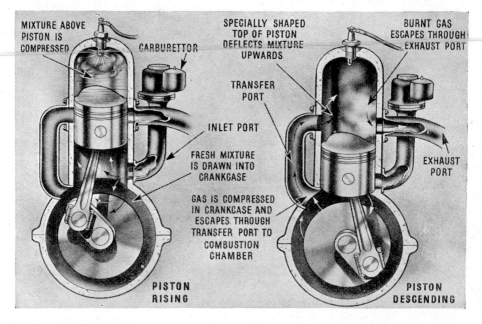

FIG. 8. TWO-STROKE ENGINE. *On the left is shown the piston rising and drawing the mixture into the crankcase through the inlet port. The plug ignites the charge at the top of its stroke and, as pictured on the right, the piston descends, opening the exhaust port. Also, the transfer port is opened and the mixture is delivered from the crankcase to the cylinder.*

16

inlet port, being deflected up into the cylinder by the specially shaped piston top and assisting in driving out the exhaust gases. It will thus be seen that a power stroke takes place during every revolution.

This is the simplest form of two-stroke engine. In order to improve efficiency, more elaborate designs have a separate cylinder and piston to force gas into the working cylinder. Some are equipped with a supercharger with the similar object of introducing a greater quantity of mixture into the working cylinder.

Compression Ratio. The fact that the gas is compressed before it is ignited in either of the two types of engine described calls for further explanation. Compression of the mixture improves the power output of the engine, since a higher compression pressure produces a higher expansion pressure. The compression ratio of an engine is simply the ratio between the volume of the charge when the piston is at the bottom of its stroke, and its reduced volume when the piston is at the top of the cylinder, with the charge confined inside the cylinder head. Fig. 9 will make this clear.

On most modern cars the charge is compressed to about one-fifth of its original volume; the compression ratio is then said to be 5 : 1. Even on family cars higher ratios are now common, ranging from 5½ : 1 to 6½ : 1. Sports cars use ratios as high as 7 : 1 or 8 : 1.

Horse-power. The term "horse-power" is used to define the rate at which work is done. It was originated by James Watt who wished to compare the performance of his steam pumping engines with that of the horses which they were intended to replace. A strong cart-horse can do work at the rate of about 22,000 foot-pounds per minute. This is equivalent to lifting a 22,000 lb. weight through a height of one foot in one minute, or, expressed differently, approximately one

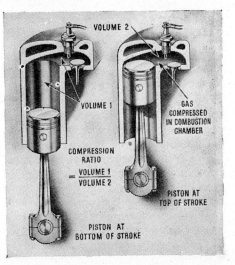

FIG. 9. *Compression ratio shown pictorially.*

ton through ten feet in one minute. In order to offer good value, Watt increased this figure by 50 per cent, and called one horse-power 33,000 foot-pounds per minute. A strong man, by comparison, can do work at the rate of 4,000 foot-pounds per minute for a short period.

The rated horse-power of an engine for taxation purposes was arrived at, until recently, by using an R.A.C. formula, in which the diameter of the cylinder in millimetres is squared, multiplied by the number of cylinders, and divided by 1,613. On early engines this gave a fairly accurate indication of the horse-power developed. Modern car engines, however, produce three or four times their rated horse-power, and with the introduction of a flat-rate system of taxation this method of assessing power becomes less common.

Brake Horse-power. A true value of the horse-power is obtained by measuring the actual power available at the flywheel by means of a mechanical brake. An engine of approximately 1,100 c.c. rated at 10 h.p., will produce about 30 to 35 brake horse-power, while a Twelve of

1,500 c.c. capacity should produce from 40 to 50 brake horse-power. Brake horse-power increases with engine speed until a critical speed is reached, when it falls off sharply. The peak power of an engine in a modern family car is reached at 3,000–4,000 revolutions per minute, while sports car engines reach their maximum power at higher speeds.

Efficiency of the Engine. Although the modern petrol engine is an efficient power unit by comparison with other types of engine, its efficiency is only about 25 per cent. In other words, for every 100 gallons of petrol supplied to the engine, only 25 gallons are used to drive the car. Put in another way, if energy amounting to one hundred horse-power is supplied to the engine by the fuel, 40 horse-power is lost in the exhaust gases, 30 horse-power is dissipated into the cooling water and by general radiation, and 5 horse-power is absorbed in overcoming internal friction in the engine. These figures are, of course, only approximate, and vary with the speed of the engine and the amount of throttle opening.

Power and Detonation. When a mixture of petrol and air is burnt in the cylinder, the expansion of the heated gases exerts a pressure on the top of the piston which can be likened to the pressure of a giant hand pressing it downwards. There is no explosion in the normal sense of the word; the mixture commences to burn in the vicinity of the sparking plug, and the flame spreads outwards through the mixture progressively, that is, provided that detonation or pinking does not take place.

Detonation, or spontaneous ignition of the mixture, occurs when the charge becomes overheated, due to the interior walls of the cylinder head retaining surplus heat which should have been dissipated by air or liquid cooling. Pinking, or knocking, as it is termed, is the audible result of this detonation, which can be compared with the effect of a hammer-blow on the piston crown, instead of a smoothly applied pressure. The higher the compression ratio of the engine, the greater the power that can be extracted from the fuel, but the greater, too, the tendency to pinking if the engine is overloaded and the temperature in the combustion chamber raised above the safety limit. Higher grades of petrol can minimize the trouble, having constituents which reduce the tendency of the fuel to detonate in high-compression engines.

The Cylinder Head. Designers have, however, substantially reduced detonation by careful attention to the shape of the combustion chamber, thus promoting a progressive flame travel, and by making sure that the local hot-spots, such as the exhaust valve and seating, are adequately cooled. In this the cylinder head plays a major part. Until recently this took the form of an iron casting, in which the water passages were formed by suitably shaped cores; on side-valve engines the head simply forms a cover which encloses the top of the cylinders, but on overhead-valve engines the head is a more elaborate casting, as it carries the valves and valve gear, and has the inlet and exhaust passages cast into it, see Fig. 13.

An increasing number of manufacturers nowadays are fitting cylinder heads made of aluminium instead of cast iron. Owing to the better thermal conductivity of aluminium, the heat of the explosion is quickly transferred to the cooling water, so that local hot-spots are less likely to occur. Highly tuned sports and racing engines are often fitted with bronze cylinder heads to ensure even better thermal conductivity. An interesting and more recent development is the cylinder head which is built up from thin sheet-metal sections, welded or brazed together; this has excellent cooling properties and may be widely used on family cars in the future as it is claimed to be cheaper to produce than a cast head.

Cylinder and Crankcase. As has already been mentioned, the cylinder head is normally bolted to a cast-iron block in which the cylinders are bored. In the early days it was not unusual for the cylinder head and block to be cast in one unit, but this form of construction is now confined to some motor cycle engines, as it increases the difficulty of maintenance. The cylinder block itself is usually integral with the crankcase below it. This houses the bearings for the crankshaft, although a separate cylinder block, bolted to an aluminium crankcase, was, at one time, a common arrangement. What the integral construction loses on the score of increased weight, it gains in increased rigidity and lower manufacturing costs.

Where weight is an important factor, the block and crankcase may be cast in aluminium; it is then necessary to fit hardened steel liners to form long-wearing cylinder bores. Even on cast-iron cylinder blocks hardened steel liners are sometimes used to reduce wear of the cylinder bores. These may be "dry" liners and a tight press fit in the block, or "wet" liners and a light push fit, rubber seals being used to ensure water-tight joints at the top and bottom of the liners.

The base of the crankcase is enclosed by a pressed steel or cast aluminium cover, termed the sump, which acts as a reservoir for the lubricating oil; this is described later.

Piston. From the point of view of minimum wear, cast-iron pistons give best results, but except in one or two instances these are no longer used on private cars, since at high engine speeds the weight of the piston is a critical factor. Aluminium alloy is, therefore, used. Besides being light, it also ensures better heat conduction.

On the average 10 h.p. engine the weight of a piston seldom exceeds one pound. At an engine speed of 4,000 revolutions per minute, which represents a road speed of about 40–45 m.p.h. in top gear, the inertia of the piston calls for a force of no less than half a ton to accelerate it at the beginning of its downward stroke, while only a slightly smaller force is required to bring it to rest in preparation for the upward stroke. Lightness is obviously of paramount importance.

Since aluminium has a high coefficient of expansion, the piston requires a fairly large clearance in the cylinder when cold to prevent it binding or seizing in the bore when hot. To allow a smaller clearance to be used, and so minimize mechanical noise, various composite designs of piston have been developed, using inserts or struts of a metal having a low coefficient of expansion to control the expansion of the piston skirt. Alternative schemes are to use slotted skirts, which are flexible enough to be compressed as the piston becomes hot, or pistons ground to a slightly oval shape when cold, becoming truly circular when hot.

Piston Rings. To maintain a gas-tight seal between the piston and the cylinder wall without generating excessive friction is not an easy task. The function is undertaken by the piston rings, which are narrow cast-iron rings fitting in grooves in the piston. At the upper end of the piston one or more compression rings, square or wedge-shaped in section, are used: these provide the gas-tight seal. Below these are the oil-seal rings. These prevent too great a quantity of lubricant from reaching the combustion chamber, where it would cause heavy carbon deposits and probably short-circuit the sparking plug electrodes. The oil control, or scraper rings, as they are often termed, may have stepped, slotted or bevelled faces to improve their scraping action.

Connecting Rods and Bearings.
The connecting rod which couples the piston to the crankshaft also represents an admirable compromise between strength and lightness. On sports and racing cars a high-strength light alloy, Duralumin, is often used, but for family cars steel connecting rods are sufficiently light and rigid.

The design of the bearing at the end

then the bearing on the crankshaft may be wider, but must carry a double load.

These difficulties have led to the production of improved bearing metal alloys, in place of the relatively soft white metal which has served for so many years. The alloys may be cast on to the bearing surfaces of the connecting rod, or may be cast on to thin shells which are placed inside the split bearing housing on the rod; in either case the removable cap is securely bolted to the rod with high-tensile steel bolts. The use of a special bearing metal is essential to ensure that the surface of the metal can be moulded or worked or rubbed down in use to form a perfect bearing surface. Should the lubrication system fail and the bearing become overheated, the bearing metal will melt instead of seizing on the crankpin, thus preventing damage to the crankshaft. Good results have, however, been obtained by using unlined duralumin connecting rods running on hardened steel crankpins. This arrangement, which has the merit of simplicity and light weight, may eventually displace the conventional lined bearing on some cars.

FIG. 10. *View of a four-cylinder engine with the oil sump removed showing location of the crankshaft and its bearings, and the connecting rod big-end bearings.*

of the connecting rod which is attached to the crankshaft, usually known as the big-end bearing, is also important, since adequate bearing area must be combined with minimum weight. On V-type engines this is something of a problem, since two connecting rod bearings must be arranged on one crankpin. If the bearings are side by side, they must necessarily be narrow. If one connecting rod is attached to the other, which in turn is connected to the crankshaft, as in articulated or forked connecting rods,

Crankshaft. Although the firing order of the cylinders is carefully arranged to reduce the stresses in the crankshaft to the minimum, this component is still one of the most highly stressed in the engine. Modern crankshafts, as will be seen from Fig. 10, are very robust steel forgings or castings; yet, when subject to the pressure exerted by the pistons on the power stroke, and the inertia of the piston and connecting rod on the exhaust and compression strokes, they twist to a certain extent.

The pistons, connecting rods, and crankshaft, considered as a whole, present a very complicated balancing problem which cannot be altogether solved in orthodox designs. Consider, for instance, a piston in a normal 10 h.p. engine when the car is cruising at 40–45 m.p.h. Starting at the top of the cylinder, the piston must be accelerated to about 50 m.p.h. in roughly $3\frac{1}{2}$ thousandths of a second, and must be brought to rest at the bottom of the cylinder in 4 thousandths of a second. As we have seen, this calls for a force of about half a ton at each end of the stroke. The inertia loads increase, moreover, as the square of the speed, being sixteen times greater at 4,000 revolutions per minute than at 1,000 revolutions per minute.

These stresses, and those caused by the power impulses, are transmitted to the crankshaft by the connecting rods. The normal springiness of the crankshaft causes it to twist slightly, and then to "unwind" when the stress is removed. Under critical combinations of engine speed and load, the vibrations could build up to such an extent that the crankshaft would be fractured, although this is a very unlikely occurrence on a modern car.

Crankshaft Vibration Dampers. To smooth out vibrations in the crankshaft, a torsional vibration damper is fitted to many engines. This consists of a small flywheel that rotates continuously with the crankshaft to which it is coupled by means of a spring-loaded friction clutch, or by an elastic bonded rubber ring. When the crankshaft twists, the small damper flywheel lags behind, and, as the two are out of step, the twisting vibration

cannot build up. Even on light car engines which are not fitted with crankshaft vibration dampers, such components as the fan, dynamo and water pump, if driven by rubber belts, have an appreciable damping effect.

Lubrication System. From the descriptions of the various parts of an engine it will be evident that a large number of metallic surfaces are either rubbing or rotating together, often under extremes of pressure and temperature. All that prevents actual metal-to-metal contact is a film of oil, seldom more than one thousandth part of an inch in thickness, and sometimes only one molecule thick.

The lubrication diagram in Fig. 11, shows how oil is carried under pressure to every vital part. The oil pump is generally of the gear-type shown in Fig. 12, the oil being carried around in the spaces between the gear teeth and the casing. Plunger-type pumps are sometimes used. This consists of a piston drawing oil into a cylinder through a valve on one stroke, and expelling it through another valve on the return stroke.

A spring-loaded valve is included in the main oil line from the pump, set to lift at a predetermined pressure, thus preventing an oil pipe from bursting should the pump pressure become excessive; for instance, when cold, viscous oil is being circulated when the engine is first started. Oil which escapes past the valve returns to the sump.

Oil Filters. The inlet to the oil pump is fitted with a gauze suction filter, which removes particles of carbon or metal that may be present in the sump. On modern cars this filter is often fitted to a floating intake, so that oil is always drawn from just below the surface of the lubricant in the sump, whatever the level may be, thus avoiding the risk of picking up sludge or heavier particles which sink to the bottom of the sump.

In addition to the suction filter, which must necessarily be of fairly coarse mesh to avoid starving the oil pump, a much finer filter is often fitted to the main pressure line. This may filter all the oil discharged from the pump, or, in the case of the latest ultra-fine filters, may deal with only a percentage of the oil at any one time. Over a period, however, all the oil in the system eventually passes through the filter. Such filters will maintain the oil in new condition almost indefinitely.

An oil pressure gauge may be fitted to the dashboard of the car to indicate the pressure in the system, but on many modern cars this is replaced by a warning light which is connected to a pressure-operated switch connected to the lubrication system.

Valves and Valve Gear. We can consider next the question of how the mixture is admitted to the cylinders and the burnt gases extracted.

Modern car engines employ a type of valve known as the poppet valve. This consists of a circular metal head, on the underside of which is a tapered seating surface which matches a corresponding surface in the cylinder block or head. Forged integrally with the head of the valve is a stem which passes through a closely-fitted guide. The valve is closed by a strong coil spring, and the seating

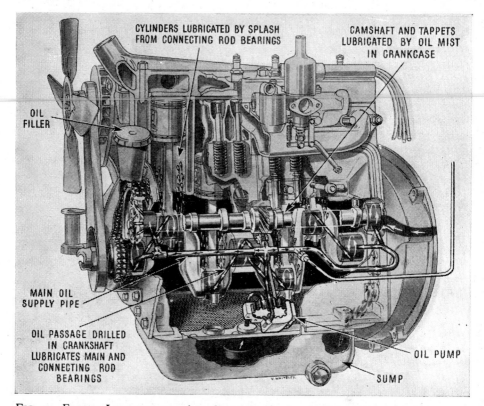

CYLINDERS LUBRICATED BY SPLASH FROM CONNECTING ROD BEARINGS

CAMSHAFT AND TAPPETS LUBRICATED BY OIL MIST IN CRANKCASE

OIL FILLER

MAIN OIL SUPPLY PIPE

OIL PASSAGE DRILLED IN CRANKSHAFT LUBRICATES MAIN AND CONNECTING ROD BEARINGS

OIL PUMP

SUMP

FIG. 11. ENGINE LUBRICATION. *A modern inline engine showing the pressure feed system. The pump which supplies the pressure oil is fed from the oil contained in the sump. The cylinders are lubricated by the oil splashing from the connecting rod bearings.*

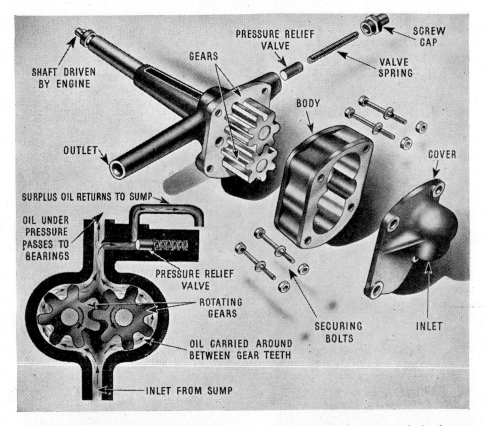

FIG. 12. PRESSURE PUMP *exploded to show the arrangement of parts, particularly the two gears that generate the pressure. The inset shows the oil circuit and the pressure relief valve.*

on its rim is accurately machined, and then matched to the seating surface on the cylinder block by grinding the two together with a fine abrasive paste, so that a gas-tight joint is obtained.

Side Valves. In the side valve engine shown in Fig. 13, the valve is opened by a metal plunger known as the tappet, which is raised by a cam on the camshaft. A cam is simply a lozenge-shaped projection on the shaft, but the contours of its sides are very carefully machined to ensure that the valve is opened and closed at the right moment. The principles of valve timing are more fully explained and illustrated in Chapter 5.

In order to allow for the expansion of the valve stem as the engine warms up, and to a lesser degree that of the tappet, a gap must exist between the top of the valve stem and the tappet when the parts are cold. This varies, from about 4 thousandths of an inch to as much as 40 thousandths, according to the design of the engine. Some form of screwed adjustment is usually provided to enable the correct gap to be obtained when the parts are assembled. Various types of adjustment are fully described in the Engine Overhaul Chapter.

On some cars a self-adjusting tappet is used, of the type shown in Fig. 14. It will

23

be seen that the tappet plunger is kept lightly in contact with the valve stem by a spring. Oil from the engine lubrication system passes into the small cylinder beneath the tappet through the non-return ball valve. It is this column of oil which carries the load of the valve spring when the tappet is raised by the cam.

Overhead Valves. With higher compression ratios, it will be evident that the combustion chamber space above the piston becomes very restricted. Since

side valves are arranged at the side of the cylinder, the incoming mixture must first pass upwards through the valve, and then suddenly reverse its direction in order to fill the cylinder. The opposite applies when the burnt gases escape through the exhaust valve. In practice, this means that in a high-speed modern engine only about half the area of the valves is really effective.

As a result, overhead valves are used on many engines because of their greater

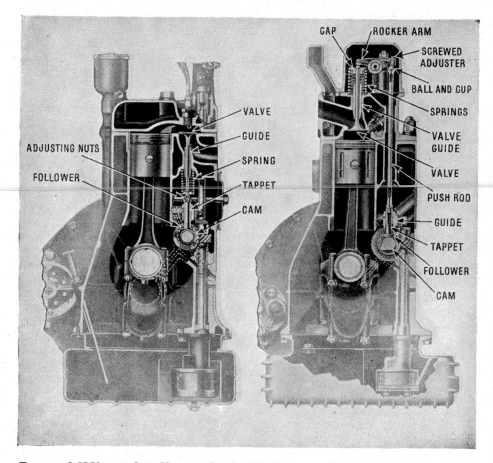

FIG. 13. O.H.V. AND SIDE VALVES. *On the left is shown a side valve mechanism, and on the right an overhead valve mechanism. The latter type is more efficient as the mixture has not to reverse its flow in order to fill the cylinder which is the case in a side valve engine. Also, adjustment can be more easily and quickly carried out.*

24

efficiency. As will be seen from Fig. 13, a simple method of operating such a valve, still using a camshaft, is to employ tubular steel rods, termed push rods, which fit into the tappets. A rocking arm carried on a shaft attached to the cylinder head transmits the motion of the push rod to the valve. An adjusting screw in the rocker arm allows the clearance between the rocker and the valve to be adjusted to compensate for expansion.

Overhead Camshaft Engines. The only disadvantage of the overhead valve gear lay-out is that the long push rod has a certain weight and inertia, which tends to slow up its movement at very high speeds, when the valve must open and close more than two thousand times per minute. On some engines the push rods are shortened by arranging the camshaft about half-way up the cylinder block. Better still, however, is to fit a camshaft in bearings mounted on the cylinder head itself. Such an engine is termed an overhead camshaft design. One end of the rocker arm bears on the cam, and the other on the end of the valve stem, so that there is a minimum of moving parts.

Sleeve and Rotary Valves. Although the poppet valve is quite efficient, it does suffer from certain disadvantages, such as restricted area and, in the case of the exhaust valve, a tendency to overheat. Designers have produced various types of valve which provide a better area of opening and which are adequately cooled.

The sleeve valve was fitted several years ago to one or two high-priced cars, and is still used on some aircraft engines. Basically, it consists of a sleeve, or cylindrical steel barrel, surrounding the cylinder. In this sleeve are cut ports which register with similar openings in the cylinder wall. The sleeve is reciprocated and rotated by a connecting rod operated by a crankshaft; this replaces the camshaft used with poppet valves.

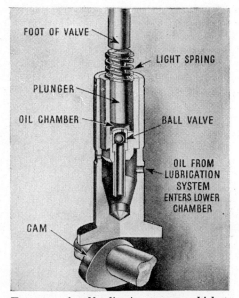

FOOT OF VALVE

LIGHT SPRING

PLUNGER

OIL CHAMBER

BALL VALVE

OIL FROM LUBRICATION SYSTEM ENTERS LOWER CHAMBER

CAM

FIG. 14. *A self-adjusting tappet which is kept lightly in contact with the foot of the valve stem by the spring.*

On some designs, double sleeve valves, one outside the other, have been used. The main disadvantage of the sleeve valve is the difficulty of securing adequate lubrication without admitting an excess of oil to the cylinder. Its higher cost, too, is a drawback.

Rotary valves are fitted above the cylinder head, and provided with ports through which the mixture is admitted and the exhaust extracted. High efficiencies have been obtained by the use of this type of valve, but high costs of production and lubrication difficulties have hampered their development. It is unlikely that they will find favour until their reliability is assured.

Driving the Camshaft. Reverting for a moment to the explanation of the four strokes of an engine, it will be recalled that the power stroke, or, for that matter, the inlet, compression or exhaust stroke, occurs only once during two revolutions of the crankshaft. If the cams are

FIG. 15. CAMSHAFT DRIVES. *A gear type camshaft drive is shown on the left, and chain type drive on the right. A feature of the latter is the automatic chain tensioner.*

to open the inlet and exhaust valves at the correct moment, the camshaft must obviously rotate at half the engine speed.

The camshaft is driven either by a chain or by gears, as shown in Fig. 15. On one or two engines ingenious drives employing eccentrics are used, but the simple chain or gear drive is almost universal. The camshaft is fitted with a chain-wheel or a gear having twice as many teeth as the driving sprocket or gear on the crankshaft, thus providing the required ratio of two turns of the crankshaft to one of the camshaft.

If the camshaft is fitted in the crankcase, the gears can be meshed together, or a very short chain drive can be used. If it is carried high on the cylinder block, however, a longer chain is required. In the case of gear drive, a vertical shaft must be used to convey the drive from the crankshaft; this calls for the use of bevel gears at the top and bottom of the shaft, since the crankshaft and the camshaft are alined at right angles to it.

THE CARBURETTOR

At this stage we must again retrace our steps to the general explanation of the four-stroke and two-stroke principles. It was assumed that a mixture of air and petrol, in the approximate proportions of 15 parts of air to 1 of petrol, was available to be admitted to the cylinder through the inlet valve.

The mixing of the petrol with the air is carried out by the carburettor. Fig. 16 shows a simple form of carburettor. It consists of a passage through which air passes to the engine; a jet through which petrol is sprayed into the passage; a float chamber, or reservoir, to maintain a supply of petrol to the jet; and a throttle, or tap, to control the amount of mixture admitted to the engine.

When air is drawn into the engine through the tube, it is usual to say that petrol is "sucked" from the jet. To be accurate, however, it should be appreciated that the petrol flows from the jet due to the fact that atmospheric pressure, which exerts a force of about 14·7 lb. per square inch on the level of the fluid in the float chamber, is greater than the pressure in the tube around the jet. It will be seen that there is a restriction in the tube, termed a choke, which forces the air to speed up at this point on its way to the cylinder, since a given amount of air has to pass through the smaller space.

It is a natural law that an increase in the velocity of air (or any other fluid) causes a decrease in the pressure which it exerts on its surroundings. In this case, the jet projects into this area of reduced pressure. Since atmospheric pressure is constantly pressing down on the surface of the fuel in the float chamber, the result is that the unbalanced pressure forces

the increased velocity of air through the choke tube results in too much petrol being supplied. At low speeds too little is available. Various methods of overcoming this difficulty have been devised. One principle employed is shown diagrammatically in Fig. 18.

In the passage leading from the float chamber to the jet is a second, smaller jet. There is also a vertical tube forming a well, filled with petrol up to the level of the fuel in the float chamber. At low engine speeds the petrol in the well passes out of the jet in the choke tube, and petrol flows through the submerged jet to replace it. At higher speeds, however, petrol flows from the jet in the choke tube faster than it can be replaced

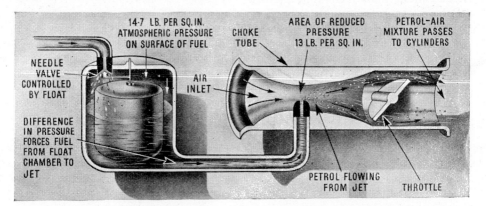

FIG. 16. A SIMPLE CARBURETTOR *illustrating how a mixture of petrol and air is fed by a jet to the cylinders and controlled by a throttle contained within the choke tube.*

petrol out of the jet; it is as if a plunger were pressed down on to the surface of the petrol in the float chamber.

It will be noticed that a hollow metal float in the float chamber controls the supply of fuel by means of a simple valve, as in the case of a domestic water cistern, thus maintaining a constant petrol level.

Mixture Correction. This simple carburettor, however, can only be arranged to supply the correct mixture at a constant engine speed. At higher speeds

by the submerged jet. The well therefore dries up. Air now enters through the well, and mixes with the petrol from the submerged jet, thus providing the necessary correction at high speeds.

To provide the correct mixture at all speeds and throttle openings, modern carburettors have a number of jets, and, in addition, economy devices to admit extra air when the car is cruising with the throttle partly closed; a small injection pump is often fitted, too, to provide a spurt of fuel if the throttle is suddenly opened, thus ensuring good acceleration.

Needle Control. One type of carburettor which operates on a different principle from those just described must be mentioned. Fig. 17 shows its function diagrammatically. The area of the jet is varied by a tapered needle which is lifted or lowered by a piston sliding in a cylinder above it. The upper side of the piston is subject, through an air passage drilled in the body of the piston, to the depression existing in the passage leading to the cylinders.

The greater the engine speed, therefore, the greater the depression above the piston, which is lifted accordingly. This withdraws the tapered needle from the jet, admitting more fuel, while the base of the piston provides an increased air passage to the cylinders: control of fuel and air is thus automatic, providing the correct combustible mixture at any speed.

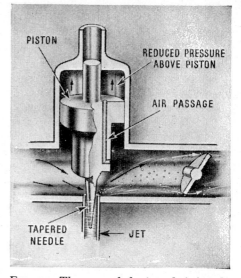

FIG. 17. *The area of the jet admitting the fuel to the choke tube, is varied by a tapered needle that is raised and lowered by the piston sliding in the cylinder.*

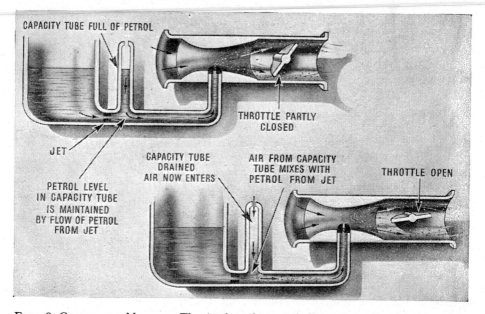

FIG. 18. CORRECTING MIXTURE. *The simple carburettor in* FIG. 16 *supplies the correct mixture only at constant engine speeds. The type shown above employs an additional jet and capacity tube for providing the necessary mixture correction at high engine speeds.*

28

Accelerator. The throttle referred to earlier is simply a disk of metal pivoted in the body of the carburettor, so that the passage can be almost closed when the engine is running slowly, or may be fully opened for maximum speed and power. It is connected by suitable linkage to the accelerator-pedal operated by the driver. A slow running control is usually to be found on the dashboard which can be set to ensure any desired engine speed when the accelerator is not in use.

Manifolds. The carburettor is connected to the cylinder by pipes or tubes, and is termed a manifold.

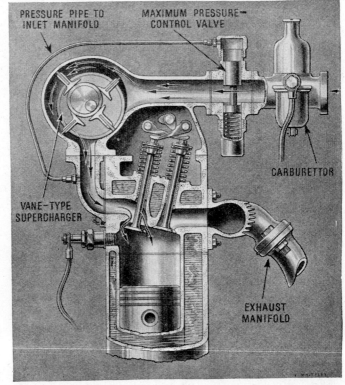

FIG. 19. *To ensure that the cylinders are filled with mixture at high engine speeds, a supercharger is sometimes fitted. The one shown above comprises vanes located in a rotating eccentric drum.*

Similarly, the exhaust ports are connected by a manifold to the exhaust pipe, and so to the silencer.

The inlet and exhaust manifolds are usually arranged to touch one another close to the point at which the mixture leaves the carburettor, providing a hot-spot which helps to vaporize the fuel. A hot-spot is mainly needed when the engine is cold and fuel is liable to condense in the branches of the manifold and on the cylinder walls. When the engine is at its normal temperature, heating of the mixture reduces its weight and causes loss of power. As a result, a special design of hot-spot is sometimes used, in which a valve, controlled by the temperature of the exhaust, deflects the exhaust gases around the inlet manifold when the engine is cold, and gradually shuts off the heat as normal working temperature is attained.

SUPERCHARGERS

Although in theory the cylinders should be completely filled with mixture during the inlet stroke, in practice only about four-fifths of the maximum possible amount of mixture is drawn in at low engine speeds, and only three-fifths at high speed. Among the factors which reduce the amount of charge drawn in are the short time during which the inlet valves are open, restriction in the car-

29

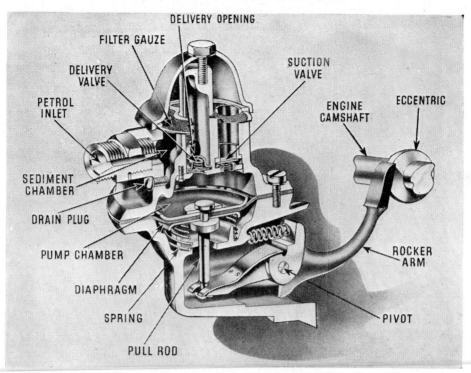

DELIVERY OPENING

FILTER GAUZE

DELIVERY VALVE

SUCTION VALVE

PETROL INLET

ENGINE CAMSHAFT

ECCENTRIC

SEDIMENT CHAMBER

DRAIN PLUG

PUMP CHAMBER

ROCKER ARM

DIAPHRAGM

SPRING

PIVOT

PULL ROD

Fig. 20. Mechanical Pump. *Petrol is drawn into the pump by the downward movement of the diaphragm and pumped to the float by its upward movement under the action of the spring.*

burettor and manifold, and the inertia of the petrol-air mixture itself.

To overcome these difficulties an air-pump, or supercharger, is sometimes fitted to draw mixture from the carburettor and supply it under pressure to the cylinders. Thus, when an inlet valve opens, the mixture is not sucked into the cylinder, but immediately begins to flow in under pressure and the cylinder is effectively filled.

On racing cars a high pressure is used to force in extra mixture and so increase the power output of the engine. The engine must, of course, be especially strengthened, to withstand the extreme pressures and temperatures which result.

By using quite a low pressure, for example, 3 lb. per sq. in. at low engine speeds and 5 lb. per sq. in. at maximum

speed, adequate filling can be obtained, yet even the engine of a family car remains docile and tractable. The performance of the car is, of course, very much improved, and reliability does not suffer.

The most common type of supercharger is that illustrated in Fig. 19. The mixture is carried around from the inlet to the outlet of the casing in the spaces between four vanes which slide in slots in a rotating eccentric drum. An alternative consists of two intermeshing rotors, or paddles, which pump the mixture through the casing. The third arrangement, used only on a few cars, consists of a vaned disk which is driven at very high speed inside a casing. Mixture enters at the centre of the casing and is flung outwards by centrifugal force, to be collected by the outer ring of the casing and fed to the cylinders.

SUPPLYING THE FUEL

The simplest method of supplying petrol to the carburettor is to fix the petrol tank as high as possible beneath the bonnet, so that the fuel will flow to the float chamber by gravity. This was, in fact, the arrangement used on many cars years ago, but today, with carburettors mounted higher and bonnets lower, some form of pump is necessary to feed the fuel from the tank at the rear of the car. A small gravity tank, mounted under the bonnet and kept supplied with fuel from the rear tank by utilizing engine suction (hence the name autovac) was the first step towards the modern pressure feed systems.

Mechanical Fuel Pump. A typical mechanical petrol pump is shown in Fig. 20. The rocker arm is operated by a cam on the camshaft, and pulls the diaphragm down against the pressure of the spring. Petrol is drawn into the chamber above the diaphragm, passing through a gauze screen and then through the inlet valve, which consists of a small disk of fibre held against its seating by a spring. When the cam allows the rocker to return, the diaphragm spring forces the diaphragm upwards; the fuel above it cannot return through the in-

let valve, and consequently lifts the outlet valve against its spring, and passes through the outlet port to the carburettor.

Notice that the only pressure generated by the pump is that produced by the diaphragm spring. If the float chamber is full and the valve closed, the pump diaphragm will remain depressed, and the rocker will simply reciprocate without pumping any fuel. An excess pressure cannot, therefore, be built up.

Electric Pump. The electric type of pump shown in Fig. 21 operates on a similar principle, a diaphragm forming the actual pumping medium. In this case, however, it is moved by a rod attached to an electro-magnet. The current to operate this passes through a contact breaker, and is cut off when the diaphragm is deflected on the suction

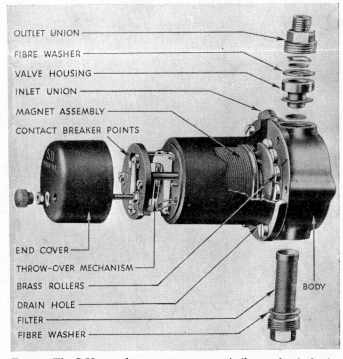

OUTLET UNION
FIBRE WASHER
VALVE HOUSING
INLET UNION
MAGNET ASSEMBLY
CONTACT BREAKER POINTS
END COVER
THROW-OVER MECHANISM
BRASS ROLLERS
DRAIN HOLE
FILTER
FIBRE WASHER
BODY

FIG. 21. *The S.U. petrol pump operates on a similar mechanical principle to that shown in Fig. 20, but is actuated by an electro-magnet.*

stroke. If the fuel does not pass to the carburettor, the diaphragm remains deflected and no current can pass to the electro-magnet.

SPARKING PLUGS

A sparking plug consists of a steel body which is screwed into the cylinder head. Into the body is fitted an insulator, made of mica, porcelain, or a synthetic compound, and through the centre of this insulator passes an electrode, or thick wire, which carries a high-tension current

which reaches it, yet must conduct heat away from the central electrode sufficiently quickly to prevent this becoming white-hot, and igniting the mixture before the spark jumps the points. The choice of the correct plug for a given engine, therefore, represents a balance between these two factors.

To persuade a current to jump the spark gap when the plug is in place in the cylinder and subject to compression pressure calls for a very high voltage. In practice from 6,000 to 7,000 volts are

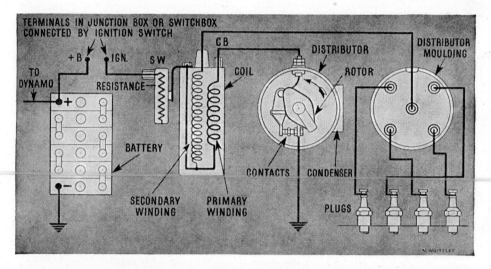

FIG. 22. IGNITION CIRCUIT. *The circuit above is typical of that employed with a four-stroke, four-cylinder engine. A detailed wiring circuit is shown in Chap. 7.*

Two well known designs are illustrated in Fig. 9, Chapter 5. Between the central electrode and one or more projections on the body is a gap of from twenty to forty-five thousandths of an inch, across which the electric current jumps in the form of a spark.

Although it may seem a simple item compared with other parts of the car, the sparking plug is the result of a great deal of experience and development. The internal insulator, for instance, must remain hot enough to burn off any oil

required in a normal engine as fitted to a family car, while even higher voltages of up to 20,000 volts are necessary with high-compression sports engines, or when wide sparking plug gaps are used.

THE IGNITION COIL

Since the only electricity available is that supplied by a 6-volt or 12-volt dynamo and battery, some method of increasing the voltage to the figure required must be employed. The ignition coil is utilized for just this purpose.

The coil consists of about 360 turns of thick wire, termed the primary winding, that is wound round, but insulated from, a secondary winding, of about 16,000 turns. At the centre of the coil is a laminated iron core.

Current from the car battery flows through the primary winding. If it is suddenly interrupted, a sudden surge of current is set up in the secondary winding, the peak voltage reaching the figure required. The reason for this is explained fully in Chapter 7. Interruption of the current is brought about by connecting a contact breaker into the wire leading from the battery to the primary winding. The spring-loaded contact is moved away from the stationary one by the cam, which makes contact with the pivoted fibre rocker carrying the contact. To prevent a low-voltage spark occurring at the contacts, a condenser is connected across them; this absorbs the momentary rush of current when the contacts first separate, so that their surfaces do not become quickly burnt and pitted. It also increases the secondary current by ensuring a quick collapse of the current in the primary coil.

THE DISTRIBUTOR

From the secondary winding the current passes to the rotating arm mounted above the contact-breaker, entering the moulded, insulated cap at the central terminal. The arm is arranged to be opposite one of the terminals, or electrodes, inside the cap whenever the contact points separate, so that the high-voltage current can jump the small gap between the rotor and the electrode. Each electrode is connected to a sparking plug, and thus the current finally reaches the sparking plug points and performs its job of firing the mixture in the cylinder.

Ignition Timing. The distributor spindle is driven by gearing from the camshaft, and, on a four-stroke engine,

runs at half the engine speed, so that the rotor will be opposite a given electrode in the cap once during every two revolutions. The spark takes place in the cylinder just before the piston reaches the top of its stroke. The order in which the sparking plugs fire depends on the number of cylinders and the valve timing. In a four-cylinder engine, for instance, a common firing order is: No. 1 cylinder, No. 3, No. 4 and No. 2, numbering the cylinders from the front of the engine. An alternative order sometimes used is 1, 2, 4, 3. The sparking plugs do not fire in a straightforward sequence, 1, 2, 3, 4, since a succession of power impulses along the crankshaft would cause severe strains. Further details of firing orders and an explanation of ignition advance will be found in Chapter 5.

THE MAGNETO

The magneto operates in the same manner as the coil ignition system just described, except that it is a self-contained unit with its own low-tension generator built into the casing, and is, therefore, independent of the car's electrical system. Its principles are explained and illustrated in Chapter 7. A magneto gives a better spark at high speeds than a coil ignition system, since at higher revolutions it generates a greater low-tension current. At low speeds, however, and when starting, its voltage is less. Magnetos are not very widely fitted nowadays, except on sports and racing cars.

THE COOLING SYSTEM

It may seem a paradox that an engine which converts fuel into heat in order to produce power should require a cooling system to dispose of heat. As we have seen, however, excessive heat in certain components can cause detonation, and loss of power. The main culprits are the cylinder head, exhaust valves and sparking plugs. The major cooling effect is therefore centred on these items.

Air Cooling. As is well known, an engine can be cooled quite effectively by air, provided that sufficient surface area is presented to the air stream. Many motor cycle and aircraft engines are cooled by means of fins cast on to the cylinder head and barrel, while a tendency to produce air-cooled car engines is now increasingly evident. The main difficulty with a car engine is that being enclosed in a bonnet at the front, or a cowling at the rear of the body, it is difficult to cool effectively unless a large fan is fitted to direct an air blast over the cooling fins. Fig. 23 shows a modern example of a two-cylinder, air-cooled engine.

Water Cooling. Most cars, however, have water-cooled power units. As will be seen from Fig. 24, the water circulates around the cylinders and through passages in the cylinder head, before flowing into a multitude of small tubes in a radiator through which an air-stream passes, generally aided by a fan. Water circulation may be by thermo-siphon action, i.e., the heated water rising to the top of the engine and passing to the radiator, while cooled water flows in at the base of the cylinder block. On many cars, however, a pump is used to provide positive circulation of the water.

As shown in Fig. 25, this consists of a vaned metal disk, termed an impeller, in a casing provided with an inlet pipe at

COWLING FOR DIRECTING AIRSTREAM FROM FAN OVER CYLINDERS

FINNED CYLINDER AND HEAD TO ASSIST COOLING

COOLING FANS

FIG. 23. AIR COOLING. *Cooling is carried out by cooling fans. These are attached to adjustable arms so that the belt slackness can be taken up when necessary. The airstream is directed to the finned aluminium cylinders by means of cowling rings. The engine is a flat-twin, four-stroke cycle, developing about 14 b.h.p. at 4,000 r.p.m.*

34

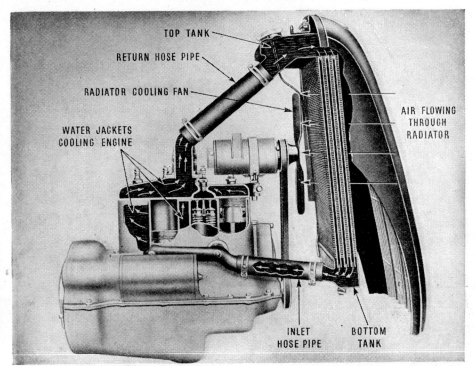

TOP TANK

RETURN HOSE PIPE

RADIATOR COOLING FAN

AIR FLOWING
THROUGH
RADIATOR

WATER JACKETS
COOLING ENGINE

INLET
HOSE PIPE

BOTTOM
TANK

FIG. 24. THERMO-SIPHON COOLING. *This water cooling system is widely used and depends on the heated water in the cylinder block rising and passing to the radiator. It is cooled by passing through the radiator which is cooled by the air flow assisted by a fan.*

the centre, and an outlet at the edge. The impeller is driven by the engine. The water between the vanes is flung outwards by centrifugal force, is collected by the outer passage in the casing, and discharged through the outlet pipe. Water is meanwhile sucked in through the inlet to replace that which has been discharged.

The outlet from the pump is often connected to a duct or tube inside the cylinder head. This has a series of openings or jets which direct the cool water on to the cylinder head around the exhaust valve and sparking plug seatings, thus keeping these critical points cool.

Since an engine must warm up quickly after a cold start to prevent wear and tear and excessive petrol consumption

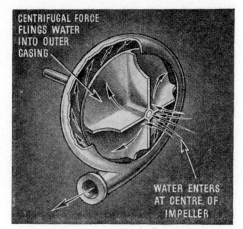

CENTRIFUGAL FORCE
FLINGS WATER
INTO OUTER
CASING

WATER ENTERS
AT CENTRE OF
IMPELLER

FIG. 25. *View showing the construction of an impeller type water pump used for providing a circulation of water to the cylinder jackets.*

35

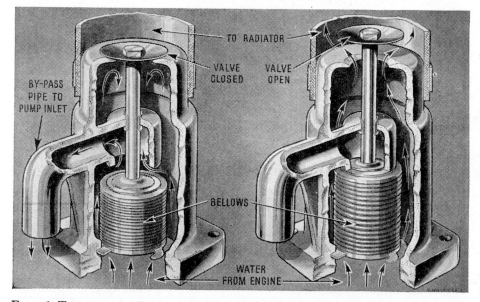

FIG. 26. THERMOSTATIC REGULATOR. *This device ensures rapid warming up when starting from cold and keeps the cooling water at a constant economic temperature.*

it is usual to fit a valve in the outlet pipe leading from the cylinder head to the radiator to restrict the flow of water until the engine has attained its normal temperature. Fig. 26 illustrates a typical example; the valve is controlled by a bellows filled with a liquid which vaporizes at the correct running temperature, opening the valve and allowing normal circulation. When the valve is closed, a by-pass pipe allows the water to circulate back to the inlet side of the pump, thus preventing excessive pressure being built up in the system.

Pressurised Cooling Systems. On a number of modern cars the water in the cooling system is maintained under a slight pressure by means of a spring-loaded valve in the radiator filler cap or overflow pipe. A pressure of, say, 4 lb. per sq. in. raises the boiling point of the water to about 223 deg. F. at sea level, a useful gain for hard driving, motoring at high altitudes or under tropical conditions. When the pressure exceeds the

safe figure the valve opens to prevent damage to the radiator. A second valve prevents the formation of a vacuum in the system when the engine cools down.

Oil Cooling. It is not always realized that the lubricating oil plays a very important part in cooling the internal components of the engine, such as the main, connecting rod, and other bearings, the pistons, timing gears, and so on. The heat absorbed by the oil is dissipated when the lubricant returns to the sump, past which air is flowing when the car is in motion. On high-efficiency engines the sump is provided with cooling ribs to increase the radiating area, while in sports and racing cars, the lubricant is often circulated through a small oil cooling radiator similar to that used for the water cooling system.

THE TRANSMISSION

As explained in the first section of this chapter, the engine may drive the rear wheels through a clutch, gearbox, propeller shaft and rear axle, or the transmission system may be, as it were, turned round completely, so that the engine drives the front wheels. Since the front wheel drive arrangements, and the less used rear engine, rear wheel drive systems, contain basically similar clutch, gearbox and differential units to those used in the conventional lay-out, this latter system will be described.

Clutch. This, the first item in the transmission, connects the engine to the gearbox; also it enables the drive from the engine to be disconnected at will. To transmit the engine power without slip, provide smooth engagement and a light operating pressure on the pedal, has called for designs of clutch which may at

first sight seem to be very complicated. The principle, however, is simple.

Imagine that the engine flywheel is spinning round, and that a disk of metal is forced into contact with its face. Due to the friction between the flywheel face and the disk, the latter will be rapidly speeded up until it is rotating at the same speed as the flywheel. If a shaft be attached to the disk, this can be used to drive the gearbox, and, through the rest of the transmission, the rear wheels. The inset in Fig. 27 shows a friction clutch in its simplest form.

Clutch Engagement. In practice, however, the disk is not forced against the flywheel by a single spring. As will be seen from Fig. 27, it is not driven until

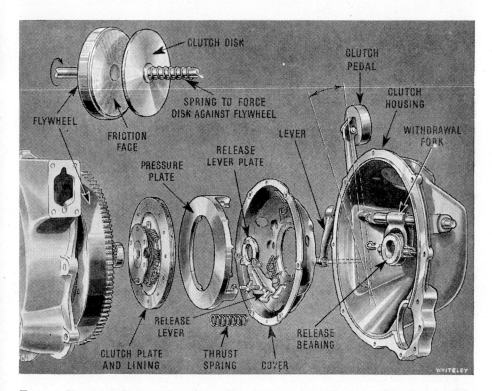

FIG. 27. FRICTION CLUTCH ASSEMBLY. *The upper drawing illustrates the principle of the friction clutch. The exploded arrangement below shows how this simple principle is applied in practice. Engagement and release is effected by the foot-operated clutch pedal.*

it is squeezed between a pressure plate and the flywheel.

The pressure plate is moved towards the flywheel by a number of coil springs which react against the casing that surrounds the whole assembly. The friction plate has a ring of asbestos material on each side and is firmly gripped between the flywheel and the pressure plate when the clutch is engaged.

The pressure plate is released by means of toggle levers moved by a linkage from the clutch pedal operated by the driver. The thrust on the inner ends of these pivoted levers is applied through a ball

matic or semi-automatic gearbox, so that a brief explanation of its principles is justified.

Referring to Fig. 29 it will be seen that the flywheel is in two parts and enclosed in an oil-tight casing. These can be best understood by imagining a motor tyre sliced in two to form two hollow rings. In these rings are fitted a number of vanes. If one ring is filled with oil, and rotated by the engine crankshaft, the oil in the pockets between the vanes will be flung outwards by centrifugal force, and, since the casing is rotating, will also be flung forwards in the direction of rotation.

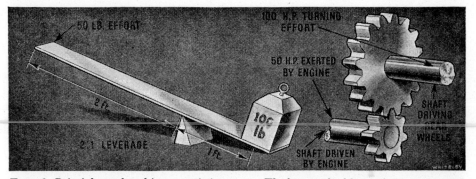

FIG. 28. *Principle employed in transmitting power. The larger wheel has twice as many teeth as the smaller, and transmits twice the horse-power. Compare with the simple 2 to 1 lever.*

bearing, or, in more modern clutches, a ring of graphite in a metal housing. The graphite thrust bearing has the advantage that it does not need lubrication.

A number of different designs of clutch working on the same basic principles have been developed, the object being to provide even smoother engagement and lighter pedal pressure. Some of the more widely used types are dealt with in Chapter 8.

Fluid Flywheel. Until recently the fluid flywheel, which is an hydraulic form of clutch, was confined to only a few makes of car. Several recent American models, however, have adopted this form of coupling, in conjuction with an auto-

If we arrange the second ring close to the first, with its hollow side towards it, the oil flung from the driven ring will strike the vanes on the second ring and rotate it. Due to the curved surface of the ring, the oil will then be directed back towards the centre, to be picked up again by the driving ring.

At first, when the driving ring is rotating slowly, the jets of oil do not exert very much turning effort on the driven half of the flywheel, which is connected to the gearbox. As the engine is speeded up, however, the turning effort is increased, and the slip diminishes. When the engine is running at about 600 revolutions per minute the slip is negligible, the gearbox being driven at about 98 per cent of the engine speed. The fluid flywheel thus forms an exceedingly smooth method of taking up the drive from a standstill.

Gearbox. The next unit in the transmission system is the gearbox. Fig. 30 shows the construction of a synchromesh type gearbox. We have already seen, when discussing brake horse-power, that a petrol engine delivers power roughly in proportion to the speed at which it is operating. To take an example, a car which is rated at 10 h.p. will actually deliver less than this when travelling at under 15 miles per hour in top gear; at 25 m.p.h., however, about 20 b.h.p. is being produced, while at something over 50 m.p.h. the maximum power at the flywheel of about 35 b.h.p. is being transmitted to the rear wheel drive pinion.

Why is a gearbox required? The answer will be obvious when it is realized that to move the car away from a standstill and to accelerate it calls for a considerable effort. For example, when the car is climbing a hill with a gradient of, say, 1 in 6, the thrust exerted by the rear wheels is equal to one sixth of the total weight of the vehicle and its occupants.

Under these conditions, therefore, it is necessary to allow the engine to run at a moderately fast speed, thus developing more power, although the car may be travelling quite slowly. This is effected by allowing the engine to drive the rear wheels through a gearbox. The term, incidentally, should, strictly speaking refer to the box or casing in which the gears are fitted, but it is now generally applied to the whole assembly of gears and their container or casing.

FLYWHEEL CASING   DRIVEN MEMBER   DRIVING MEMBER

FIG. 29. FLUID FLYWHEEL. *View showing construction of the two main members and the flywheel casing. The driving member, attached to the crankshaft, flings oil onto the vanes of the driven member. The curved surface of the vanes directs the oil back to the centre where it is picked up again by the driving member. This form of transmission ensures that the drive is taken up smoothly from a standstill.*

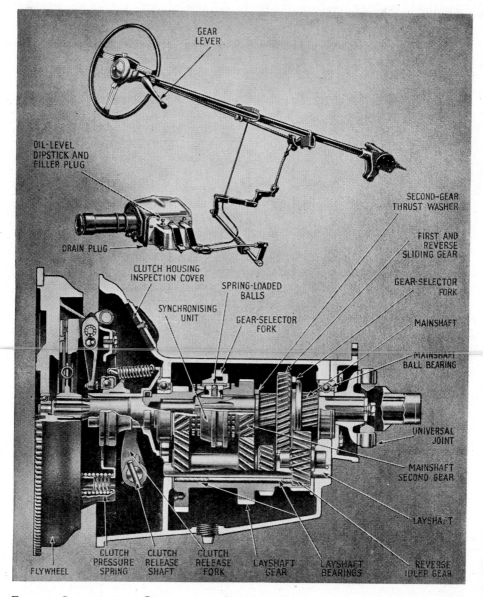

FIG. 30. SYNCHROMESH GEARBOX AND STEERING COLUMN SELECTOR MECHANISM. *A three-speed gearbox cut away to show the arrangement of gears, synchromesh cones and gear selector mechanism. The cones are integral with the gears and come into contact before the dogs of the gears mesh. The speeds of the two are synchronized and their meshing is carried out smoothly, i.e., without crashing. First and reverse gears are not fitted with synchromesh cones, being engaged by sliding them into mesh. Selectors are mounted on shafts at the side of the gearbox and are actuated by linkage from the steering-column lever.*

Fig. 28 shows two simple gears, one having twice as many teeth as the other. If the smaller gear is driven by the engine, and the larger drives the propeller shaft leading to the rear axle, the engine will rotate twice every time the propeller shaft revolves. By choosing a suitable number of teeth for each gear, any ratio of engine revolutions to propeller shaft revolutions can be obtained. The engine can thus be allowed to develop the power required for the conditions prevailing at the moment.

Arrangement of Gears. In practice, the normal gearbox has only two or three indirect gears, as they are termed, that is, in addition to the direct drive from the engine to the propeller shaft. The gearbox is then said to be a three-speed or a four-speed type.

Fig. 31 shows a four-speed gearbox in a very much simplified form. The engine drives the small gear at the left-hand end of the upper shaft: this gear is permanently in mesh with another gear fitted to a second shaft in the gearbox, termed the layshaft, on which there are four gears. There is a third shaft in the gearbox, in line with the engine shaft; this drives the propeller shaft, and is called the mainshaft. On it are gears which rotate with it, but are free to slide along it.

In Fig. 31 the smallest gear on the layshaft is meshing with the large gear on the mainshaft. This provides the lowest ratio, first or bottom gear, used when the car is starting from a standstill or climbing a very steep hill.

In Fig. 31 the larger gears on the layshaft engage with corresponding smaller gears on the mainshaft. These gears provide intermediate ratios, termed second and third gears, used for normal hill climbing and traffic work. When the top gear is engaged, the clutch shaft is connected to the mainshaft so that a direct drive to the transmission is obtained.

An extra pair of gears, carried on a third shaft which is not shown in the sketches, is brought into action to reverse the direction of rotation of the mainshaft, thus causing the car to travel backwards.

Synchronization. The appropriate pair of gears is selected by sliding the required gear along the mainshaft until it meshes with its fellow on the layshaft. On modern gearboxes, however, the mainshaft and layshaft gears are permanently in mesh, but the mainshaft gears are not fixed to the shaft. Instead, the required gear is temporarily locked to the mainshaft by a dog clutch similar to that used to engage top gear. This clutch has internal projections which slide on grooves, or splines, in the mainshaft. To render it easy to engage the dogs with those on the gear, most modern gearboxes are fitted with synchromesh mechanism. This consists of a cone attached to the gear. The two cones come into contact before the dogs meet, so that the speeds of the two gears are synchronized, enabling the teeth of the dogs to slide into mesh without grating or noise.

Gear Selection. Fig. 32 shows a normal gear lever, which has a ball joint at its base, where it enters the gearbox, allowing it to be swung from side to side, or backwards and forwards. A projection on the gear lever below this ball can thus be moved to one side or the other, so that it enters a slot in one of the selector forks.

These are mounted on rods in the gearbox, and engage with grooves on the dog clutches; when slid backwards or forwards, therefore, they move the clutch into engagement with the appropriate gear. Before another gear can be selected the lever must first be returned to the central or neutral position so that it is impossible to engage two gear ratios at once; Fig. 32 illustrates the gear lever positions for a three-speed gearbox and the location of the selector fork.

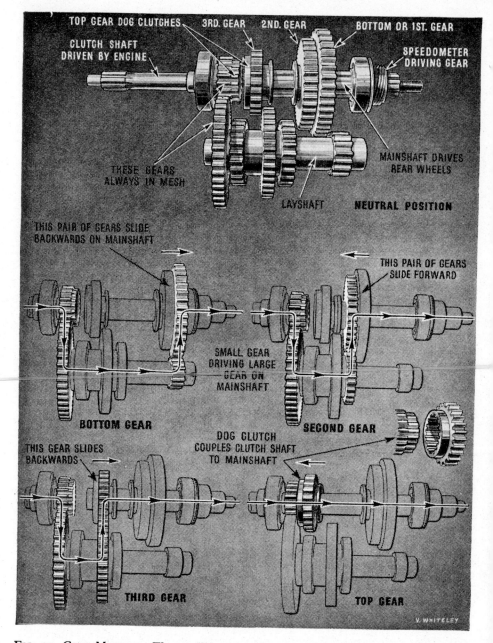

FIG. 31. GEAR MESHING. *The top illustration shows in detail the gears in a crash type, four-speed gearbox (neutral position). Below are the four positions that can be selected by the operation of the gear change lever. It should be noted that in TOP GEAR the clutch shaft is coupled directly to the mainshaft by means of a dog clutch.*

FIG. 32. Here are shown
the four positions of
the gear lever. Below
the ball joint the gear
lever locates the selec-
tor forks. These are
mounted on rods and
engage in a groove on
the dog clutches. When
moved backwards or
forwards, they move
the clutch into engage-
ment with the appro-
priate gear.

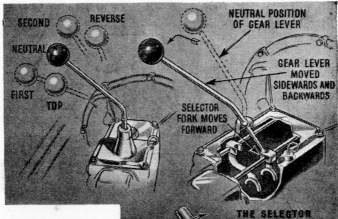

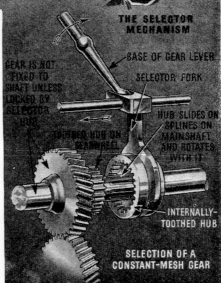

On the majority of modern cars, the gear lever mounted on the gearbox has been replaced by a lever on the steering-column, the lever being linked to the gearbox by rod and cable controls.

Overdrive. The overdrive is becoming an increasingly popular feature on medium-sized and large cars.

Consisting of a step-up gear mounted behind the gearbox, it enables high cruising speeds to be maintained with relatively low engine revolutions. This reduces engine wear and gives better fuel consumption and quieter running.

The overdrive, which usually operates only on the two upper gears (but on some cars may operate on second, third and fourth gears of a four-speed gearbox), may be brought into operation by means of a switch—mounted on the steering column or the dashboard—controlling the solenoid which effects engagement of the epicyclic gears in the overdrive. The extra gear (as the overdrive unit may loosely be described) can be engaged or disengaged while the engine is pulling.

An alternative arrangement is for the overdrive to be engaged automatically whenever the throttle pedal is released at speeds over about 30 m.p.h. in top gear. The overdrive then remains in operation until speed is reduced to below 30 m.p.h., unless the throttle pedal is pressed to the limit of its travel, when a switch is operated which interrupts the ignition circuit and re-engages direct drive.

Automatic Gear Changing. On some modern cars, chiefly of American origin, automatic control of the gearbox is adopted. The transmission system consists of a fluid flywheel which is coupled to a gearbox of specialized and complicated design. Broadly speaking, there are two systems in use. In the first, the driver has a measure of control over the gearbox, a small lever on the steering column being placed in the high position

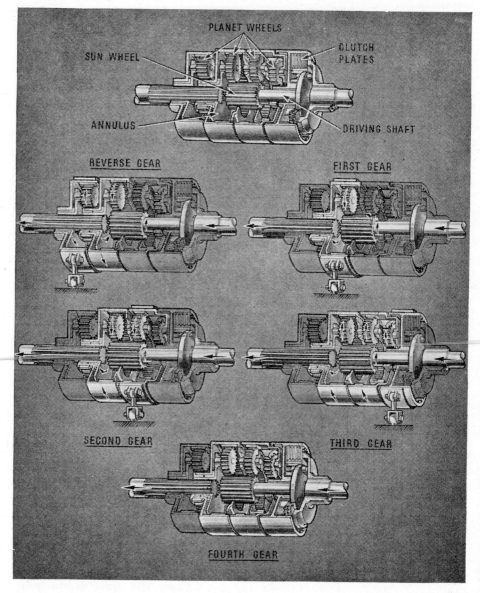

FIG. 33. A PRE-SELECTOR GEARBOX *comprises three main assemblies; the running gear, the brake harness and the control mechanism. The running gear consists of four epicyclic trains of gears interconnected so that four different ratios and a reverse can be obtained by compounding the various trains. In top gear all the trains are locked together and drive the output shaft at engine speed. The function of the brake harness is to put any required gear into action by gripping the drum or annulus in which the gear trains are housed. Operation of the brake harness is by a toggle linkage and gear control lever.*

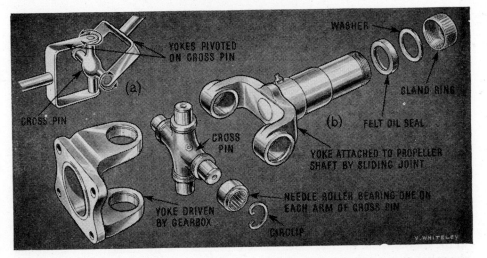

FIG. 34. UNIVERSAL JOINT. *This joint couples the gearbox to propeller shaft and propeller shaft to rear axle, and allows for vertical movement of the rear axle.*

for normal driving, and at low when starting on a hill or in mud or sand.

High provides two ratios equivalent to third and top gears on a normal car. The change from third to top takes place automatically at road speeds of over 15–20 m.p.h. By depressing the accelerator pedal beyond its normal travel third is regained. Third is automatically selected if the road speed falls below 15 m.p.h.

The low position of the lever provides the equivalent of first and second gears on a normal transmission. As in high, the change of ratio is controlled either by the accelerator pedal or road speed, bottom gear being obtainable up to 27 m.p.h., and an automatic change down from second to bottom occurring at about 8 m.p.h.

In the second type of transmission, changes of gear ratio occur automatically according to the road speed of the car and the driving conditions; that this design is complicated may be appreciated from the fact that the gear changes are effected by hydraulic cylinders, and the various control circuits call for up to six different oil pressures in the system at one time.

Hydraulic Drives. It is possible that in the future the present transmission system may be superseded by the installation of a high-pressure hydraulic pump attached to the engine in place of the clutch; this pump would operate small hydraulic motors attached to either the two front or rear wheels, or to all four. Due to the low inertia of the small motors, outstanding acceleration would be possible, coupled with a high degree of controllability.

Propeller Shaft. Reverting, however, to the conventional lay-out, a propeller shaft is necessary to transmit the drive from the gearbox to the rear axle. Since the rear wheels are carried by springs and are subject to appreciable vertical movements, the shaft is coupled to the gearbox and back axle by universal joints. The principle of a simple mechanical universal joint can best be understood by referring to Fig. 34 from which it will be seen that the two pivots arranged at right angles allow universal action of the joint. A modern development of this primitive arrangement is also shown; it is provided with needle-roller bearings on the pivots, and has a sliding joint which compensates for the slight change in effective length of the propeller shaft which takes place as the rear axle moves up and down.

A reinforced fabric disk was sometimes used on light cars instead of a metal universal joint, but this is uncommon on modern cars. An alternative is the rubber bushed type of joint in which the elasticity of the rubber, which is bonded to the inner and outer parts of the joint, provides the necessary flexibility. This type of joint, of course, does not develop slackness due to wear, and needs no lubrication.

Rear Axle. So we come to the last unit in the transmission: the rear axle. Inside the metal casing is the mechanism which carries the drive from the propeller shaft through a right-angle turn to the two axle shafts attached to the wheels, and at the same time divides the power between the wheels so that one wheel can rotate faster than the other when the car is being steered round a corner or bend.

From Fig. 35 it will be seen that the drive from the propeller shaft is transmitted to a large bevel gear, called a crown wheel, by a smaller pinion, thus turning the drive through a right angle to each wheel, and also providing a reduction in gear ratio, which is generally between 4 : 1 and 5½ : 1.

To render the gears quiet in operation, the teeth are cut so as to form part of a spiral; the term "spiral bevel final drive" appears in the specifications of most cars today. To enable the propeller shaft to be lowered so that the floor in the rear compartment of the car may be flat, instead of being divided by the usual propeller shaft tunnel, the centre-line of the pinion is sometimes set below that of the crown wheel.

The gears then have a special tooth shape, and are termed hypoid gears. Another design is the worm and wheel, in which the axis of the driving worm is below that of the worm wheel, this arrangement is illustrated in Fig. 37.

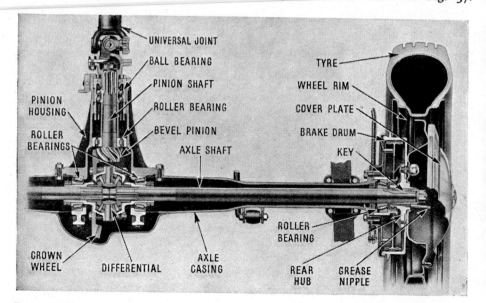

UNIVERSAL JOINT
BALL BEARING
PINION SHAFT
ROLLER BEARING
BEVEL PINION
AXLE SHAFT
PINION HOUSING
ROLLER BEARINGS
CROWN WHEEL
DIFFERENTIAL
AXLE CASING

TYRE
WHEEL RIM
COVER PLATE
BRAKE DRUM
KEY
ROLLER BEARING
REAR HUB
GREASE NIPPLE

FIG. 35. TRANSMITTING THE DRIVE. *This horizontal section shows the general arrangement of parts in the rear axle, differential, and rear wheel and hub assembly.*

Whichever type of differential drive is being used, the crown wheel or the worm wheel is not connected directly to the axle shafts, but to an intermediate set of gears. When the car is turning a corner, the outer wheel follows a longer path than the inner and must, therefore, rotate more quickly. This would be impossible if the two wheels were driven by a solid axle. An ingenious mechanism known as a differential is, therefore, used to drive two shafts, one attached to each wheel.

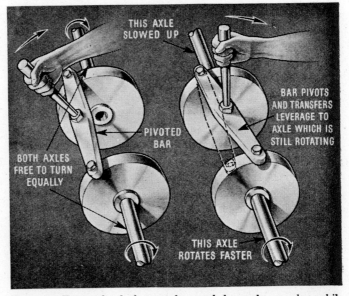

FIG. 36. *Two axle shafts may be coupled together so that while both wheels are driven, the one can rotate faster than the other.*

Since the average beginner finds it difficult to understand the principle of a differential gear, a simple analogy is shown in Fig. 36. The first sketch shows two axle shafts, fitted with disks which are coupled together by a bar, which is pivoted to the rim of each disk.

If the disks are rotated by pulling on the rod attached to the bar, the disks will both turn by the same amount. This represents the state of affairs existing when the car is moving forward.

If one shaft is slowed down, however, as happens to the inner wheel when turning a corner, the bar connecting the two disks will pivot, allowing the other disk to rotate further. This is the principle of the differential action required, but a rigid bar can only allow slight relative movement of the two disks.

The next step is to replace the disks by two bevel gears, and to connect them together by placing two bevel pinions between them. The pinions are mounted on shafts, and by rotating these we can turn the gears attached to the axle shaft. The logical method of doing this is to fit the pinion shafts into a cage or frame which is attached to the crown wheel driven by the propeller shaft pinion.

Step by step we have built up a complete differential unit as fitted to most cars. It only remains to watch it at work. When the crown wheel rotates and carries the pinion cage around, the pinions, being interlocked with the bevels on the axle shafts, turn these through an equal amount. Notice that the differential pinions do not rotate; the whole assembly turns as a unit.

If one rear wheel is slowed down, however, the bevel pinions will begin to rotate round the gear attached to that axle shaft. In doing so, they will exert a driving effect on the other axle shaft bevel gear. Notice that this turning effect is additional to that due to rotation of the whole assembly with the crown wheel.

47

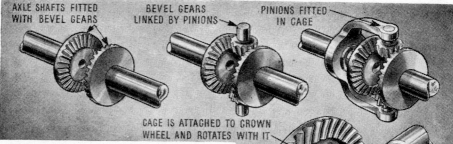

AXLE SHAFTS FITTED
WITH BEVEL GEARS

BEVEL GEARS
LINKED BY PINIONS

PINIONS FITTED
IN CAGE

CAGE IS ATTACHED TO CROWN
WHEEL AND ROTATES WITH IT

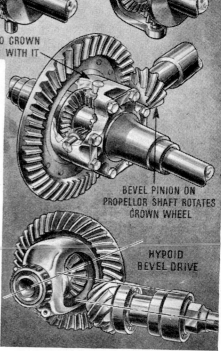

BEVEL PINION ON
PROPELLOR SHAFT ROTATES
CROWN WHEEL

HYPOID
BEVEL DRIVE

FIG. 37. *Four stages in the construction of a differential employing a normal bevel pinion and crown wheel. The differential unit rotates as a unit. Lower sketch shows a hypoid bevel drive used to allow propeller shaft to be carried at a lower level.*

In other words, if one road wheel is slowed down, the other is automatically speeded up, which is just what is required when turning a corner.

This effect can prove a decided drawback, however, if one wheel is resting on a slippery or soft surface, while the other is on hard ground, since the differential will speed up the wheel which is not exerting a grip to twice its normal speed, while the other remains stationary. While special designs of differential have been developed to overcome this difficulty they are not fitted to the normal car due to their greater complexity and cost.

Axle Shafts. The shafts which drive the rear wheels are usually attached to the bevel gears by splines, but on some cars the gears are forged onto the ends of the shafts. The outer ends of the shafts are fixed to the wheel hubs by means of a taper and key, or by splines in the case of fully floating axles. Fig. 38 illustrates the meaning of the term semi-floating, three-quarter floating and fully floating axles.

Front Wheel Drive. As has been mentioned at the beginning of this chapter, there has been for may years a small proportion of cars in which the front wheels are driven directly instead of the rear wheels being driven.

The engine, clutch, and gearbox are turned round in the chassis, and a differential is built into the gearbox, driving the front wheels through short axle shafts fitted with a special design of universal joint which will work effectively throughout the wide angularity caused by the vertical movement of the very short driving shafts.

On some of the most recent American and Continental cars, a different lay-out is used, the clutch and gearbox being behind the engine as in normal practice, and a short propeller shaft passing forward beneath the engine to a differential and driving unit. This forms a compact layout which allows a more roomy body to be used, but the centre of gravity of the engine is necessarily higher than usual due to the driving shaft and differential being beneath it.

THE SUSPENSION

For many years the conventional method of isolating the car from road shocks has been to mount the front and rear axles on laminated springs attached to the chassis at each corner. A leaf spring as it is termed, needs little explanation; Fig. 39 makes its construction clear. It will be seen that one end, generally the rear, is attached to the chassis by means of a swinging link, to accommodate the alteration in length of the spring as it flexes.

Many present-day cars are fitted with independent suspension systems, either at the front, or at both front and rear. In this case the wheels are not connected by a rigid axle, but are free to rise and fall independently in response to road surface irregularities. Each wheel is attached to the chassis by a pair of hinged arms, or by a single pivoted arm. Either a leaf spring, coil spring, or a torsion bar may supply the necessary resilient suspension. Fig. 41 shows some typical examples of modern systems.

Torsion Bar Suspension. The torsion bar method of suspension calls for some explanation. In this case the springing is provided by the elasticity of a rod or tube which is twisted. One end is attached to the chassis, and the other to the arm carrying the wheel.

When the wheel rises, the bar is twisted, and, in attempting to unwind, provides the necessary resilience. In one example which is employed a rod and a tube are used, to provide a more compact unit than a single rod of double the length. The rod is attached to the wheel arm at the outer end, and passes through

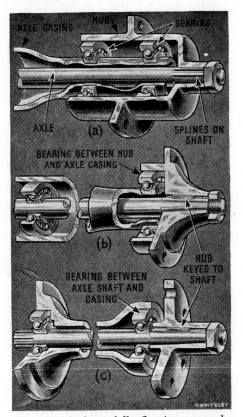

FIG. 38. (*a*) *shows fully-floating rear axle, the load is carried by the axle casing;* (*b*) *three-quarter floating axle, the casing and axle share the load;* (*c*) *semi-floating axle where the shaft carries the entire load.*

the tube to which its inner end is attached. The twisting effect thus passes from the rod through the tube and back to the point at which the tube is anchored to the chassis.

The principle of torsion bar suspension is not new: the familiar coil spring is simply a torsion bar coiled into a helical shape, its resistance to compression being the result of twisting the wire from which it is made.

Future Possibilities. It is likely that suspension systems employing rubber as an elastic medium may challenge the

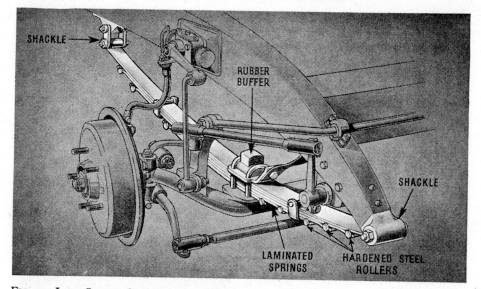

FIG. 39. LEAF-SPRING SUSPENSION. *View showing a leaf-spring anchored to the chassis and the U-bolts strapping it to the front axle.*

orthodox designs in the future. Rubber has inherent damping properties which render the use of shock absorbers unnecessary. An alternative possibility is the wider use of hydraulic suspension systems of the type already employed, for example, on the Citroen D.S. 19.

Shock Absorbers and Stabilizers.
If a length of spring steel is bent and then suddenly released, it will vibrate several times before coming to rest. The same thing occurs when a road wheel attached to any of the springing systems just described encounters a bump. To prevent

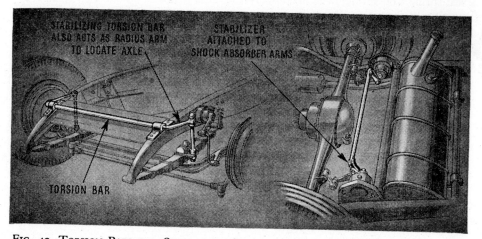

FIG. 40. TORSION BARS AND STABILIZERS *fitted to prevent lateral rolling when travelling round corners, and the twisting of the axle when the brakes are applied.*

FIG. 41. MODERN INDEPENDENT SUSPENSION *systems fitted to front wheels. The upper view shows the use of torsion bars and hydraulic telescopic dampers. The centre view illustrates the use of laminated transverse springs with piston type hydraulic shock absorbers, and the lower view, coil springs with hydraulic shock absorbers.*

51

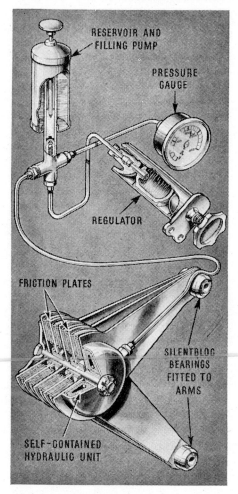

FIG. 42. A Multi-disk friction type shock absorber. It is hydraulically controlled by means of a regulator from the driving seat.

another when it is flexed, and this accounts for its popularity until today.

Since the modern demand for comfort dictates more flexible springs, however, various methods of reducing the friction between the spring leaves have been adopted, such as small rollers fitted between the tip of each leaf and the one above, or zinc disks similarly engaged. This, or the use of coil springs, or torsion bars which have no inherent damping effect, has called for the development of more efficient shock absorbers. Figs. 42 and 43 illustrate two types of shock absorbers, and other common types are referred to in Chapter 9.

Body-roll and Axle-twisting. More flexible suspension systems have intensified two further problems: the tendency of the car to roll on corners, and, in the case of leaf springs, the rotation of the axle when the brakes are applied, due to distortion of the spring.

The first fault can be cured by the anti-roll torsion bar shown in Fig. 40. Provided that both wheels rise and fall together, the bar does no work. If the body rolls to one side, however, one arm

the wheel from bouncing up and down, and the car as a whole bouncing on the springs, some form of damper or shock absorber is required.

This is fitted between the spring and the chassis, and may be a simple friction device which prevents any bouncing tendency. The leaf spring itself has an inherent damping action, due to the friction of the leaves as they slide over one

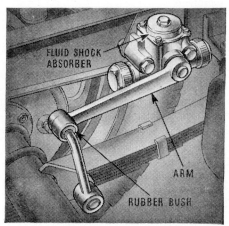

FIG. 43. A piston type hydraulic shock absorber located between the chassis and axle. The link arm is housed in rubber bushes.

is depressed and the other lifted, tending to twist the bar, which resists the roll. The second fault, twisting of the axle under brake torque reaction, can be eliminated by the same anti-roll bar, the arms of which function as radius rods to locate the front or rear axle. This method is usually adopted nowadays in preference to fitting separate radius arms or steel cables, anchored at one end to a bracket on the axle and the other to the chassis.

THE STEERING GEAR

Modern designs of steering gear represent many years of development and specialization; they must combine accuracy and sensitive control with directional stability and ease of operation.

Fig. 45 shows the lay-out of a typical steering gear, and it is almost self-explanatory. It will be seen from Fig. 45 that the steering wheel in the driving compartment moves one front wheel through a gearbox and linkage, and this movement is transmitted to the other wheel through a transverse coupling rod termed a track rod.

Two basic principles, however, are not apparent from this illustration. The first is that allowance must be made for the fact that when the car is driven round a bend, the inner wheel follows a smaller arc or circular path than

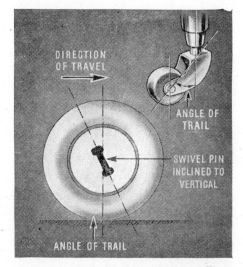

FIG. 44. *Castor action is obtained by placing steering pivot in advance of wheel axle.*

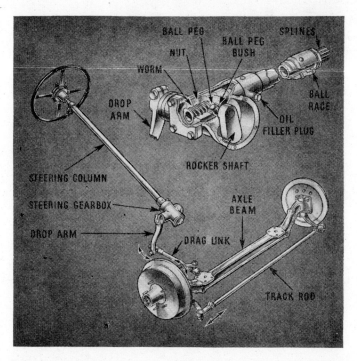

FIG. 45. *General layout of steering gear. The steering gearbox shown employs a worm and nut. Movement of the nut is conveyed by the rocker shaft to the drop arm and drag link, and then to the track rod.*

53

the outer and must, therefore, turn through a greater angle. This is achieved by arranging the steering arms so that they converge slightly, resulting in the front wheels turning through a different angle.

Castor Principle. The second is the ability of the wheels to return to the straight-ahead position of their own accord when the steering wheel is released.

This self-alining action is due to the castoring effect caused by inclining the pivot pins slightly backwards, as shown in Fig. 44. The effect is similar to the self-alining property of the ordinary castor fitted to a chair or dinner wagon.

Of the several different types of steering gearbox used, one of which is shown in Fig. 46, space does not permit detailed discussion. Further information regarding these, and the various types of joint will be found in Chapter 9.

THE BRAKES

The braking systems on modern cars can be divided into two groups: those employing mechanical operation by rods or cables, and hydraulic braking systems.

Both employ the same principle, the forcing apart of two shoes inside a drum.

The brake shoes are faced with a heat-proof friction material, and are carried on a backplate attached to the axle, while the drum is attached to the wheel hub and rotates with it. If the shoes are forced against the inside of the drum, the friction created will retard the drum and bring the wheel to rest.

The power exerted by a brake is surprising. In bringing the car to a standstill from 40 m.p.h. within a distance of about 25 yards, for in-

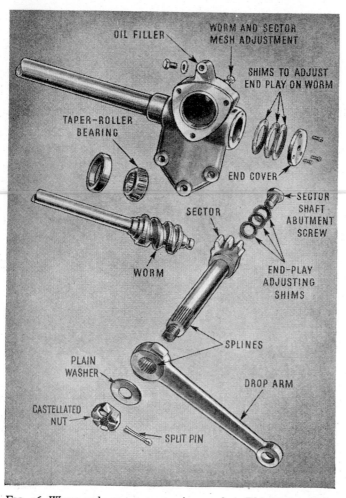

FIG. 46. *Worm and sector type steering gearbox. This is more direct and sensitive. Slightest movement of the worm actuates the sector.*

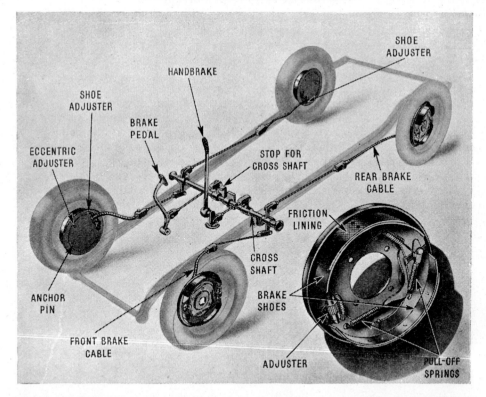

FIG. 47. MECHANICAL BRAKING. *The shoes are expanded by a cam or wedges and plungers. Expanders are coupled to the brake pedal and handbrake by rods and cables*

stance, each brake performs work that is equal to over 33 h.p. The power exerted by one brake, in fact, is roughly equal to that required to drive the car at 40 m.p.h. on a level road.

Mechanical Brakes. A number of different methods of expanding the shoes inside the drums are in use. A simple cam, which, when rotated by an arm pivoted to the backplate, forces the shoes apart may be used. To reduce friction, some designers employ steel balls or rollers which are forced between the tapered faces of plungers in contact with the ends of the brake shoes. This wedging action provides a powerful leverage.

Fig. 47 shows a typical lay-out of the operating rods and cables of a system of this type. All four brakes are applied by the foot pedal and the hand lever. On some designs the hand lever applies the rear brakes only.

Hydraulic Brakes. The hydraulic braking system makes use of the fact that when a fluid is compressed, it exerts an equal pressure in all directions on its container. If a piston, operated by a foot pedal, compresses a fluid contained in a cylinder which has outlets communicating with pipes running to the four wheel brakes, it follows that the pressures in all pipes will be equal; by fitting a small cylinder to each brake backplate, and using two pistons to force the shoes apart, powerful and balanced braking is obtained. Fig. 48 illustrates the system.

Servo-operated braking systems, which were, until recently, confined to larger cars and commercial vehicles, are now to be found on a number of medium-sized cars. The servo assistance is provided by a vacuum-operated piston which is connected, through a control valve, to the induction manifold. A rod attached to the vacuum piston operates a plunger in the master cylinder of the hydraulic system. The control valve is operated by the normal hydraulic pressure in the system, whenever the driver depresses or releases the brake pedal.

THE WHEELS AND TYRES

A wheel consists, basically, of a rim to which the tyre is attached, and a central portion which is bolted or otherwise attached to the hub which runs on bearings on the axle of the car, the two parts being connected by spokes or a disk.

At one time, the rim and centre were held together by wooden or hollow metal spokes: this was termed an artillery wheel. On modern cars, the wheel is usually a steel pressing, with some sections welded together; the construction is at once strong, light, and easy to clean.

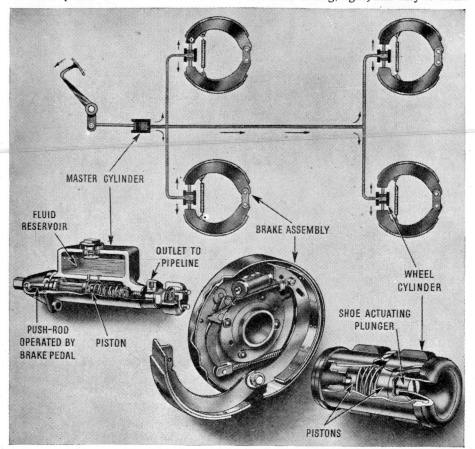

MASTER CYLINDER

FLUID RESERVOIR

OUTLET TO PIPELINE

BRAKE ASSEMBLY

WHEEL CYLINDER

SHOE ACTUATING PLUNGER

PUSH-ROD OPERATED BY BRAKE PEDAL   PISTON

PISTONS

FIG. 48. HYDRAULIC BRAKING. *The system is operated by fluid pressure that forces apart pistons in a cylinder mounted on a back-plate. When the brake is applied, the pistons expand the shoes which contact the drums and retard the movement of the car.*

56

On sports cars, however, the wire-spoked wheel is still used to a certain extent. In this design, the weight of the car is borne by a number of wires in tension. By arranging the spokes at a tangent to the hub and rim, acceleration and braking forces are also resisted by the wires, which are in a state of tension.

On most cars the wheels are bolted to the hubs. On sports cars, however, the hub is often splined, while the interior of the wheel centre is also splined to match. By sliding the wheel on to the hub until it is home against a tapered seating, and screwing up a large hub nut, the wheel is firmly held. The hub nut may have "ears", so that it can be given several blows with a copper hammer to tighten or loosen it, or may be made to fit a large ring spanner.

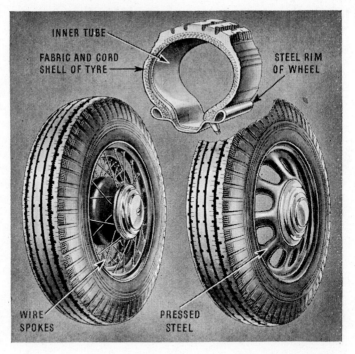

FIG. 49. *The upper drawing shows clearly the construction of a low-pressure tyre, and location of the inner tube and air inlet valve. A wire spoke and pressed steel wheel are shown below.*

Hub nuts are given a right-hand thread on the nearside wheels, and a left-hand thread on the offside, so that they are self-tightening; wheel nuts are sometimes similarly arranged.

Tyres. The tyres, which provide a resilient cushion to absorb minor road shocks and to afford good adhesion, consists of a moulded outer cover, reinforced by several plies of cotton cords, or, in the latest designs, by rayon or nylon. The outer cover is automatically locked in place on the rim of the wheel when expanded to shape by an inflated inner tube, which contains air under a pressure of 15 to 40 lb. per sq. in. or more, depending on the weight of the car and the design of the tyres. It is most essential to keep the tyres inflated to the pressure recommended by the manufacturer. In addition, attention should be paid to such factors as, front wheel track, removing small stones, tacks, etc. from the outer cover, driving on the brakes and rapid and erratic acceleration.

When the tyres are of the tubeless type, the casing is rendered impervious to air, so that the conventional inner tube can be dispensed with.

The valve is then fitted directly into the rim of the wheel and the outer edges of the tyre beads are so constructed as to form an airtight seal against the rim.

Correct initial assembly is essential.

CHAPTER 2

FIRST STEPS IN MOTORING

BEFORE buying a car, the following points should be carefully considered. First, there is the question of cost. Remember it is not only the initial outlay which comes under this heading; thought must be given to depreciation and running costs. The higher the horse-power, the heavier the insurance, petrol consumption, and so on.

Choice of Body. Next comes the question of the type of car. The choice will, to some degree, depend on the age of the prospective owner and his passengers, on the use to which the car will be put, and other considerations. As with the cost, no general rules can be laid down, although assistance can be given by a survey of the different types of body.

The Saloon Model. The most popular type of body in Great Britain is the saloon. For the driver who proposes to use his car as much in winter as in summer, and for whom it is essential that a vehicle be waterproof and draughtproof, the saloon body is the obvious choice. Generally speaking, it is the cheapest type of car to buy, and has much to recommend it from all points of view.

Modern window ventilation is so efficient that the feeling of stuffiness, even in a small saloon car, is no longer present. In many saloon models the windscreen is made to open outwards to increase the flow of air into the car during the hot weather, and an added means of ventilation is sometimes provided by a sliding roof. Ventilation units circulating a stream of fresh air by means of a fan are also available as additional fitments, or built into the car.

Saloon cars are designed to carry upwards of four people, including the driver. Sometimes two doors only are provided, but four are to be preferred and can generally be obtained at a slightly higher initial outlay. The advantages of the extra doors will be felt most, of course, by the driver who is in the habit of carrying passengers. A two-door fitment means repeated alighting and tipping of seats by those in front for the convenience of those in the back of the car.

There is really only one type of driver to whom the saloon model may not commend itself. This is the person who suffers from claustrophobia—the feeling of oppression and dread in a confined space, like a small room or even a compartment of an underground railway. Any such feeling of discomfort will prevent proper relaxation at the wheel, which is what all drivers should aim at.

Touring Bodies. At the other end of the scale is the open touring model, with collapsible hood and removable side-screens. This does not coincide with everybody's idea of comfortable motoring, but there are many experienced drivers who would choose no other type. Certainly, given reasonable weather, it is the ideal vehicle for summer touring.

Many motorists drive seven-eighths of their total annual mileage during the summer months. Some even garage their car for the winter. Others, while using their car a great deal for pleasure, also have a business use for it, and for these latter a tourer might not prove a practical proposition.

The tourer is no longer as popular as it was in pre-war days, but quite a number of current models are available in this version. The sporting motorist, of course, insists on touring-type sports cars, but these form rather a different class.

The great advantages of a touring body are that, with the hood down, driver and passengers alike are open to the air, and that full appreciation of the passing countryside can be indulged in. The drawback is that in the British climate there are comparatively few occasions when it is safe to venture out in a tourer without some protection against rain, wind or cold. In spring or autumn, when the sun feels quite warm overhead for ordinary purposes, it strikes definitely cold when passing through the air at thirty or forty miles an hour in an open car.

Protection against bad weather was provided with older touring models in the form of removable side-screens and a collapsible hood. These take no time at all to fix and remove. They are, of course, waterproof, although not necessarily draughtproof. In any event, in winter the touring car, even when totally closed, is bound to be chillier than a saloon car and also rather less waterproof. Further, with constant use the hood wears out faster than the bodywork of a saloon car.

The modern tourer is often known as a convertible, and the removable screens have been replaced by wind-up safety-glass windows, making the body as weatherproof as a saloon when closed.

It is worth remembering, by the way, that a two-seater open car is far more easily convertible than a four-seater. Raising and lowering the hood on the latter type can be a difficult task for one person unaided.

The Sunshine Roof. The main requirement of any car is that it shall be an efficient means of transport. For practical purposes, the saloon is the popular choice. If, on the other hand, the driver is a lover of fresh air and does not mind the slight discomforts which are inevitable, an

open touring model is probably the car that will give the greatest pleasure. There are, however, certain compromises to be considered.

One such compromise is the sliding-head or sunshine-roof saloon, as it has come to be known; that is to say, a saloon of which part of the roof slides back, leaving an area open to the sky. Many motorists regret that far fewer sliding roofs are now fitted as standard equipment than used to be the case.

The advantages of a sliding roof in a saloon have to be experienced to be fully appreciated. In bad weather it is kept closed, of course, but its easy opening from the driver's seat during fine, warm periods brings sun and air to those within, and takes away completely the feeling of oppression of which some saloon motorists complain.

The Drop-head Coupé. Another compromise is the coupé, the head of which is dropped to convert it from what might almost be called a saloon to what is undoubtedly a tourer of a better class. The side windows are of glass, and the hood can be rolled back half-way or dropped completely, as desired. Within limits, this type of body embraces all the advantages of the saloon and touring models.

When closed the drop-head coupé model is as windproof and watertight as a saloon body. When open it is a genuine touring car. As with the ordinary tourer, care must be taken with the hood, although the wearing qualities of modern drop-heads are very good.

A point to be considered is that the drop-head coupé is not a standard body, and, therefore, generally costs more than the ordinary saloon or tourer. If, however, the car is to be used both in town and country, the extra cost should prove a worth-while investment.

One word of caution. Some drop-head coupés seat only two or three people in comfort, rear seats being often cramped. In general, therefore, if the need is a family car for carrying four or five people in comfort, a drop-head coupé should be avoided. On every other ground it is the ideal body.

Choosing a Car. When the would-be motor car owner has decided the type of car he would like to buy, thought must be given to its size in relation to its horse-power. There is a wide field between small cars and high-powered cars, and the choice is not entirely a matter of cost, although that must, of course, be taken into account.

There are on the market today relatively high-powered makes of cars which are priced lower than some of lower horse-power. However, the tendency in design has been to increase the roominess of even the low-powered cars, so that an average modern saloon of whatever horse-power will carry four adults in the maximum of comfort.

The advantages of a high-powered engine are flexibility, avoidance of excessive gear-changing on hills and in traffic, swift acceleration, and, generally, a much longer period of use before the engine shows signs of wear. In other words, extended journeys can be undertaken with ease and at relatively high speeds in a high-powered car, whereas they might prove a strain on the driver of a smaller-powered car.

Cost apart, everything depends on the use to which the car is to be put. If its main purpose is to carry the owner on a number of long journeys, the need is for a high-powered model. If, on the other hand, the car is to be used as a runabout with only occasional long journeys, then size does not matter so much, and in times of over-crowded garages and parking-places, there are obvious advantages in having a small car for town use.

Another, if somewhat similar, factor to be considered is the annual mileage it is proposed to cover. This varies enormously between different types of car users. The average family car, with occasional week-end trips to the sea and the more extended runs on summer holidays, covers between 4,000 and 8,000 miles a year at the most, but it is quite normal for a car used by a commercial traveller to average upwards of 25,000 miles in twelve months.

Running Costs. Let us see how mileage can affect running costs, assuming the following items: tax at £12. 10s. per annum; private comprehensive insurance; petrol at, say, 4s. 6d. per gallon; average mileage per gallon for an 8 h.p. car forty and for a 20 h.p. car twenty; a depreciation during the year of £80 in the case of a light car and £150 in that of a larger model.

It must be understood that the figures given can vary considerably according to circumstances. For example, the depreciation of some models is very slight during the first few years; with other models it can be much higher than the figures quoted. Much depends on the popularity of the model and, therefore, on its availability in the open market. Depreciation is smaller in amount as a car becomes older, but the saving might well be offset by the greater cost of repairs and replacements.

The cost of insurance also varies over a wide range. It is highest in London and certain industrial areas, and lower in most rural areas. The figure also varies with the value of the car and the record of the driver: a rebate is normally allowed to a driver who has not made a claim during the preceding year. Special rebates are also allowed where a driver is prepared to accept responsibility in respect of, say, the first £10 of each and every claim.

Where only the third-party insurance legally necessary is effected the rate is under half that for comprehensive cover. On the other hand, the cost of in-

	8 h.p. 40 m.p.g.		20 h.p. 20 m.p.g.	
Annual mileage	5,000	25,000	5,000	25,000
	£	£	£	£
Depreciation	80 0	80 0	150 0	150 0
Tax	12 10	12 10	12 10	12 10
Insurance (Comprehensive), say . . .	17 0	17 0	24 0	24 0
Petrol (at, say, 4s. 6d. a gallon) to nearest £1	28 0	163 0	56 0	326 0
	137 10	272 10	242 10	512 10
Average cost per mile to nearest ¼d. . .	6½d.	2½d.	11½d.	5d.

Note: The cost of oil, garage, repairs and replacements have been ignored.

surance is appreciably increased when the car is used for business purposes and when goods or samples are carried.

The table above offers two lessons. First, and obviously, that the average cost per mile on any car decreases as the total mileage increases. Secondly, that the larger the potential mileage, the less difference there is in the average cost per mile between that done in a large as against a small-powered car. In actual fact, the cost per mile is less for a 20 h.p. car with a 25,000 mile average than for an 8 h.p. car with a 5,000 average.

Buying a Second-hand Car. How to buy a second-hand car is the problem that confronts large numbers of people as their first step in taking to the road. Assuming that a good second-hand car can be bought, it remains to be decided whether its acquisition would be sound policy, or whether it would be better to face what is in normal circumstances the greater expenditure of a new car.

The buying of a very old car is always something of a gamble unless the buyer is a mechanic. Occasionally the gamble comes off very successfully, but more frequently a car which has seen any length of service is not a reliable means of transport, and the new owner finds he is always having to put his hand in his pocket to

pay for running repairs, the replacement of parts, reconditioning, and so on.

If the would-be owner plans to cover a big mileage—say, in the region of 20,000 miles a year—it will nearly always be more economical to buy a new car rather than one of doubtful origin. Given due care and attention, particularly in the initial running-in stages, a new car will give many thousands of miles of comfortable travel without any major replacement or repairs.

If absolute reliability is essential for, say, business reasons (and few motorists are likely to do such a mileage as 20,000 unless their cars are used for business), it may easily prove most economical to buy a new car every year, obtaining the keenest price possible for the old model in part exchange. This arrangement of car replacement is often done by contract; otherwise, it should be remembered that the depreciation of new models is particularly high during the first twelve months in the absence of exceptional circumstances, such as shortage of cars.

Running Economy. From the above reasoning it follows that a car which is only a year or two old, and which has done nothing big in the way of mileage, might prove an economical proposition. This is especially true if the car is to be

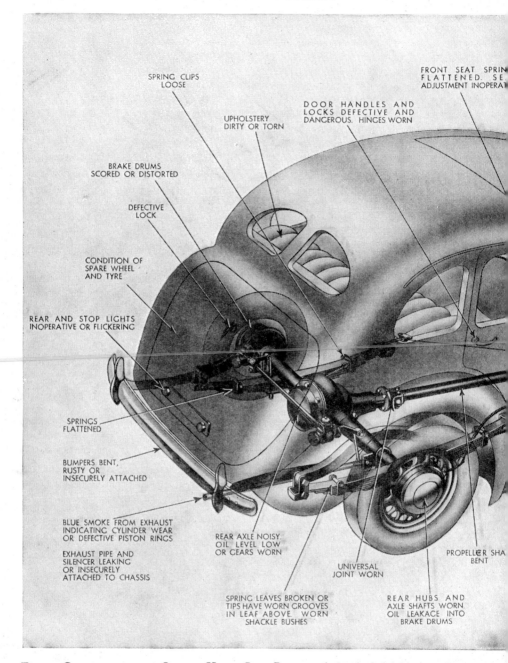

SPRING CLIPS
LOOSE

DOOR HANDLES AND
LOCKS DEFECTIVE AND
DANGEROUS. HINGES WORN

FRONT SEAT SPRIN
FLATTENED. SE
ADJUSTMENT INOPERAT

UPHOLSTERY
DIRTY OR TORN

BRAKE DRUMS
SCORED OR DISTORTED

DEFECTIVE
LOCK

CONDITION OF
SPARE WHEEL
AND TYRE

REAR AND STOP LIGHTS
INOPERATIVE OR FLICKERING

SPRINGS
FLATTENED

BUMPERS BENT,
RUSTY OR
INSECURELY ATTACHED

BLUE SMOKE FROM EXHAUST
INDICATING CYLINDER WEAR
OR DEFECTIVE PISTON RINGS

REAR AXLE NOISY.
OIL LEVEL LOW
OR GEARS WORN

PROPELLER SHA
BENT

EXHAUST PIPE AND
SILENCER LEAKING
OR INSECURELY
ATTACHED TO CHASSIS

UNIVERSAL
JOINT WORN

SPRING LEAVES BROKEN OR
TIPS HAVE WORN GROOVES
IN LEAF ABOVE. WORN
SHACKLE BUSHES

REAR HUBS AND
AXLE SHAFTS WORN.
OIL LEAKAGE INTO
BRAKE DRUMS

FIG. 1. CHECKING OVER A SECOND-HAND CAR. *Because of the doubtful history of most second-hand cars it is advisable to have them checked over. It is better to have an experienced mechanic go over the car, but if one is not available, the illustration can be very helpful as*

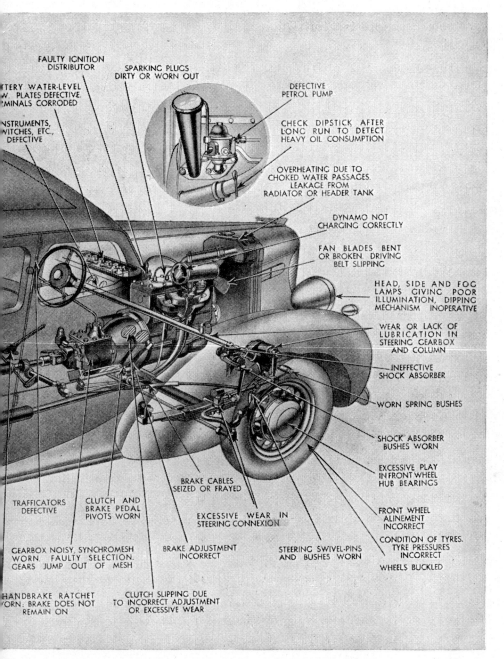

FAULTY IGNITION DISTRIBUTOR

SPARKING PLUGS DIRTY OR WORN OUT

TERY WATER-LEVEL W. PLATES DEFECTIVE. MINALS CORRODED

DEFECTIVE PETROL PUMP

NSTRUMENTS, WITCHES, ETC., DEFECTIVE

CHECK DIPSTICK AFTER LONG RUN TO DETECT HEAVY OIL CONSUMPTION

OVERHEATING DUE TO CHOKED WATER PASSAGES. LEAKAGE FROM RADIATOR OR HEADER TANK

DYNAMO NOT CHARGING CORRECTLY

FAN BLADES BENT OR BROKEN. DRIVING BELT SLIPPING

HEAD, SIDE AND FOG LAMPS GIVING POOR ILLUMINATION, DIPPING MECHANISM INOPERATIVE

WEAR OR LACK OF LUBRICATION IN STEERING GEARBOX AND COLUMN

INEFFECTIVE SHOCK ABSORBER

WORN SPRING BUSHES

SHOCK ABSORBER BUSHES WORN

EXCESSIVE PLAY IN FRONT WHEEL HUB BEARINGS

TRAFFICATORS DEFECTIVE

CLUTCH AND BRAKE PEDAL PIVOTS WORN

BRAKE CABLES SEIZED OR FRAYED

EXCESSIVE WEAR IN STEERING CONNEXION

FRONT WHEEL ALINEMENT INCORRECT

GEARBOX NOISY, SYNCHROMESH WORN. FAULTY SELECTION. GEARS JUMP OUT OF MESH

BRAKE ADJUSTMENT INCORRECT

STEERING SWIVEL-PINS AND BUSHES WORN

CONDITION OF TYRES. TYRE PRESSURES INCORRECT

WHEELS BUCKLED

HANDBRAKE RATCHET ORN. BRAKE DOES NOT REMAIN ON

CLUTCH SLIPPING DUE TO INCORRECT ADJUSTMENT OR EXCESSIVE WEAR

it spotlights those points that should be given attention. Of importance are the engine and transmission, also the braking and steering systems. The purchaser should drive the car to check for gearbox and body noises at different speeds and in varying road conditions.

63

used mainly for pleasure and only a reasonable mileage is contemplated, for clearly, the running repairs of a second-hand car on a small mileage will be proportionately less than on a big mileage.

On the other hand, there is a lot to be said for meeting the extra initial cost of a new car, providing there goes with the payment the determination to treat the vehicle with care and give it the attention recommended by the manufacturers. If a new light car is bought for £500, and is run 5,000 miles a year for ten years, with only such minor replacements as tyres, the owner cannot complain that his motoring has been unduly extravagant.

Some manufacturers have a scheme whereby a worn engine can be replaced by a new or reconditioned engine at a very moderate cost. This may well prolong the life of the car almost indefinitely, because with practised handling the strain on the transmission system is small. It is usually the engine of a car which first begins to give major trouble.

Points to Watch. A second-hand car seldom carries a guarantee, and in these circumstances it is helpful either to know the history of the particular car or else to know something about cars in general. The former is the better proposition. In fact, the ideal is to buy a car from a friend who bought it new in the first place, who has treated it carefully, not driven it over long distances at excessive speeds, and not been involved in a major accident.

If the history of the car is unknown, as is the case with many cars that exchange hands, it is worth obtaining an expert's report on it before deciding to purchase. The leading motoring associations arrange for such reports at a small fee, and the advice they give is strictly unbiased. However, any large and up-to-date garage will supply a mechanic to carefully check over the mechanical and electrical installations of a particular car, especially if it is privately owned.

Failing expert advice, the services of a friend with long experience of motoring are not to be despised. Generally, the following points are useful to bear in mind when making judgment on a second-hand car, although it is seldom possible to check on more than a few of them:

1. Examine the condition of the coachwork. See not only whether it is dented or marked in any way, but whether it has been kept well-washed and polished. A careful driver takes pride in the appearance of his car.

2. Look inside the bonnet. This may prompt the seller to point out certain defects, but look particularly for cleanliness. A dirty, oily-looking engine probably means that little care has been taken of it.

3. Look at the mileage registered by the speedometer. This may give a false reading, however, and is not always to be relied upon.

4. Examine the tyres for general condition. Look especially at the front tyres. If there are traces of markedly uneven wear or feathering, it may only mean that the front wheels are not in proper alinement. The cause may possibly be more serious, however—perhaps a buckled chassis as the result of a collision, in which case a heavy repair bill may be incurred, or frequent renewing of tyres may be found necessary.

5. Insert the starting handle and test the compression of the engine by turning slowly. This will reveal more to the expert than the novice, and is a test that tells much more about the condition of an engine.

6. Have the engine started up from cold. If it is slow or difficult in starting, the fault may be in the petrol supply (choked or faulty pump or carburettor) or ignition (weak battery, worn or faulty distributor contacts, dirty or outworn sparking plugs with faulty ignition).

7. Rev up the engine quickly in bottom gear and then decelerate immediately. Listen for a thumping noise in the engine. If this occurs during acceleration it is less serious than if it occurs on the over-run. In the latter case it may imply worn big-end bearings. Though these can be renewed at comparatively small cost, there is probably some underlying cause to account for the wear.

8. Look at the exhaust when the engine is being revved up. If smoke billows out (particularly blue smoke) in great quantities, the cause is generally excessive wear in the cylinders. This will mean that the consumption of oil will be very heavy.

9. Test the steering. Make sure that play in the wheel is not excessive, and that there is no undue drag to left or right. This is something that may or may not be serious, but it is unwise to take it on trust.

10. Have the car driven past you and note whether any of the wheels wobble. This may only be looseness of nuts (suggesting carelessness) or may denote some previous accident.

11. If possible, take the car on a reasonably long drive on varied roads, making several starts and stops. This will reveal the presence or otherwise of faults not usually traceable when the car is at rest.

12. Test the brakes by pulling up the car as rapidly as possible. If they do not act efficiently, the probability is that they need relining. The trouble may not be as simple as that, however. Excessive use may have worn the brake drums oval.

13. Listen for any noise emanating from the back axle when the car is being driven in top gear. If there is a distinctive hum, the crown wheel and pinion are probably worn, and may produce serious trouble at any time.

14. Ask to see the registration book (or "log-book" as it is commonly known). If produced, this should give much useful information about the car—the number of owners, how often taxed, date of original registration, and so on.

Any of the foregoing precautions may be the means of revealing flaws in a car offered for sale. An expert is better able to make a true assessment, particularly if arrangements are made for him to drive the car over a route with which he is familiar, but an expert is not infallible and, as previously stated, the buying of a second-hand car is always something of a gamble, even though everything possible be done to reduce the odds of picking a loser.

Garage. Having obtained a car and arranged for it to be taxed and insured, the next essential is its home. A private lock-up is to be preferred to a public garage. The latter has many facilities to offer, but also obvious drawbacks. In a large public garage, for instance, cars may have to be moved from time to time, and it is expecting too much of human nature to hope that the steering will never be wrenched, or that scratches will never appear on the bodywork.

If the car is to be housed in a private garage or lock-up, try to ensure that there is enough space not only for the car, but to walk around it. This is vital for the periodic attention which an owner must give his car.

If possible, it is worth having a small bench, on which to keep tools and to carry out small maintenance jobs. It is a great economy to be able to do minor repair work, as well as more satisfactory for one's own peace of mind.

A water tap is essential in the ideal garage, and there should be ready to hand either a can or a long piece of rubber tubing for filling the radiator when necessary.

Finally, a warning. Never in any circumstances run the car engine in a garage when the doors are closed. The carbon monoxide fumes which are given off from the exhaust pipe are poisonous, and can be fatal if inhaled for any length of time.

CHAPTER 3

LEARNING TO DRIVE

LEARNING to drive a motor car is like learning to do anything else. Success comes only by careful study and long practice. In the case of driving, skill is attained by going through three stages, the first two of which can be described as theory and the third as practice.

The first stage is to get to know the car and its controls. Before setting the car in motion, before even starting the engine, the beginner should familiarize himself with the position of these controls and should go through the motions of using them again and again, until the depression of a certain pedal or the changing of a gear at the correct moment becomes a habit.

It is probably not too much to say that good driving is based on good habits. The experienced driver does not appear to think what he is going to do next, although, in fact, his every action is the result of thought and planning. The actions become almost reflex, so smooth and inevitable is the sequence of hand and foot motions.

The second stage is to master the handling of the controls while the car is in motion on a quiet road. This is really a mechanical stage, in which the slower the progress the more lasting the results. But this second stage is also a very dangerous one, because so many would-be drivers imagine themselves to be competent with very little experience and nothing more than a round-the-houses trial run.

The third stage is to drive on the open road and in traffic. In this stage many new factors have to be taken into account, mainly other people, pedestrians, as well as other drivers. It is at this stage, however, that the learner comes to master the niceties of steering and control which are the hallmark of a good driver.

IN THE DRIVING SEAT

The first part of these instructions is designed for those who have never driven a car, and who are learning from the beginning. The second part, which deals more with the art of good driving, may be useful as a refresher course even for those who consider themselves experienced.

If a driver has been taught badly, there may be a number of things which he does badly or even incorrectly. His experience may have taught him to choose, say, speed before carefulness, in which case his experience has proved dangerous. He, in particular, would do well to reconsider the art of driving from its elementary stages.

Getting to know the car to be driven is the first stage. In different makes of cars the controls are not always placed in exactly the same position, and the description that follows may differ slightly from the lay-out of the model used. The general arrangement of the principal controls is very similar, however, and any variation will be revealed in the instruction book which is supplied with every new car. (For the owner of a second-hand vehicle an instruction book can generally be obtained at a small cost by post from the makers.)

The first essential of good driving is comfort at the steering wheel. The driver should take his place in the driving seat and *feel* himself into a forward-facing position that is erect, and yet comfortable, without any suggestion of discomfort. A clear view of the road ahead should be obtainable through the windscreen without any noticeable movement of head or back, or for that matter of the body at all.

If the correct position has been found, the feet should make contact with the foot controls in such a way that pressure on them can be exerted without undue effort. If that is not the case, the position is too far forward or too far back. If the driving seat is adjustable, as most are, it should be pulled forwards or backwards, as required. On some models seats are adjustable for height.

This changing of positions to make the controls accessible is vital to good driving. An uncomfortable driving position increases the difficulty of every operation and lessens the confidence of the learner. If the driving seat is fixed, or has been altered to its fullest extent without comfort having been attained, a cushion placed behind the back may help.

FIG. 2. *Comfort at the wheel is an essential of good driving. If necessary, adjust the position of the driving seat to obtain this.*

THE CONTROLS EXPLAINED

On the floor of the car, arranged on either side of the steering column, are three foot controls; the clutch pedal, the footbrake and the accelerator, or throttle pedal. The accelerator pedal is on the extreme right, the brake pedal is next to it, and the clutch pedal is on the left of the base of the steering column.

The two hand levers should next be noted, and in most cars these are placed centrally and in a position convenient for operation by the left hand. These are the handbrake lever and the gear change lever. The handbrake lever is pulled towards the driver for braking, while the gear change lever cannot only be moved in a forward and backward direction, but also to the left and right. It should be noted that on some modern cars the gear lever is attached to the steering column.

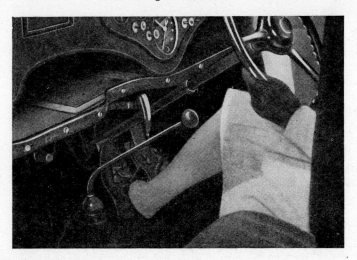

FIG. 1. *The driver's feet should make contact with the foot controls so that pressure can be exerted without undue effort having to be made.*

67

FIG. 3. THE DRIVING SEAT. *This view shows the disposition of the driving controls. All instruments and controls are grouped on one panel for ease of observation and use.*

Immediately in front of the driver as he sits at the wheel is the dashboard, facia panel, or instrument panel, as it is variously called. On it will be found dials which may include an ammeter, speedometer, oil pressure gauge and petrol gauge, all very important to the motorist, although not to be confused by the learner with the actual mechanical means of driving.

On the panel are certain controls which need to be used before the car can start. These are the choke, the ignition switch (or key) and the self-starter button, the ignition switch being often combined with the side-lights and headlights switch.

Each of the controls mentioned above will be discussed under a separate heading, but the first thing is to memorize their positions, so that when each is wanted in its turn the hand or foot will go automatically to the desired control without conscious thought.

The Steering Wheel. Of all the controls on the modern car the steering is perhaps the simplest to understand. On all makes the response is on the front wheels, and the rules of forward steering are as easy as they are obvious. If it is desired to steer the car to the right, the steering wheel is turned in a clockwise direction; if to the left, then the reverse, or anti-clockwise, turn of the wheel is made.

The great thing to remember about steering is that a slight turn of the wheel will produce an appreciable change of direction. The phrase "finger-light steering" may have been heard, and in modern cars the tendency is for steering to become lighter and lighter. Theoretically, at least (road safety precludes the practice) it should be possible to steer even quite large cars with one finger.

There is always a certain degree of play in the steering wheel, that is to say, the wheel can be turned a fraction (the actual distance varies in different makes, and is naturally more pronounced in old cars)

without meeting any resistance or altering the course of the car. The amount of play in the wheel should be judged carefully before the car is taken on the road.

A light touch is essential to good steering. However light the pressure needed to make a turn, the wheel should be held firmly with both hands, except when performing a necessary driving function. The best position for the hands is that which ensures the maximum control, and in practice many drivers have found a good hold to be that illustrated in Fig. 2, with the left hand at about eight o'clock and the right at about two o'clock.

Alternative positions used are with the right hand at three o'clock and the left hand at nine o'clock (not completely satisfactory), and with the right hand at

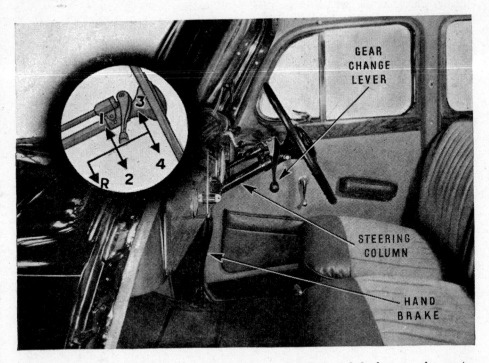

FIG. 4. GEAR CHANGING. *A recent development is the placing of the lever on the steering column to facilitate quicker operation. The inset shows the movement of the lever for selection of the four ratios and reverse. Clutch operation is the same as with a normal gear lever.*

three o'clock and the left hand at eight (frequently seen). The thing to ensure is comfort with efficiency, and it will be found that the position illustrated gives far better control than that which strikes many learners as the more obvious, with the left hand at nine or ten o'clock and the right hand at five.

With the position illustrated, it is easy to pull down the wheel or to push it up with the right hand alone, a move which may be necessary many times during a run while the left hand is withdrawn from the wheel to perform the necessary function of changing gear.

Always hold the steering wheel by the rim, never by the spokes. The nearer the grip is to the centre of the wheel, the less control there is and the less subtle are the movements it is possible to make. Finally, when holding the wheel see that the elbows rest comfortably at the sides. The practice adopted by some drivers of resting the right elbow on the window ledge restricts movement in the case of an emergency.

The Clutch Pedal. On almost every make of car the clutch pedal is situated in the floorboards on the left of the steering column. Its function is to connect or disconnect the drive between the engine and gearbox. In brief, the engine is freed with the depression of the pedal, and connected when the pedal is allowed to rise to its normal position (providing, of course, that a gear is engaged).

In order to depress the clutch with the firmness required, it is necessary to place the sole of the left foot squarely on the pedal and to exert a definite muscular pressure. If the attempt is made to operate it with only the toe of the shoe, the foot tends to slip off the pedal near the bottom of its travel, and there is less positive control.

It will be noticed that there is a clearance, or tolerance, in the clutch pedal; that is to say, it is only at a certain point in its downward travel that resistance to the foot pressure is felt. The amount of clearance varies not only between different cars, but also on the same make of car, according to the adjustment of the pedal. It is important that the driver of any car should first test the feel of the clutch before going on the road.

Clutch practice is especially beneficial to the learner, and it should be the aim to depress the pedal with the minimum effort and the maximum assurance. Try depressing it to its fullest extent in one positive movement, and then letting it slip back slowly into its normal position. Skill in releasing the clutch gently in this way will make for smoothness in engaging and changing gears when the time comes to drive the car.

When the car is in motion do not rest the foot on the clutch pedal. The weight of the foot is sufficient to cause premature wear of the clutch operating mechanism and may easily cause the clutch to slip slightly.

The Gear Change Lever. This is a lever which on most standard makes of car is placed centrally in the front part of the car, in a position convenient for operation by the left hand. By its manipulation in conjunction with the clutch pedal it is possible to engage three or four forward gears (as well as a reverse gear) which have different ratios.

Gear changing is the most important of the manual processes involved in driving a car, and it is essential that the learner understands its operation.

Power and Speed. It will suffice here to say that when a car is driven in low gear, speed is sacrificed for power. In a low gear the engine develops a high power relative to the speed of travel of the car, so that a low gear is required for the initial momentum, to provide the reserve of power necessary for swift acceleration from low speeds, and for climbing a hill.

Conversely, in a high gear power is exchanged for speed. The ratio of the highest gear is that at which the engine develops its most effective usefulness at what the manufacturers consider the best cruising speed of the particular car. The drive is said to be direct when the top gear is engaged.

The top gear is the gear for use under normal conditions, on a road that is level, moderately straight, unencumbered by heavy traffic, and with few built-up areas and their consequent crossings. In fact, once reached in normal circumstances, top gear should be maintained until it is necessary to reduce speed below about twenty miles per hour.

Auxiliary Gears. The gears other than top may be regarded as auxiliary. They are used principally for starting, for manœuvring at corners and in traffic, and for climbing hills. For starting (moving from a stationary position) the lowest gear must be engaged first. It is true that higher-powered cars can be started with seeming ease on one or other of the higher gears, but this puts an unnecessary strain on the transmission and is a practice which should be avoided.

It is as well to give the manufacturers credit for knowing something about the capabilities of the car they have produced. They have considered fully the gear ratio necessary to start a car with the maximum efficiency from rest, therefore, in fairness to them the lowest gear ratio is the one to use for normal starting.

Whatever personal opinions a motorist may have on this matter, he may sometimes be compelled to start in bottom gear, as, for instance, on a hill or against the camber of the road. It is obviously better for the learner to begin as he means to go on, and not to seek any apparent short cuts to quick progress.

As a preliminary, the various gear positions on the particular car should be found. Often they are marked on the handle of the change lever; otherwise, they will be indicated in the instruction manual. Number One is the bottom gear, the highest numbered is the top gear, and R stands for reverse.

A four-speed gearbox, which has become the most popular type, has been selected as an example for this chapter. In the main the directions given will also be applicable to three-speed boxes, except that there will be one less movement. On a four-speed box bottom gear is normally in the left-hand forward position, the second gear left and backward, the third gear right and forward, the top gear right and backward. The inset in Fig. 4 shows the gear selection movements when the gear change lever is attached to the steering wheel.

Mastering the Gears. It is essential to get the feel of these positions. It may be found that, without the engine running, the gear lever will not slip easily into the required positions. This does not matter. The important thing is to master the directions in which to move the lever for a particular gear engagement, so that the movement becomes a semi-automatic operation.

Practise moving the lever about from one position to another. Then, when this has been done a number of times, try depressing the clutch pedal between each movement. This is good training because, as previously mentioned, before making a change of gear it is necessary to disengage the engine and the gearbox by throwing out the clutch.

Although it may not be used in the first lessons, it is also advisable to get the feel of the reverse gear. Generally, more difficulty is experienced in engaging this gear than any of the others. This is designed by the manufacturers to safeguard against changing into reverse when attempting to engage a forward gear.

On four-speed models the reverse gear engagement is made by lifting or pushing the gear change lever against a spring. Some cars have the additional precaution of a button or ratchet which must be pressed or lifted before the reverse gear can be engaged.

There will be a good deal more to learn about the use of gears as soon as the car is on the road. However, preliminary drill in locating and engaging gears will be found invaluable in practice, providing it is carried out thoroughly and often enough.

The Footbrake. In the course of driving the brakes are operated by the pedal on the immediate right of the steering column, that is to say, by the central of the three foot controls. The brake pedal is connected with the brake mechanism operating on all four wheels, and its depression will bring the system into operation in a greater or lesser degree according to the pressure applied.

There are many different systems of braking, and they operate with extraordinary variety of action. It is true to say that the brakes on no two cars are alike. Some are fierce and sudden, others more gentle. Corresponding with this difference of action, a different degree of pressure is necessary on the brake pedal, so that no precise rule can be given until the brakes of a car have been tested in practice.

The only rule which applies to every car is that the pressure on the brake pedal must be even and square, the action of the foot being similar to that recommended for depressing the clutch pedal, except that in this instance the right foot is used. In fact, it is a good rule when driving never to do anything suddenly. Apart from the inherent danger of sudden movements, an unnecessary strain is put on the car's mechanism.

The Handbrake. This is operated by a lever which is nearly always centrally placed, and in a position convenient for application by the left hand. Its type will

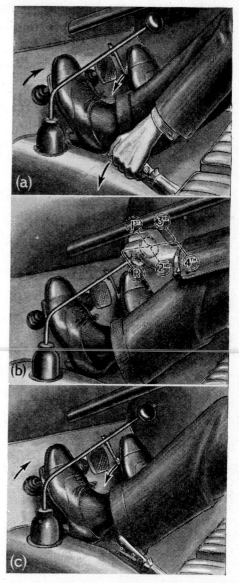

FIG. 5. *Sequence of operations when moving away from rest; (a) shows the handbrake being released, the clutch being engaged and the accelerator slightly depressed; the gear lever is in 1st gear position; (b) changing up from 1st to 4th gear position, the five positions of the gear lever are shown; (c) letting-in the clutch and depressing the accelerator.*

72

depend on the make of car, but generally it is operated by a pull towards the driver, either backwards or upwards.

On some models the handbrake operates on all four wheels, on others on the back wheels only. Whatever the action, its purpose and functions are the same; the handbrake lever provides a second means of operating the braking system either in an emergency, continual application of the brakes without sustained flywheel effort or for holding the brakes "on" when the car is parked.

The application of the handbrake is simple in principle, but to release the lever quickly and effectively is more difficult. Generally, it is held in place by a ratchet, and it is necessary for the user to pull the lever further towards him to effect its release.

On most models the operation of a small supplementary lever, or a knob at the top of the main lever, will free the ratchet; it is advisable to use this both in the application and release of the handbrake. Once it is released from its ratchet, the main lever will slip back to its off position. None the less, it is as well to give it a final forward or downward press to make sure that the brakes are properly off before attempting to move the car from its stationary position.

The Accelerator Pedal. This is the foot control on the extreme right-hand side of the floorboards. It is operated by the right foot in the same way as the footbrake, but its application must be infinitely more subtle and gentle. Practice depressing it slowly and gently, and then letting it back to its normal position just as carefully.

Avoid any jerky or sudden movement of the accelerator pedal, and treat it always as the delicate control it is. Remember that more damage is done to the transmission of a car in the normal course of usage by sudden or jerky acceleration or deceleration than by any other cause. When on the road sudden acceleration will spoil the feeling of control, especially in low gears. It is also the cause of excessive wear on tyres.

Sudden acceleration can be the means of skidding on wet or icy roads. The effect of a quick depression of the accelerator pedal is for the back wheels to be forced suddenly into rapid rotation. At a given point the adhesion between the back wheels and the road will cease to be effective, and the wheels will spin, with an immediate likelihood of a skid.

There is one other drill necessary before starting the engine. That is to practise alternate depression of the accelerator and footbrake pedals with the right foot in rapid succession. The aim should be certainty of changing the foot from one to the other quickly and avoiding depressing the edge of the accelerator pedal when operating the footbrake.

This rapid changing of pedals cannot be practised too often. Faulty location of one or the other with the foot is one of the most frequent errors in the early stages of driving, and perhaps the most dangerous. It has been a plea of defence in court cases in which motorists of many years experience have been involved.

ON THE ROAD

If the learner has familiarized himself with the position of the controls and has carried out all the preliminary drill described in the preceding pages, the first stages of actual driving should present no real difficulty. There may well be an initial tenseness, but there should not be the slightest hesitancy in handling the controls because all the essential movements may be assumed already to be habitual, and capable of being performed without conscious effort.

For this second stage of mastering the controls it is to be assumed that a friend or instructor holding a full licence has driven the learner to a suitable stretch of quiet road, that the learner is himself in possession of a provisional licence, and that the L plates of the official dimensions are displayed one at the front and one at the rear of the car. These points are obligatory if it is desired to practise driving on the public highway.

The best kind of thoroughfare on which to practise is a fairly long straight stretch carrying as little traffic as possible. It is far better first to master the art of driving without the distraction of traffic, and then at a later date, to study the separate art of driving in traffic, rather than to attempt the two together.

The instructor having parked the car on the near side of the road and switched off the engine, the learner should take his place at the wheel, as previously described. The learner should then be allowed to start the engine, having been warned beforehand to make absolutely certain that the gear lever is in the neutral position.

This *must* be a routine check every time the engine is started, just as it should be routine to leave the gear lever in neutral after stopping. If the car is in gear when the engine is started, it will shoot forward. Providentially, the engine may stall; on the other hand, a serious accident may result.

This double check is just as essential with a driver of experience; more so, perhaps, because he will often be starting a car in a position where a sudden forward movement might be extremely dangerous.

HOW TO START THE ENGINE

There are three controls on the dashboard, or instrument panel, with which the learner must familiarize himself before he can start the engine. These are the ignition switch, the choke and the starter. The first step is to switch on the ignition (and, therefore, the engine), which is ordinarily performed by turning a removable key to the right or left. This also switches on the electric petrol pump, and at its turning the petrol gauge on the dash will register.

Most modern cars have fitted to the distributor (see Chapter 7) fully automatic ignition control, in which case there is no manual control. On other cars, older cars in particular, a manual control is provided for the purpose of adjusting the ignition timing. In the ordinary course of events this should not be touched on a new car by an amateur, because, at the factory, it has been set to give best all-round results.

With most older cars the ignition control took the form of a lever on the upper part of the steering column, its arc of movement being terminated by positions marked "Advance" and "Retard". These positions coincide with the "A" and "R" at either end of a graduated scale which today is often fitted on the distributor securing clamp, and by which delicate adjustments can be made if found necessary.

On cars fitted with the steering column lever, it was customary to use the "Retard" position for starting, and then to move the lever towards "Advance" as the engine warmed. Such manipulations are no longer necessary, and, if not automatically controlled, the timing should be fixed by a mechanic to give the best results. It will be seen that generally the spark is advanced by an adjustment of the distributor body in a clockwise direction, and retarded by a reverse movement.

Use of the Choke. The choke control is usually in the form of a pull-out knob on the dashboard, and its purpose is to control the strength of the mixture supplied by the carburettor (see Chapter 4) to the engine. When pulled out, the air reaching the petrol combustion chamber is minimized, and the mixture correspondingly enriched.

When starting from cold, particularly when the weather is severe, the richest possible mixture is necessary and the choke must, therefore, be held out to its fullest extent. When the engine is warm, the choke is not needed; in fact, difficult starting arises less from under-choking then over-choking, but more of this later. The choke button should be pushed home as soon as possible to avoid the flow of neat petrol into the cylinders.

The starter is usually either a press button or pull-out knob on the dashboard, but on some older models it is a foot press button on the floorboards. Assuming the ignition to be switched on and the choke pulled out, it is necessary only to operate the starter for the engine to fire.

If the engine fires after two or three seconds and then fades out, the probability is that the choke is not out far enough. In that case pull it right out and start again. If, on the other hand, there is no response to the operation of the starter after six or seven seconds, it is probable that the mixture is too rich; that is to say, the choke is being used too much.

This is a condition which needs attention. It is of no use letting in the choke and then starting again; the surplus fuel has first to be expelled from the combustion chamber before the engine will fire. To do this, switch off, push home the choke, press down the accelerator to its fullest extent, and operate the starter for ten or fifteen seconds. Then release the pressure on the accelerator, and, with the switch on, and either no choke or very little, press the starter again.

If there is still difficulty in starting, rather than overstrain the battery by continuing to operate the starter motor, do nothing for about five minutes, by which time most of the surplus petrol will have evaporated; in certain conditions it may be necessary to remove the plugs and dry them. Then endeavour to start again according to the directions given.

Once started, the engine needs to be kept going at a reasonable speed if it is to warm up as soon as possible. Some cars have a starting control incorporated in the choke, others have separate fitments, but their object is the same, to effect a steady acceleration of the engine until warm. Failing either of these, the accelerator pedal should be depressed so that the engine turns over fairly fast, the choke being released as soon as the rich mixture causes the engine to run erratically.

MOVING OFF

Once the engine has been started and is considered warm enough, the driver should prepare to move off and change up through the gears. The precise sequence of operations is as follows, and can best be seen in tabular form (a four-speed gearbox is assumed, as before):

1. Depress the clutch pedal to its fullest extent, and move the gear lever left and forward into bottom gear.
2. Release the handbrake lever.
3. Give a slight, but steady pressure on the accelerator pedal, and simultaneously let the clutch pedal return gently to its normal position.

About half-way between the "out" and "in" positions of the clutch pedal (that is to say, as the clutch itself is engaged) the car will begin to move. It should pull away gently, and without any noticeable jerk. The smoothness of this operation depends on how gently the clutch is let in, and, to some extent, on the evenness of the pressure maintained on the accelerator pedal.

Changing Gear. The car is now being driven in first gear, and the pressure on the accelerator pedal may be increased gradually until the speedometer indicates a speed of about eight miles an hour. This is the time to change up into second gear, and here the sequence of operations is similar to that detailed above:

1. Depress the clutch pedal to its fullest extent, and simultaneously release the pressure on the accelerator pedal.
2. Move the gear change lever through neutral into the second gear position.
3. Let in the clutch (rather more quickly than before), and as the gear is engaged gently depress the accelerator.

The essence of this change (and the subsequent ones) is the quickness with which it is carried out. Obviously, the quicker the change is made the less speed will be lost. What is happening when a change is made either up or down, is that what is often called an "equation" is obtained between the speed of the engine and the speed of the driving wheels as modified by the gear.

In the lowest gear a car can, with the same number of engine revolutions per minute, travel slower than in second gear, and slower in second gear than in third gear, and so on. So that when the change is made to a higher gear, it is necessary for the engine to have the opportunity of slowing down until its revolutions are adjusted to the appropriate revolutions at the same speed in the higher gear. Letting in the clutch helps to slow down the engine, and consequently makes a more rapid change possible.

Never force home the gear lever if there seems to be some resistance. By its correct manipulation the gears should engage easily; in fact, most modern makes of cars are fitted with various devices which make it next to impossible to crash the higher gears, although extra care is sometimes needed in engaging the bottom gear.

Reverting to the last change made, the car is now being driven in second gear. Again, gently depress the accelerator pedal. When the speedometer needle hovers around the fifteen miles per hour

mark, the moment has arrived to change into the next, and third gear. This sequence of operations is as for the previous change, except for the position of the new gear, namely:

1. Depress the clutch pedal, simultaneously releasing the pressure on the accelerator pedal.
2. Move the gear change lever through neutral, right and forward into third gear.
3. Let in the clutch, and gently depress the accelerator.

It is advisable to make the final change upwards when the car is travelling at between twenty and twenty-five miles an hour, although this and all the other changes is largely a matter for the discretion of the individual. The change from third to top is accomplished by repeating the process of operations given above, the gear lever being moved straight back, through neutral, to the position indicated for the top gear.

Stop the car at this stage, and start again. The correct sequence of operations for stopping the car is as follows:

1. Gently release the pressure on the accelerator pedal.
2. Depress the clutch and brake pedals firmly.
3. Move the gear lever forward into neutral, and let in the clutch.
4. Steer slightly to the left, so that the car comes to rest as near to the kerb as possible.
5. Apply the handbrake.

Now repeat the process of moving off, changing up through the gears, and stopping, until these operations become automatic. A little experience will show that driving is not so difficult as may have been imagined. Once the learner is accustomed to the feel of the car in motion, confidence will come, and then proficiency will soon follow with practice.

The chief faults of the beginner in moving off are (i) starting with a jerk, (ii)

76

stalling (stopping) the engine. A jerky start will result if the clutch is let in too rapidly, or if the accelerator is depressed too quickly. The engine will tend to stall if the power is not enough, particularly if at the same time the clutch is let in too quickly. Following a stall, move the gear lever into neutral and start all over again.

It may at first be difficult to move the gear lever from one position to another, or even into neutral, with any degree of accuracy or speed, and in consequence too much speed may be lost in changing from one gear to the next. In this, as in every sphere of driving, skill will come with practice, and these are minor points which may soon be put right.

POINTS TO REMEMBER

When driving a car, it is important to keep the eyes fixed on the road ahead at all times. Never be tempted to look for the controls. Momentarily, of course, the steering will have to be done with one hand as the other is engaged in changing gear. The temptation to keep the gear change hand on the lever when no change is required should be avoided.

When a change has been completed, the operating hand should be returned to the steering wheel at once. It may be thought that adequate control is provided by the one hand, but this is not so, as has been proved many times in an emergency, such as a dog running across the road at a critical moment. The same principles hold good when using the right hand to give a signal of some kind.

Be sure that the road is clear behind as well as in front before moving off from a stationary position. In starting it is necessary to draw away slightly from the kerb (this should be

Fig. 6. *Whenever practicable, and it usually is, park near to the kerb and not a foot or two away from it as illustrated in upper view.*

three inches, and the front and rear wheels should be parallel with the line of the kerb, except when parking on hills, when for safety's sake it is advisable to leave the forward wheels turned towards the kerb.

Judging distances, of which more later, is a vital part of driving which requires a great deal of practice. The kerb should be avoided and should *never* be hit, even when stopping (quite apart from the fact that doing so damages the best of tyres). As explained above, however, the car should be parked as close to the kerb as is reasonably possible; an important point, this, in narrow or crowded thoroughfares.

FIG. 7. *Never drive on the crown of the road (upper view); keep near to the kerb (lower view). This allows any overtaking traffic to pass without cutting across the oncoming traffic lane.*

indicated by the appropriate hand signal), as without timely warning a driver coming on behind may find it difficult to avoid a collision. To obviate such crises, make a habit of looking in the mirror before moving off. To be doubly certain, before starting look round through the rear window.

Judging of Distances. When a stop is made, the handbrake should be applied firmly. In the early stages of driving it is as well to get out of the car and look to see the distance between the car and the edge of the kerb after parking. This should not be more than six nor less than

Dashboard Instruments. As soon as the engine is started, some of the instruments on the dashboard begin to register. An occasional glance at these instruments is necessary, but not to the prejudice of road safety. The reading should be made as quickly as possible in order not to lose sight of the road ahead.

The speedometer is the instrument which will need most frequent study. This shows the mileage done by the car, and also indicates the speed of the car in miles per hour. With practice it is possible to estimate the speed, and all that is required is observation of the speedometer when driving in a restricted area where the speed limit in force must be observed.

The purpose of the oil gauge, if one is fitted, is to indicate the pressure of oil being fed to the engine. It will show a high pressure on first starting the engine, especially if the engine is cold.

I WANT TO TURN
TO MY LEFT

I AM READY TO BE
OVERTAKEN

I AM GOING TO
SLOW DOWN OR STOP

I AM GOING TO
TURN TO MY RIGHT

This pressure will tend to fall as the engine warms and the oil becomes more fluid, but that is nothing to worry about: in fact, it is to be expected. The approximate pressure to look for on a particular car will be noted in the instruction manual.

If at any time the oil gauge ceases to register, or registers a figure very different from that prescribed, the car should be stopped and the advice of an expert sought. It may be that the oil pump is not functioning properly, in which case the moving parts of the engine will become overheated. To continue driving may cause extensive damage.

Similarly, the ammeter, an instrument for measuring the charge or discharge from the electrical system, must be watched carefully. Its pointer or needle should swing either to the right (indicating that the battery is being charged) or the left (discharge), according to what is happening at the time.

When the ignition switch is turned on during the day (that is, when no lights are being used), the ammeter needle should swing to the right, until a reading of eight to ten amperes is given when the car is travelling at about twenty miles per hour. When all the lights are switched on the

FIG. 8. *Above are the hand signals which a driver should use to indicate his intentions to other road users. On his right are the hand signals which should be used to indicate to a police constable regulating traffic, the direction in which the driver wishes to proceed. The signals shown are those which are authorized in Great Britain*

I WANT TO TURN
TO MY LEFT

I WANT TO TURN
TO MY RIGHT

I WANT TO GO STRAIGHT AHEAD

ammeter will read zero, that is, the charge is balancing the discharge. If this is not the case, it is advisable to have the electrical system inspected by a mechanic at the earliest opportunity.

CHANGING DOWN

To revert to the mechanics of driving. Once the sequence of operations connected with upward gear changing has been mastered, changing down presents no real difficulty, except for the additional process of double de-clutching.

The aim of changing down is to obtain more power from the engine.

It is necessary to change down if the speed drops below that at which adequate acceleration can be obtained; for example, when ascending hills, at corners, and in traffic. Forcing the acceleration when it is not spontaneous causes strain on the transmission, and the life of the car is prolonged if a change down is made when the need is apparent.

One way of engaging a lower gear in such circumstances is to stop the car and start again in bottom. In the case of a bungled change, that is quite a sound thing to do. All the same, it is not feasible to be constantly stopping in a stream of traffic, so that the technique of changing down through the gears should be mastered.

Imagine that the car is climbing a steep hill in top gear and that the speed has fallen to about ten or fifteen miles an hour. At such a speed the engine labours badly if the attempt is made to accelerate. A change to a lower gear should, therefore, be made, and the sequence of operations is as follows:

1. Release the accelerator pedal, firmly press down the clutch pedal, and slip the gear change lever into neutral.
2. Release the clutch pedal, and, immediately afterwards, sharply depress the accelerator pedal.

3. Release the accelerator pedal, depress the clutch pedal, and move the gear lever into the required position.
4. Release the clutch pedal, and press down the accelerator pedal until the required speed is obtained.

The secret of carrying out this operation successfully depends upon various factors, chief of which is flexibility and speed in performing the sequence described. Another important factor concerns the amount of pressure given to the accelerator pedal in the middle of the change.

It is essential to engage the lower gear when the engine is turning at the number of revolutions per minute appropriate to the speed of the car in that gear. Only experience can teach exactly what that speed is, and a few bad changes are inevitable at first. When a mistake has been made, never force home the gear lever; rather start again.

If a still lower gear than that engaged by the first change down is required (and a reduction through the whole box may at times prove necessary, principally on steep hills), the sequence of operations is precisely the same as that already described except that, following the first change down, the gear lever must be moved next from the third to the second gear position, and then from second to first.

GEAR CHANGING
SIMPLIFIED

The sequence of operations for changing down listed above is that generally approved for all standard makes of cars (a similar process is often recommended for changing up) and the mastering of this technique is to be preferred. It is not essential with cars designed to facilitate easy gear changing, however.

Fitments of this kind are detailed in a later chapter of this work, and those mterested should turn m particular to the section on the fluid flywheel in Chapter I. The two types of advanced gear-changing devices ordinarily encountered are the synchromesh gearbox and the pre-selector. The steering column type of gear change lever now being increasingly adopted also merits some mention here.

Synchromesh. The primary aim of the synchromesh control is to enable a smooth change to be made and to avoid gear crashing. With this fitment an easier engagement is assured when changing either up or down; in fact, for a downward change in the higher gears (on some makes of cars the synchromesh mechanism does not apply to the lowest gears) the following procedure may be adopted:

1. Depress the clutch pedal, at the same time increasing the speed of the engine by acceleration.
2. Move the gear lever from its high position, through neutral, to its lower position, making a slight pause before engaging.
3. Release the clutch pedal gradually, simultaneously adjusting the engine speed by means of the accelerator.
4. Accelerate as required.

The secret of this change, simple as it may appear by contrast with the double de-clutching method, is in adjusting the speed of the engine so that the drive is taken up steadily without jar or shock. The engine *must* have the opportunity of increasing its speed when a change is made from a high to a lower gear; when this is not given, the shock to the transmission can in time prove serious.

Pre-selector. The device known as a pre-selector consists, so far as the driver is concerned, of a lever fitted to the steering wheel which can be moved across an arc marked with the respective gear positions. With such a fitment gear changing becomes very simple.

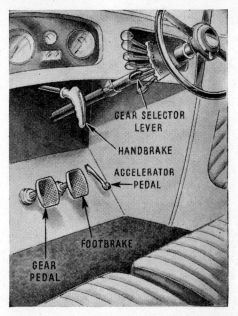

FIG. 9. *Pre-selector gear change lever. The gear is engaged by depressing the gear pedal.*

The procedure with the pre-selector is to move the lever to the position marked for the next gear required; that is to say, the next highest gear if the process is changing up, or the next lowest if the car is already in, say, top, or if it is thought a change down may be necessary. When the time comes to make the change, all that is required is to depress the clutch pedal and release it again, adjusting the speed of the engine as usual with the accelerator pedal.

When such devices become standard on all motor cars, much of the mechanical work of driving will be unnecessary. At present, however, advanced gearboxes of this and similar design are the exception rather than the rule.

Steering Column Gear Lever. The gear change lever that is fitted on the steering column of some cars is not to be confused with the pre-selector already described. Its position makes it easy of access and gives added room space in the front of the car, but in other respects it must be operated in conjunction with the clutch pedal in the same way as the more usual gear lever on the floor. Its operation of the gears is effected by levers linked from the steering column to selectors on the off-side of the gearbox.

REVERSING

So far we have been concerned with propelling the car in the normal way through the engagement of the forward gears. It remains for the learner to acquire the art of reversing, a by no means difficult task on a straight stretch of road

The position required by the gear change lever for the engagement of reverse gear should by now have been ascertained. Assuming the engine to be running and the car to be stationary, the sequence is to depress the clutch pedal, move the gear lever into the reverse position, and then to release the clutch pedal and depress the accelerator in the same simultaneous, but gradual way as when moving off in a forward position.

As movement is felt, the pressure of the accelerator pedal can be increased as required, although high speeds are never to be recommended in reverse, particularly with a beginner at the wheel. To stop, it is only necessary to release the accelerator pedal and depress the clutch and brake pedals. Care should be taken to ensure that the gear lever is moved into the neutral position before the clutch pedal is finally released. This completes the mechanical operations necessary to drive a motor car.

MORE ADVANCED DRIVING TECHNIQUE

Once the elementary principles of driving have been mastered, and the necessary mechanical actions can be carried out with speed and precision, the new motorist will feel capable of dealing with any and every situation. until there arises an emergency which has not been visualized.

This is where the art and science of good driving, the ability to visualize emergencies before they arise, comes in. Commonly known as road sense, this ability presupposes a lively imagination, intelligence and the facility of learning from "near squeaks" how to avoid them in future.

Beware particularly of that fatal sense of security which afflicts novices and experienced drivers alike. It is the easiest thing in the world to propel a car at sixty miles an hour, but by no means so easy to judge precisely when the circumstances are favourable for so doing.

Learning by Stages. The speed at which a car should be driven depends on the proficiency of the driver, the car's size and capability, the kind of road being used, and the state of the traffic, not to mention the weather. It is a good rule to progress by slow and easy stages, and not to try anything where the slightest element of risk is involved.

Thirty miles an hour might well be considered the maximum speed at which a learner should drive during his first six months on the road. For the next six months up to forty miles an hour might be permitted. Speeds of fifty and upwards should be attempted only very occasionally, and then on an absolutely straight and clear stretch of arterial road.

When an emergency arises, it may make all the difference whether the car is travelling five miles an hour faster than the safe speed. The crux of the matter is how quickly a car can be brought to rest, and it should be remembered that the distance needed to stop a car in bad road or weather conditions, or if the vehicle is not in good order, is considerably greater than that required in normal circumstances.

Assuming perfectly adjusted brakes and good conditions generally, the dis-

Never in any circumstances, particularly when on a narrow or twisting road, exceed a speed at which the car can easily be halted within the limits of vision; the point being, of course, that what is beyond the field of vision is a mystery. This will mean slow cornering, and perhaps dropping to a walking pace at a blind corner, but do not regard this as unnecessary. The safety of the driver, his passengers, and other road users depends upon such precautions being taken.

The rule of driving within one's vision applies equally on a straight main road, but with modification. Here it is more often the side-turnings which have to be considered. We now reach a new rule: Never exceed a speed at which the car can be pulled up before reaching the next cross-road or side turning.

FIG. 10. (a) to bring on a vehicle from the front (beckoning movement); (b) to bring on a vehicle from behind; (c) to bring on a vehicle from right or left (beckoning movement); (d), (e) and (f) are "stop" signals.

tance required to stop a car varies approximately according to the square of the relative speed of travel. In other words, it does not take twice as far to come to a halt from a speed of forty miles an hour as from a speed of twenty miles an hour, but four times as far.

Speed and Safety. What is a safe speed? The question is frequently asked, but it is one which admits of no answer except in general terms. Thus it is safe to drive at a speed from which the car can be stopped within the distance that any conceivable emergency may arise. Generally speaking, this is the distance to which the view extends.

ROAD SIGNS AND RULES

To enable a driver to judge when such side turnings can be expected road signs are provided by the local authorities or one of the motoring associations. Never neglect these signs. Never, in any circumstances, drive straight over a cross-road in the hope that nothing is coming in the other direction. Another driver may quite easily be thinking the same thing!

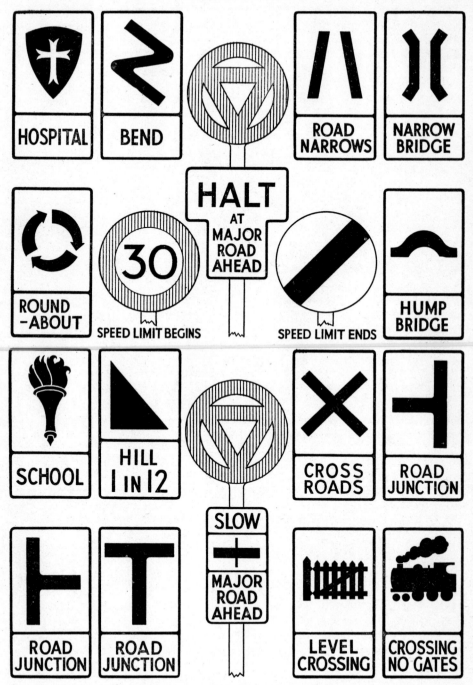

FIG. 11. ROAD SIGNS. *Official caution signs and pictorial signs used in Great Britain.*

When travelling on a minor road in the direction of a major crossing, there will probably be a warning sign to that effect, with instruction either to halt or go slow. (A halt should always be made where there is the slightest doubt.) However inopportune these warnings may be, strict notice must be taken of them.

Halt means stop, and it must be realized that there is a very good reason why this instruction is given. Slow means slowing down to the point at which the driver can be quite sure that no other traffic is approaching. For the rest, the safe speed for ordinary driving is the speed at which no risks are taken; precisely what this is can only be judged by experience.

In built-up areas generally, and on a few other restricted roads, a speed limit of thirty miles an hour is imposed. There may be times at which this limit seems unnecessary, but to exceed it is an offence, and may also be a risk. Remember that thirty miles an hour is the intended *limit* of speed, not the average speed to be maintained.

The point to be observed is that a road which is safe for high speeds at one time of the day may be most unsafe at another. In congested shopping areas, for instance, twenty miles an hour may be an unsafe speed, and often is, because of pedestrians. Which brings us to another rule: Always expect the other man to do the wrong thing, and be prepared to cope with it.

Jay-walking in certain circumstances is an offence against the law, and the Highway Code lays it down that a pedestrian must not loiter on an approved crossing or wilfully cause obstruction of the highway. All the same, there will always be jay-walkers, just as there will always be drivers who shoot over a crossing, or corner on the wrong side of the road. This is just one more reason why it is essential to keep the speed of the car down to what appears to be the margin of safety.

Keeping to the Left. The rule of the road in Britain is to keep as near to the left-hand side as it is safe to drive. Like every rule, however, this needs some interpretation.

Generally speaking, a car must be driven well to the left of the crown of the road whenever there is any weight of traffic, or if the road is one that bends and has blind corners. But, as every motorist comes to know with experience, the roads of Britain vary in character.

On those roads which have a gentle camber, there is no hardship in driving near to the left edge; but some roads have a very steep camber, and on these, particularly in wet weather, it may be dangerous to hug the left edge too closely.

On roads in this second category, assuming them to be fairly straight and free of obstructions, there is no reason why the crown should not be used. No element of risk should be involved, however, and watch should be kept in the mirror for traffic coming from behind. If another car is seen to be overtaking, the car on the crown of the road must draw immediately to the left, so that the other driver has an opportunity to pass.

Bends and Corners. The rule about keeping to the left is particularly important when taking bends in the road, whether left or right, although many drivers have a tendency to pull out in such circumstances. When taking a left bend it is more difficult and more dangerous to draw out from the left edge. In point of fact, if the left edge is hugged the camber will help the car round the bend.

With a right-hand bend the left side of the road must still be used, although here the case is somewhat different. It is sometimes easier to take the bend at a higher speed on the right. It is grossly wrong to give in to this temptation, however; in fact, this failing on the part of some drivers is one of the greatest causes of serious accidents.

Apart from the fact that travelling on the right is contrary to the accepted rule of the road, it must be borne in mind that there may also be a driver coming in the opposite direction, and he may have pulled out, too! In the interests of safety alone, it is policy at right-hand bends to keep strictly to the left.

The only time when it is permissible to cut a corner (as this driving on the right is sometimes known) is when a car is being driven on an empty stretch of road and there is a clear view round the bend and for some distance ahead. Even then it is a bad thing to do, because the very action may lay the foundations of an undesirable habit.

With corners, as distinct from bends, the rules of the road must still be adhered to as far as possible. When a left-hand corner is to be taken, for instance, obviously the driver must keep strictly to the left. A change down should be made, the appropriate hand signal given, and at the turn the driver should avoid making a preliminary swing to the right.

With a right-hand corner the circumstances are different. When approaching the corner, the driver should pull out on to the crown of the road, having given indication of his intention to turn right. A change down should be made, and the road should be entered in such a way that the car is on the left-hand side immediately upon arrival. The corner should in no circumstances be cut, and the turning car should give way to all direct traffic.

A common fault in driving, which should be avoided particularly at corners, is that of slowing down too late. In such circumstances the driver is often compelled to brake during cornering, and after the corner has been turned. Such braking sometimes resulting in a loss of

FIG. 12. *Do not drive "en echelon." It is bad driving and can lead to serious consequences.*

control. At every acute bend or corner, the thing to do is to slow down well in advance. Practice will develop precise judgment as to the best moment to begin.

Change down, then, before reaching the corner. When it is reached, accelerate round it if it is not too sharp, or immediately after the turn has been made if circumstances do not permit it earlier. In other words, at the actual moment of cornering the car should be, if not accelerating, then certainly moving freely. It should definitely not be braking. Quite apart from any other factor, braking when cornering is to invite a skid.

OVERTAKING

Passing a slower vehicle on the road is an operation which always requires care and skill. Very often it also requires patience. An accident in these circumstances is frequently caused by impatience on the part of the driver of the overtaking vehicle.

The conditions of overtaking are: First, to ascertain that the road ahead is clear for a great enough distance to enable a car to complete the act of overtaking and then to draw in again to the left side; second, to ensure that there are no other vehicles coming on from behind to prevent this manœuvre. Approaching traffic must not be impeded.

If the driver has any doubts that both these conditions are fulfilled, it is wiser not to overtake. Never take a chance. Further, one driver should never attempt to overtake another car that is travelling at approximately the same speed, unless the overtaking car has a good deal of speed in reserve or the driver of the car in front slows down and waves him on.

If the driver of the car to be overtaken is a courteous motorist, he *will* slow down and invite passing with a hand signal. Unfortunately, however, there are discourteous, as well as courteous, drivers, and these are known to increase their speed if another motorist dares to attempt to pass them. Though this may often constitute dangerous driving, allowances have to be made for it.

When it is desired to overtake another vehicle, and the above conditions have been fulfilled, a clear signal should be given before drawing out. It may be necessary to sound the horn as an indication to the driver in front, but confident acceleration is essential so that the overtaking is completed as quickly as possible. The movement of the car when over-taking should be in the form of an arc, and angles and sudden swerves should be avoided.

Never overtake at or near a bend or corner, nor when approaching the crest of a hill. Overtake only when it is unavoidable in fog, on a slippery road, or on a road which has a steep camber. Above all, never overtake if the movement impedes those travelling in the opposite direction. Finally, make quite sure that the driver in front will not be moving out from the left side of the road to avoid an obstacle ahead, or to pass a still slower moving vehicle.

If difficulty is experienced in passing another vehicle, do not, as so many bad drivers do, drive in echelon formation, that is, with the nose of the car edging out to the offside of the car in front. A car that has been baulked in overtaking should drop back into position, and try again later when the circumstances are better. Remember that the aim of the good motorist is to drive in such a way that the safety of all road users is ensured.

Right of Way. When passing a stationary vehicle, think of it as moving, and observe the same precautions. If the movement of passing is likely to impede the progress of traffic coming in the opposite direction, observe the rules governing right of way and wait (stop dead if needs be) until the oncoming vehicle has passed. In practice distances will be judged ever more accurately, and the necessity to stop will be avoided by slowing down well in advance of reaching the stationary vehicle.

This point about right of way is im-

FIG. 13. *"Cutting in" is an example of very bad driving and shows a complete lack of consideration for other motorists on the road.*

portant. Generally speaking, any vehicle which is on its own and lawful side of the road (that is, on the left side of the road) has the right of way over any vehicle which, in order to proceed, has to cross the crown of the road. On hills, the right of way is ordinarily given to the car ascending, as against the car descending.

CLIMBING HILLS

The golden rule when ascending hills is to change down before the engine begins to labour. If a steep hill is being approached, the best time to change down is at something near the maximum speed at which the car will travel in the lower gear; if a further change down has to be made, the same principle applies the second time.

There are very few hills in the British Isles which a modern car of even the lowest horse-power will not ascend without difficulty, assuming that the gear changes are made in time. There are, however, some (Porlock Hill in Somerset or the road over the Kirkstone Pass are examples) where it is still possible to see an occasional car in difficulties.

These difficulties are nearly always the result of bad driving. They arise either from changing down too late, so that the car loses the necessary momentum, or through failing to change down again near the top of the hill in the hope that the car will breast the summit in its present gear, with the result that the engine stalls.

Avoiding Engine Strain. If the engine does stall, or the car stops for any other reason on a steep hill, moving off again can be something of a problem to the beginner. Careful judgment is necessary to know exactly when to release the handbrake, and a great strain is put on the clutch by letting it in slowly when the engine must be revved up comparatively fast to develop sufficient power to move forward.

If possible, it is advisable in such circumstances to let the car run back slightly until one of the rear wheels is resting against the kerb or bank. The car having then a fixed starting place, the task of moving off is much less difficult, as the handbrake can be released as originally instructed. Further, assuming the road to be clear, instead of pulling straight up the hill, the car can be started off at an angle, which will prove much easier.

For a novice with any doubts of his ability to negotiate the necessary changes of gear on a very steep hill, the best thing is to stop at the foot and drive up in bottom gear. By that somewhat primitive method almost any climb could be accomplished, and the cooling of modern engines is so efficient that there is little risk of the water boiling.

USE OF THE BRAKES

It is no exaggeration to say that the best brake is the engine compression of a car, and the less strain put on the actual braking system the better. Applying the brake pedal vigorously and often, the process known as "driving on the brakes," not only rapidly wears away the brake linings, but also the treads of the tyres, as well as jarring and perhaps damaging the transmission.

The golden rule for brakes is: Use as little as possible, and never brake suddenly except in an emergency. The observance of this rule will make little if any, difference to the overall time of a journey; in fact, using the engine as a brake gives more gentle retardation and quicker acceleration.

Try to anticipate when it will be necessary to slow down or stop, then release the accelerator while remaining in gear. In top gear, especially at higher speeds, this action has a noticeable braking effect, while the effect is correspondingly greater in the lower gears.

When a slackening of speed is

88

visualized as necessary (as, for instance, when approaching a sharp bend, and more especially before a sharp right or left turn) a change down to a lower gear than that being used should be made well in advance. As well as saving the brakes, the lower gear will give more rapid acceleration when the manœuvre of turning has been completed. The same process can be adopted with advantage when overtaking or driving among heavy traffic.

The footbrake will need to be applied in certain circumstances even after the speed of the car has been reduced by the engine. However, this last-minute braking entails very little wear on the brake linings compared with the erratic, harsh and often dangerous braking at speed.

Emergency Braking. In the case of an emergency it may not always be possible to go through the motions of gear changing. At such a time the foot-brake should be used in no uncertain manner. If the brakes are properly adjusted, the car will stop in a short distance, depending on the speed at the time of the application of the brakes and the condition of the road surface. At the time of such emergency braking, depress the clutch pedal so that the engine is freed.

It is essential to have the brakes of a car adjusted regularly by an expert; instructions for the adjustment of the brakes is given in Chapter 10. It is an offence to drive with brakes that are inefficient or out of adjustment, just as much as it is to drive without a licence, both for the driver and the vehicle, or without at least a third-party insurance cover.

The art of descending hills is linked with the proper use of the engine as a brake. It is a good rule to descend a hill in the same gear that would be needed to ascend it. If applied, it will seldom be necessary to use the brakes.

The rule is a sound one for use on hills the ascent of which has been experienced. In other cases, where the course of a hill and its gradient are in doubt, it is as well to engage a lower gear than might at first be thought necessary. Then, as the hill makes itself known, a change up through the gears can be made, a higher gear being engaged each time the drag of the engine is greater than the momentum of the car.

SKIDDING

The use of the brakes is closely related to skidding, because many skids originate through the brakes being applied carelessly. Other contributory causes are wet, greasy and ice-bound roads. A wet oily surface is especially dangerous, and over-quick acceleration, particularly at corners, is responsible for many skids.

Racing motorists are in the habit of skidding deliberately, in order to corner more rapidly. Every driver will, at some time or another, experience a slight skid on a corner, and, after the first skid, some idea may be obtained of how the principle works. Deliberate skidding at corners should be avoided, however, for not only can it prove dangerous to other road users, but great skill is required to know to what extent a car can skid and remain under effective control.

Although care should be taken to avoid skids in the course of normal driving, a certain amount of practice with them is worth while; the experience gained will assist in coping with the emergency when it arises. For this practice a wide empty stretch of wet, and if possible, greasy road should be selected. Choose the emptiest straight stretch possible, and practise at a time when the traffic is lightest.

Why Skids Occur. The routine advice for dealing with a skid is to endeavour to steer into it. This really means that the skid should be allowed to "have its head."

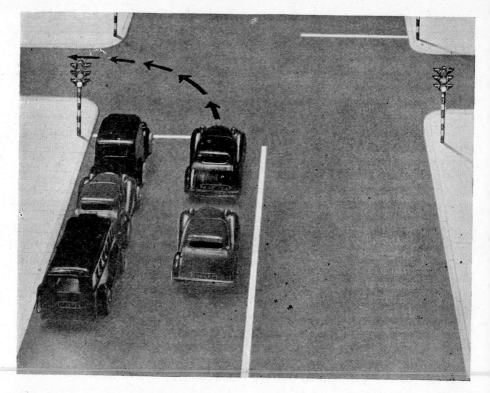

FIG. 14. LEFT-HAND TURN. *Always keep to the left-hand traffic lane if you wish to make a left turn, even if it means queueing. Do not cut across the bows of another car as illustrated above.*

In general, a skid arises when a car is required to change its direction or speed so rapidly that the normal adhesion between the tyres and the road surface fails. Then the car continues in the same direction in which it was travelling before the change of direction or speed was made.

To make this clear, imagine a car to be travelling along a straight and level road when, for some reason, the brakes are applied rapidly. If the road is wet or greasy, particularly if the tyres of the car are in bad condition, a skid may develop and the car will shoot straight ahead, with all four wheels locked. In practice, it will often skid into the camber, but if the road were absolutely flat it would not.

If a skid is experienced when negotiating a left-hand corner, the front wheels of the car will take the corner but the back wheels will follow the previous course of the car; that is to say, they will seem to swing right, or outwards. In such a case the method adopted to correct the skid is to turn the steering wheel to the right, that is, steer the car in the direction in which it was travelling before the corner was begun.

In the same way, if a skid is experienced when turning right, the steering wheel should be turned to the left. If the wheel is turned sufficiently and at the right moment, the skid will correct itself in a second. Unfortunately, however, such manœuvres as have been prescribed may mean steering into oncoming traffic. That is why a skid is to be avoided if at all possible.

If a skid is experienced through braking (usually over-braking), release the pressure on the brake pedal. If through acceleration (usually over-acceleration), decelerate. By practising these simple rules a few times on an empty stretch of road, confidence will be gained. To repeat sound advice, if you develop a skid, then correct it by steering into it.

DRIVING IN TRAFFIC

Driving in towns, where traffic is sometimes congested, is an art in itself. The correct procedure is to become a unit in a stream. A bad driver is one who is constantly changing from the left-hand stream to the right-hand stream, trying to pass other cars and failing.

If there are two lines of traffic in each direction, stay in the left-hand one if driving slowly or if intending to turn to the left. Use the outside stream only when overtaking, or as a prelude to a right-hand turn. Never try to gain a minute by sudden acceleration and fierce braking. Two cars may be passed with a net gain of ten seconds. Never cut in on another car.

Above all, never do anything without giving the appropriate signal (if by hand, then with the arm well extended from the car). Signals to be given by drivers to indicate their intentions are illustrated in Fig. 8. It should be noted, however, that the "signals are for the purpose of giving information, *and not instructions,* to others."

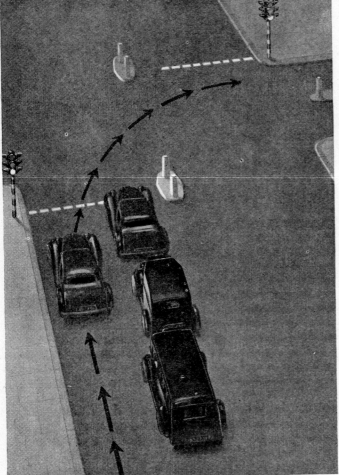

FIG. 15. RIGHT-HAND TURN. *Never "cut across" a stream of traffic as shown above. Always keep to the right-hand traffic stream if you wish to make a right turn.*

Most modern cars are fitted with direction indicators, or trafficators as they are known. These are of great assistance when turning to the left or right, particularly at night or during inclement weather. It should be remembered, however, that the use of trafficators does not excuse the driver from making other signals, of which probably the most important is "I am about to slow down." After use, a trafficator should be returned at once to neutral.

Traffic Lights. Watch for traffic lights carefully, and learn their sequence. Simultaneous lighting of red and amber does not mean "Go," but "Prepare to go," while amber when it is shown means "Stop," unless to do so is dangerous. Never turn left, that is, filter, against the lights unless waved on by a policeman, or unless a subsidiary green light (usually an arrow) indicates that it is permissible to do so at that point.

If a right-hand turn is necessary, avoid cutting across the stream of traffic approaching from the opposite direction. The oncoming traffic has the right of way, and a wait should be made until there is adequate space to pass across it. Turning right in these circumstances is often the most difficult of traffic manœuvres.

Second in difficulty is crossing a main road from one side street into another. The traffic on the main road has the right of way, of course. If this is a broad city road and there are no traffic lights, it may be necessary to cross it in two "hops," first moving out to the centre of the road, stopping, and then completing the crossing, each "hop" being made as the streams of traffic permit.

The ideal is to avoid causing another driver to slow down. That is a policy of perfection, however, and occasionally it may be necessary to turn right or cross a main road at some minor inconvenience to another road user. Beginners should

not manœuvre against a heavy stream of traffic except at a crossing controlled either by a policeman or traffic lights.

Pedestrians and Cyclists. The careful driver studies pedestrians and cyclists, as well as other motorists. The policy advocated is to give them plenty of room because of their vulnerability. In these days most children are taught road drill, but, like too many adults, some still step suddenly into the road without first observing the traffic. A special danger are those people who walk out from behind a stationary vehicle.

In most towns pedestrian crossings exist for the better safety of foot passengers. Where they are not controlled by police or light signals, pedestrians have precedence over vehicular traffic. Care should be taken when approaching them, and the speed should only be such from which a stop can be made if required.

Driving Fatigue. When undertaking a long journey the driver of a car is sometimes overcome by temporary fatigue or sleepiness, and cases are not unknown where drivers have indeed fallen asleep. At the first symptoms of drowsiness, stop the car, get out and exercise the limbs. Never drive in a comatose condition.

NIGHT DRIVING

Driving at night is different from driving by day only because visibility is limited by the lights used. The good night driver is he who translates everything that has been said in the preceding pages into terms of that limited visibility.

In brief, drive at a pace from which a stop can be made within the distance that is visible. If this theory is adopted, there is no additional risk when there is little traffic about. Actually rather less; for instance, a car approaching a crossroads at night can usually be detected by its lights, whereas during the daytime it would be hidden from view by obstructions, such as buildings or hedges.

Special watch should be kept for the car or lorry that has a rear light which is not functioning, pedestrians in dark clothes, and bicycles with inefficient rear lights. These and other things should be seen perfectly well in the light of normal, properly adjusted headlights. The difficulty arises when there is heavy traffic coming from the opposite direction.

Dazzle from Headlights. Unfortunately, there is no uniformity in dipping or extinguishing headlights, and it happens that sometimes a motorist is dazzled by the lights of approaching traffic. The practice is to dim, dip or switch off headlights at the approach of another car; all modern cars are provided with dipping headlights and combined dipping and switching headlights.

If the other driver fails to return the courtesy, slow down and, if necessary, stop. It will not help if the first motorist switches on his headlights again, however much the bad manners of the other driver may be deplored; in fact, a double dazzle will only make matters worse.

Never hesitate to stop when dazzled. It is dangerous in such circumstances to drive on, or to attempt to steer, as so many drivers do, by the lights of the oncoming car. There may be an obstruction or a cyclist ahead of which the dazzled driver is completely unaware.

Immediately the other car has passed, headlights may be switched on again. When proceeding care should be taken to avoid the tendency to steer outwards which always follows dazzling. In heavy traffic it will be found more convenient to drive with permanently-dipped headlights, or with a spotlight only. The rule of driving within the range of visibility must still be observed.

Changes in road surface are more difficult to detect at night than by day, and keen observation is therefore necessary, especially when passing from a good non-skid surface to an inferior kind of road. In winter, too, it is possible sometimes to enter, without realizing it, a stretch of road that is flooded or has a coating of ice on it.

DRIVING IN FOG

The real bane of night driving is fog or mist. Fog by day is rarely thick enough to impede slow driving, but in either case the rule here is the same as that already given, namely, drive only within the range of visibility. If the visibility becomes nil, then stop.

In daytime it is seldom that visibility is reduced to such a low ebb, and then only when the fog is polluted by smoke in big cities. At night the problem is rather different. The fog particles are reflected back by the car's lights, and even a relatively slight fog can reduce visibility. Various kinds of fog lights are on the market, but none of them solves the problem completely.

In reduced visibility experience offers three suggestions. In a mist the headlights are best kept on. In slight fog the best visibility will be obtained by having only the nearside headlight switched on, and this directed towards the kerb. In really thick fog the best results are obtained by having side-lights only and opening the windscreen wide.

In all the above circumstances concentrate on the left edge of the road, and reasonable progress may be made. If a centre white line on the road is still visible, this will also help, but care should be taken to keep this on the right. Never in any circumstances drive by the right-hand kerb, a proceeding which is inviting a head-on crash.

If the fog is so thick that driving as described above is impossible, there are two courses open. One is to abandon the car, in which case it should be driven off the road so that it does not present an obstruction to other road users. The other is to ask someone carrying a newspaper,

Fig. 16. Parking a car into a confined space is usually better achieved by backing in, because once the rear of the car is approaching its final position, the front end will swing into line more rapidly when reversing than when moving forward.

reverse, as previously explained, has been mastered, however, the secret of parking successfully is quite simple.

The first essential is to ensure that the space available is at least sufficient for the car. This having been ascertained, the car should be driven past the space in a forward gear, a stop made, the reverse gear engaged, and then, by very gentle acceleration and the use of the mirror, the car can be negotiated into position.

It is often of help in reversing to look through either the side or rear window, but the great thing to remember is that steering in reverse is much the same as steering forward. If the car is to go to the right, the wheel should be turned to the right (that is, clockwise); if to the left, turn the wheel to the left (anticlockwise). As all steering is carried out by means of the front wheels these will, of course, turn first, but their movement will promote corresponding turning of the rear. It should be remembered that the rear wheels describe a smaller arc than the front wheels. Because of this the rear of the car should be brought nearly opposite to the opening of the parking space.

or other bold white object, to walk in front of the car.

PARKING

Many experienced drivers find difficulty in reversing, particularly when parking in crowded places, and when it may be necessary to reverse into a confined area. Once the art of driving in

CHAPTER 4

CARBURETTORS AND FUEL SYSTEMS

ALTHOUGH the carburettor is a moderately complex instrument, it seldom gives trouble, provided that one or two routine maintenance jobs are performed at the appropriate intervals. One of its chief enemies is dust and grit. In most instances, therefore, the carburettor is provided with some form of air cleaner. A typical example is illustrated in Fig. 1; the cylindrical body of the cleaner contains a woven metallic mesh which is wetted with oil, to which the dust adheres. The lower part of the body forms a silencer which damps out the hiss or power roar which could otherwise be heard at the intake to the carburettor.

Other types of filter employ gauze or horsehair as a filtering medium, and work on similar principles.

Cleaning the Air Filter. If the filter performs its task efficiently, it follows that in time the filtering medium will become choked by an accumulation of dust and other material. This will restrict the flow of air to the carburettor, leading to loss of power and heavy petrol consumption. The filter should, therefore, be removed at approximately 5,000-mile intervals, or more frequently when it is operating in a dusty atmosphere, and should be cleaned by swilling it in a bowl of petrol or paraffin. If the filtering

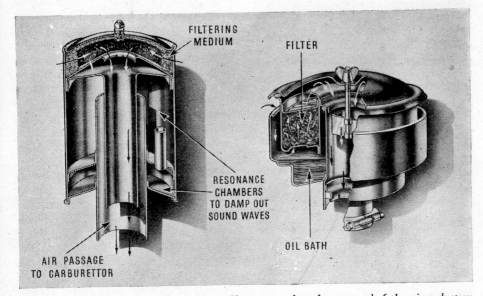

FILTERING MEDIUM

FILTER

RESONANCE CHAMBERS TO DAMP OUT SOUND WAVES

AIR PASSAGE TO CARBURETTOR

OIL BATH

FIG. 1. AIR FILTERS. *Two designs of air filter mounted on the open end of the air-induction pipe to prevent dust and grit passing to the carburettor. The design on the left incorporates resonance chambers to damp the sound vibrations emanating from the carburettor. In the design on the right the air is drawn through the oil bath before reaching the filtering medium.*

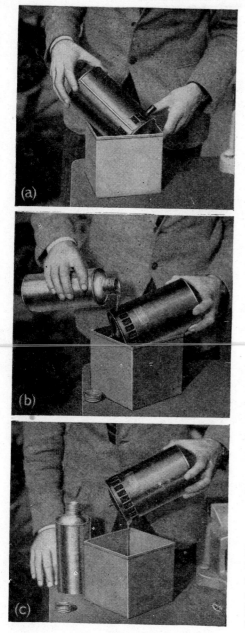

element is of the oil-wetted type, it should be sparingly re-oiled with clean engine oil, allowing the surplus oil to drain off before the filter is refitted to the engine.

Cleaning Petrol Filters. Since the carburettor is an accurate metering instrument, tiny particles of sediment will clog the jets or the internal passages; water, too, will have the same effect.

The S.U. carburettor does not experience this trouble since the single jet is of large diameter, and is very rarely blocked by sediment or water. Grit may cause the needle valve in the float chamber to bind, however, causing either flooding of the carburettor or petrol starvation. These troubles will, however, be discussed later.

The petrol is, of course, filtered before it reaches the carburettor, since gauze filters are fitted to the suction pipe in the petrol tank, and to the inlet of the fuel pump. The third line of defence is a small filter in the union which connects the petrol pipe to the carburettor. This may be withdrawn by unscrewing the union nut. The filter may be conical in shape, retained in the float chamber boss by a small spring, or may take the form of a cylinder of gauze surrounding the body of a hollow bolt which couples the union to the float chamber. The method of removing is illustrated in Fig. 3.

When cleaning the filter, a tooth-brush will be useful in dislodging sediment and fluff from the gauze, but care must be taken not to damage the mesh. When reassembling, make sure that the filter is not crushed, and do not overlook the fibre washer, or washers, between the union nut and the float chamber, which ensure a petrol-tight joint. Filters should be cleaned at regular intervals; the owner, however, should consult the Instruction Book to see the interval recommended by the manufacturer.

FIG. 2. *Stages in the cleaning and re-oiling of an air cleaner. This operation should be carried out periodically to prevent the accumulated dust choking the air supply.*

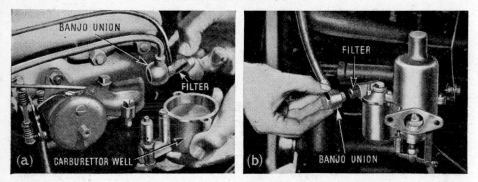

FIG. 3. CARBURETTOR FILTERS. *These are fitted in the inlet connexion to prevent sediment clogging the jets or grit binding the needle valve: (a) shows the type of filter fitted in the union of a Solex carburettor and (b) the S.U. carburettor filter.*

Cleaning the Float Chamber. Even systematic cleaning of the filters does not always prevent the accumulation of sediment and water in the float chamber. Inspection of the float chamber after, say, 5,000 miles, will generally reveal the presence of a reddish sediment, fluff, and possibly a few globules of water.

On most horizontal carburettors the float chamber is attached to the main carburettor body by two or more square-headed bolts, which generally have screw-driver slots cut in them. Sometimes one large hexagonal bolt is used. On slackening the bolt, or bolts, the float chamber can be lowered from the carburettor. It will be necessary to disconnect the petrol feed pipe in most cases. On downdraught carburettors it is more usual for the float chamber to be embodied in the carburettor casting, access to it being obtained by removing the lid, which is secured by bolts or screws.

When reassembling the float chamber it is advisable to fill it with petrol to eliminate the possibility of an air lock, and save overworking the battery as operating the starter is the favourite way of refilling the fuel system.

Unscrewing the jets. Inside the float chamber is the float itself, usually a hollow brass vessel. This should be examined before it is lifted out, as it must subsequently be replaced the right side up. Sediment can now be swilled out of the bowl, and the interior wiped with a clean, non-fluffy cloth. It will do no harm to unscrew any jets which are fitted in the base of the bowl, to ensure that no sediment enters them. One of the float chamber retaining bolts often has a square cut on its lower end so that it may be used as a key to unscrew the jets. If the jets have a screwdriver slot cut in them, use care in unscrewing them, as the jet orifice may be damaged if the screwdriver slips.

The passages beneath the jets can now be swilled out, and every trace of sediment removed. If water is present in the float chamber, as indicated by drops or globules of a different appearance from the petrol, it should be dried out carefully with a cloth; as water has a habit of finding its way into the most inaccessible drillings and passages, however, the best plan is to flush out the float chamber, jets and passages with methylated spirit, since alcohol absorbs a large percentage of water.

Cleaning the Jets. If any jet appears to be clogged, it may be cleared by blowing through it in the reverse direction to that in which the fuel enters it.

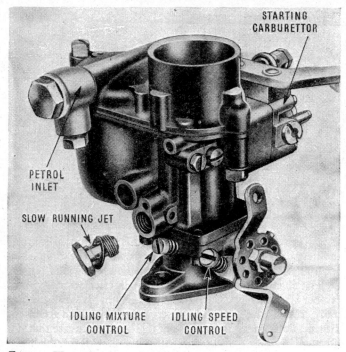

STARTING
CARBURETTOR

PETROL
INLET

SLOW RUNNING JET

IDLING MIXTURE
CONTROL

IDLING SPEED
CONTROL

FIG. 4. *The mixture and idling speed regulating screws on a Solex carburettor. Note the starting carburettor attached to the rear face of the body.*

of the mixture supplied when the engine is idling. In practice this adjustment has a definite effect on the economy or performance of the engine, so that a little trouble to obtain the correct setting is well repaid. The variation in mixture strength also affects the idling speed; adjustment of the throttle opening is necessary at the same time.

It is a fairly simple matter to identify the adjusting screws on most carburettors. Both generally have milled heads, and are provided with screwdriver slots, while beneath the head is a small spring which retains the screw in any desired position. The mixture adjusting screw may be on top of the carburettor close to the main barrel, or at the side, or even underneath. It is easily identified on inspection. The idling speed adjustment is simply a small setscrew which limits the extent to which the throttle closes, and is, therefore, to be found adjacent to the throttle lever to which the operating linkage is attached. Figs. 4, 9, and 10, show typical examples.

On no account be tempted to use a length of fine wire to clear the obstruction, as the jet orifice may be enlarged. Even if this does not happen, the internal surface will almost certainly be affected, and this is quite sufficient to alter the characteristics of the jet. During manufacture, for instance, the jets are drilled to ultra-fine limits of accuracy, yet when a batch which have all been drilled with the same drill are tested, it is found that individual jets vary in their output, calling for correction and calibration. Even the countersinking on one side of the jet affects the flow of petrol through it, so that it will be evident that a jet cannot be treated with too great care.

Adjusting and Tuning the Carburettor. The only adjustment which need be carried out on the average carburettor is that which affects the strength

The Idling Mixture Control. Suppose that we begin by screwing the mixture control screw inwards. If this screw controls the air supply, the mixture will become richer, and the engine will begin to run unevenly, alternately speeding up slightly and slowing down, or hunting, as it is termed. Slight black smoke will be evident from the exhaust, and the exhaust gas will have a sweet odour.

If the screw controls the petrol supply, the mixture will become weaker. The engine may speed up slightly, and then will run irregularly. On listening to the exhaust note, a splashy sound is usually evident, and the engine may miss several beats. The exhaust gas will be practically odourless.

If either adjustment is carried to excess, the engine will stall. In order to determine whether this is due to an excessively rich or weak mixture, turn the screw back a little, restart the engine, and open the throttle sharply. If the engine hesitates, spits back, or stalls, the mixture is too weak; if it accelerates rapidly, the mixture is rich.

Once the effect of the screw has been determined, screw it inwards or outwards until the engine runs evenly and at the highest idling speed. If this is now too high, unscrew the throttle-adjusting screw slightly. Any adjustment of engine speed will call for a slight readjustment of mixture strength, so that each screw in turn will require slight rotation. For maximum economy, the mixture screw should be turned until the engine begins to hesitate, and then turned back a shade until even running is obtained. For high performance, the mixture should be a trifle on the rich side.

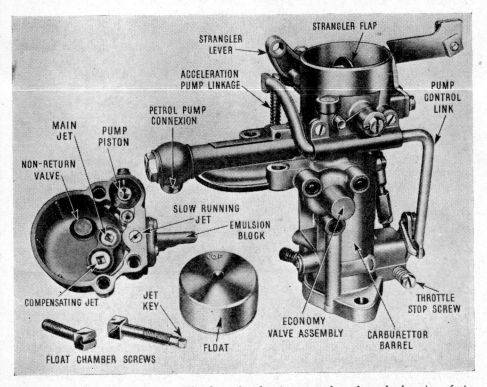

FIG. 5. ZENITH CARBURETTOR. *The float chamber is removed to show the location of the jets, non-return valve and acceleration pump. The acceleration pump is coupled to the throttle control by the pump control link so that as the throttle is opened, the pump is operated automatically. The throttle opening is adjusted on the throttle stop screw.*

ADJUSTING
THE S.U. CARBURETTOR

The adjustment of the S. U. carburettor differs from the types just described. In this case the mixture strength is controlled by the position of the jet in relation to the needle, thus varying the size of the opening through which the petrol flows. The jet is lowered by the mixture control to provide a rich mixture for starting from cold; when the engine is at its normal running temperature and the mixture control is pushed home, the jet rests against the large brass nut beneath the body of the carburettor shown in Fig. 13. If this nut is screwed upwards, the jet will move closer to the needle, thus weakening the mixture; conversely, screwing the nut downwards holds the jet farther away from the needle and provides a richer mixture.

Before carrying out this adjustment, disconnect the mixture control rod or wire from the operating arm on the carburettor, and keep the jet against the nut throughout the adjusting operations. The procedure is otherwise the same as that just described for other types of

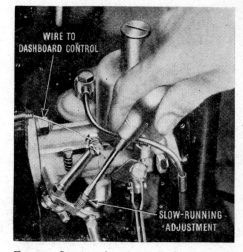

FIG. 7. *Setting the clearance between the mixture and throttle interconnecting lever on the adjusting screw.*

carburettor. When the correct setting has been obtained, connect up the mixture control while the dashboard knob is in the "weak" position.

Positioning the Needle. It is sometimes found that the mixture appears to be too rich even with the jet adjusting nut screwed up as far as it will go. First check that the level of the petrol in the jet is not too high, due to flooding of the carburettor. If petrol is not seeping from the jet, remove the suction chamber as described in the next paragraph, slacken the screw which secures the needle in the piston, and gently pull the needle out about $\frac{1}{64}$-in. Great care must be taken not to bend the needle.

Removing the Suction Chamber and Piston. This operation is required when it is necessary to alter the position of the needle, or to clean the piston and suction chamber. It should not be tackled unnecessarily by the novice, although it is quite straightforward. Unscrew the two fixing screws, and lift the suction chamber off, being careful not to tilt it in the process. The piston must similarly be extracted with care, to avoid bending the

FIG. 6. *Adjusting the idling speed by means of the spring-loaded screw on S.U. carburettors.*

needle. Two points should be watched. If the base of the suction chamber and the body of the carburettor are not marked to show the correct method of refitting the chamber, do so before dismantling. Also, notice that a locating screw in the body of the carburettor engages with a slot in the piston to ensure correct assembly.

The second point concerns the cleanliness of the piston and the internal bore of the suction chamber. If grit or carbon is present on these surfaces, the piston may bind slightly, upsetting the mixture strength. Clean the parts carefully, and do not be tempted to oil them before reassembly. The only item requiring a few drops of thin machine oil is the steel plunger at the top of the piston, which slides in the narrow section of the suction chamber.

FIG. 8. *Checking the freedom of the piston in an S.U. carburettor. Access is obtained by removing the air silencer assembly.*

Centring the Jet. After refitting the piston and suction chamber, lift the piston and let it drop on to its seating. It should fall with a definite click. If it binds at all, the jet requires centring, as wear will occur if the needle rubs against it. This should, strictly speaking, be left to an expert. It is carried out by slackening the large gland nut above the jet adjusting nut. This leaves the jet free to move slightly when the needle enters it. By allowing the piston to drop once or twice, and tightening the gland nut after each trial, a position will be found in which the needle enters the jet without binding. The jet must be up against the stop nut during this process. Make sure that the gland nut is fully tightened, or petrol will leak down the outside of the jet.

TUNING CARBURETTORS FOR ECONOMY OR POWER

It must be emphasized at the outset that the standard setting of the carburettor, as determined by the manufacturer, represents the best all-round compromise between maximum speed, power, and reasonable economy. It is seldom advisable, therefore, to alter the jets or choke tube in an effort to improve on the standard setting.

Many owners believe that after a considerable mileage carburettor jets become worn, but this is a fallacy. The moving parts of the carburettor, on the other hand, such as the throttle spindle, needle valve, acceleration pump and economy

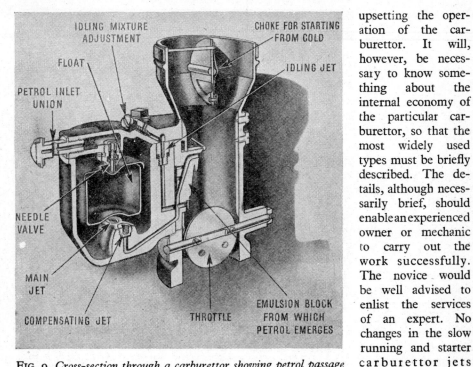

FIG. 9. *Cross-section through a carburettor showing petrol passage ways or channels in the body of the float chamber and emulsion block.*

upsetting the operation of the carburettor. It will, however, be necessary to know something about the internal economy of the particular carburettor, so that the most widely used types must be briefly described. The details, although necessarily brief, should enable an experienced owner or mechanic to carry out the work successfully. The novice would be well advised to enlist the services of an expert. No changes in the slow running and starter carburettor jets are recommended,

device do wear in time, so that it is always wise to have the carburettor reconditioned when a major engine overhaul is due.

Modern S.U. carburettors are provided with an hydraulic damper (Fig. 13, page 105) consisting of a small piston working in a chamber which should be filled with winter-grade engine oil (S.A.E. 20). If acceleration is poor the most likely cause is that the damper chamber is empty.

Alternative Jet Sizes. When slightly more economical running, or a moderate increase in performance is required, carburettor manufacturers can generally supply alternative jets to those fitted as standard. Usually suitable combinations which will provide a weak or a rich setting are quoted for each model of a given make of car. In this case, the owner who wishes to experiment can generally effect the necessary substitution without the risk of

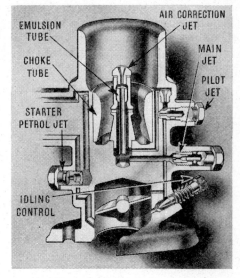

FIG. 10. *The arrangement of the jets in the Solex F.I. and F.I.P. type carburettors.*

as the sizes of those jets should never need alteration under normal conditions.

SOLEX CARBURETTORS

During recent years the F and B.F. self-starting types of carburettors have been widely used. With this model the main and slow running jets are only accessible when the float chamber is removed. To remove the main jet a protecting cap has to be unscrewed. The jet is marked with two numbers: 112–57S, to take an example. The first represents the jet size, and the second its correction or compensation factor, determined by the horizontal holes drilled in it.

If a richer or a weaker mixture is required over the whole range of running, a jet having a larger or smaller number must be used, but the correction number must be the same. In the case first quoted, for instance, a weaker setting would call for a 105–57S or a 100–57S jet. If a change in mixture strength is required only at low speeds or high speeds, a jet having the same size of fuel orifice, but a different correction number, is required.

Separate Air Correction Jet. The Solex F.I. and F.I.P. downdraught carburettors differ from that just dealt with in having a separate air correction jet. The main jet is fitted in a carrier screwed into the main body of the carburettor, as shown in Fig. 10, and petrol is fed from the jet through a passage to a vertical tube in the choke tube, and is sprayed from a series of holes around this tube. An air correction jet is screwed into the top of the vertical tube, and beneath this a hollow emulsion tube, into which air passes. The air then escapes through holes drilled in the lower part of the emulsion tube, to mix with the petrol from the main jet, thus forming a well-atomized mixture.

With this arrangement a change of main jet will result in an alteration in mixture strength over the whole of the

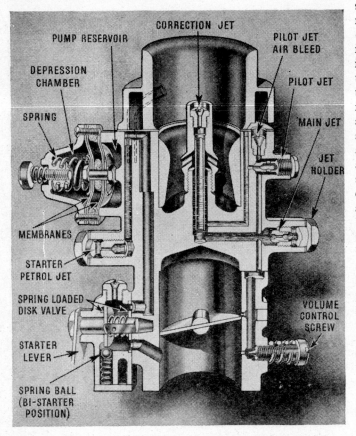

PUMP RESERVOIR
CORRECTION JET
DEPRESSION CHAMBER
SPRING
MEMBRANES
STARTER PETROL JET
SPRING LOADED DISK VALVE
STARTER LEVER
SPRING BALL (BI-STARTER POSITION)
PILOT JET AIR BLEED
PILOT JET
MAIN JET
JET HOLDER
VOLUME CONTROL SCREW

FIG. II. *The Solex A.I.P. carburettor shown above is similar to that illustrated in* FIG. 10, *but incorporates an acceleration pump.*

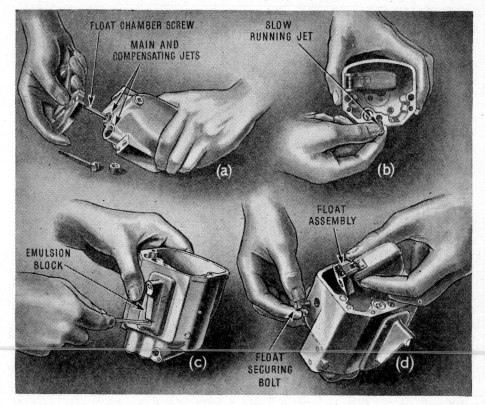

FIG. 12. SERVICING THE CARBURETTOR. *Removing the jets for cleaning on a Zenith carburettor. The float has to be removed from the chamber before the jets can be withdrawn.*

speed range. If a richer mixture is required only at lower speeds, a larger correction jet will be required. Fitting a larger correction jet, while leaving the main jet unchanged, will weaken the mixture at higher speeds only.

It will be evident that there is considerable scope for variations in mixture strength at different speeds. Main jets can be obtained from the makers, and are graded in steps of 5, that is, 100, 105, 110, and so on, while correction jets range in steps of 10.

A.I.P. Carburettor. This is similar to the instrument just described, but has an acceleration pump consisting of a spring-loaded fabric diaphragm in an airtight chamber. As shown in Fig. 11 the diaphragm is drawn back at small throttle openings due to the depression in the chamber, which is in communication with the induction pipe on the engine side of the throttle by a passage which is not shown. Petrol flows through a non-return valve to the fuel chamber. When the throttle is opened for acceleration, the suction behind the diaphragm falls, so that the spring returns it; petrol is thus forced through the power jet, supplementing the fuel which is provided by the main jet. This takes care of snap acceleration.

If the throttle is held open, the delivery from the fuel chamber will soon cease. A depression develops around the power jet, however, and this is communicated to the fuel in the passage which feeds the jet. As a result, petrol begins to issue from the power jet again, and continues to do so as long as a wide throttle opening is maintained.

When the principle is understood, it will be evident that in addition to variations in size of the main and correction jets, the amount of movement of the diaphragm will also affect the acceleration. This is adjustable by means of the screw which projects from the pump casing. The main jet can be adjusted to give a much weaker mixture than in the case of the earlier types of carburettor, since it only functions alone at small throttle openings. The power jet is not adjustable.

Recent Solex Designs. The carburettor illustrated in Fig. 13 resembles earlier designs except that the initial mixture for cold starting is drawn from the starter petrol jet and the small air bleed. As soon as the engine fires, the increased manifold depression draws back an air valve against the pressure of the smaller spring, thus admitting extra air through the starter air jet and weakening the mixture.

As with the earlier type of zero starter, an intermediate position of the starting control is provided, additional air being admitted through a dished opening (not shown in the illustration) in the starter petrol valve.

The squat, downdraught version of the carburettor illustrated is the ZIC-3 model which incorporates a ring diffuser to give better atomization of the fuel. This is, in effect, a small secondary venturi, and is representative of design on some other types of carburettor. Some premium petrols cause icing troubles, and the use of a ring diffuser reduces the liability of ice formation on the spraying orifice, while the emulsion tube is also well protected against ice. Notice also that the float chamber is vented to the carburettor intake, thus rendering the main carburettor dustproof.

On the type of acceleration pump shown in Fig. 14, the diaphragm is actuated mechanically by a lever which is

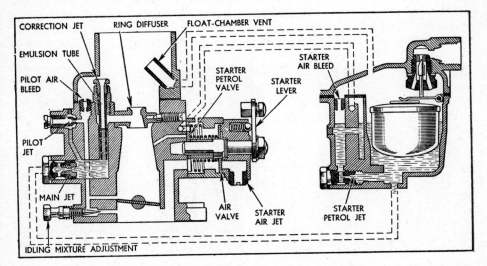

FIG. 13. *Solex 26ZIC carburettor, in which a ring diffuser gives better spraying, presents the minimum surface to the air stream and reduces the risk of icing.*

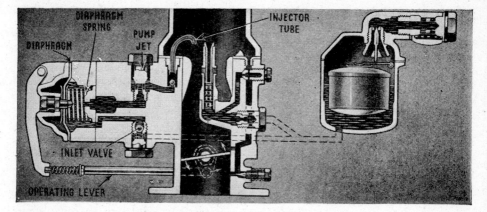

FIG. 14. *In this Solex carburettor, the acceleration pump is actuated by a lever attached by a spring-loaded rod to the throttle spindle.*

attached by a spring-loaded rod to another lever on the throttle spindle. When the throttle is closed, a spring presses the diaphragm outwards so that a supply of petrol is drawn through a non-return valve into the diaphragm chamber. Immediately on opening the throttle, the lever forces the diaphragm forward and the petrol passes through a metering jet and a second ball valve to an injector tube which projects into the main air stream.

The travel of the lever can be adjusted by altering the position of the split-pin which controls the tension of the spring

on the operating rod. The rate of flow for each injection is controlled by the size of the pump jet.

A development of this system shown in Fig. 15, incorporates a spring-loaded valve in the exit from the diaphragm chamber. It will be seen that as a result of the presence of this valve, when the accelerator pedal is depressed, pressure is built up in the diaphragm chamber until the valve is forced momentarily off its seating, allowing a quantity of fuel that is proportional to the throttle movement to pass through the pump jet into the in-

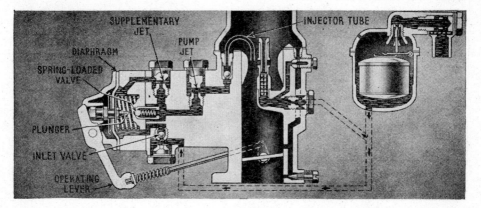

FIG. 15. *This Solex carburettor is similar to that shown in* FIG. 14, *except for the spring-loaded ball valve in the delivery passage from the pump.*

jector tube. Once the pressure has been relieved, the spring-loaded valve closes and at cruising speeds the engine operates on the main-jet system.

ZENITH CARBURETTORS

The Zenith carburettor in general use today is the "V-type", which is supplied in various horizontal, downdraught and updraught versions. Zenith carburettors, which resemble the Stromberg (Fig 16), in some respects, rely on a main jet,

running jet. Acceleration is controlled mainly by the size of the compensating jet, and the adjustment of idling mixture strength. When an acceleration pump is fitted, adjustment may be provided to vary the stroke of the plunger, but in exceptional cases a larger discharge jet may be necessary. Conversely, by moving the plunger-lever fulcrum to provide a shorter stroke, fuel economy can be improved.

On some V-type carburettors an

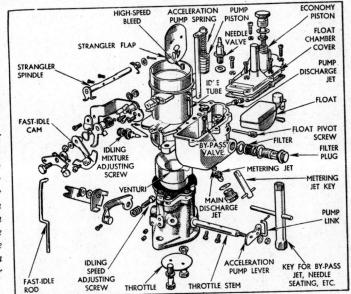

FIG. 16. *Stromberg DIV42 carburettor fitted to Humber Super Snipe, Mark IV. The quantity of fuel delivered by the acceleration pump is controlled by the size of the pump discharge jet, and the duration of the charge by the strength of the pump spring. The stroke may be altered by engaging the pump link with either of the holes in the pump lever on the throttle stem. The inner hole gives a shorter stroke, for summer running.*

which provides the main supply of petrol for power, a compensating jet which supplies the richer mixture necessary for acceleration, and the usual slow-running jet and idling adjustment. Some models are also fitted with acceleration pumps.

On V-type carburettors, the jets are accessible when the float chamber is removed, as shown in Fig. 18. On some later carburettors, the main and compensator jets can be unscrewed after removing external jet plugs; it is still necessary to remove the float chamber, however, to obtain access to the slow-

economy device is fitted. This consists of a spring-loaded diaphragm in a housing, similar to that described on Solex carburettors. In this case, however, the diaphragm controls a valve which admits extra air during part-throttle running, providing a lean mixture under cruising conditions. This valve is not adjustable.

Typical modern Zenith carburettors are shown in Figs. 17, 18 and 19. The simple carburettor fitted to the Austin A30 (Fig. 17) illustrates the basic principles of Zenith downdraught designs except for the fact that the main and

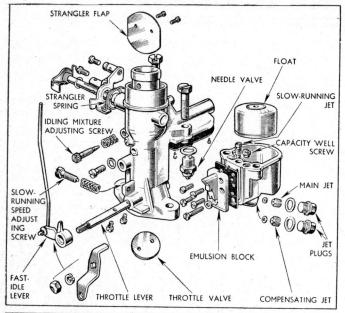

STRANGLER FLAP

FLOAT

NEEDLE VALVE

STRANGLER SPRING

SLOW-RUNNING JET

IDLING MIXTURE ADJUSTING SCREW

CAPACITY WELL SCREW

MAIN JET

SLOW-RUNNING SPEED ADJUSTING SCREW

JET PLUGS

FAST-IDLE LEVER

EMULSION BLOCK

THROTTLE LEVER   THROTTLE VALVE   COMPENSATING JET

FIG. 17. The simple Zenith 26VME carburettor fitted to the Austin A30. This has a manually operated strangler to provide a rich starting mixture, the flap being spring-loaded so that it will open when the engine fires. Note the positions of the main and compensating jets; they are accessible from outside the carburettor, instead of being fitted in the base of the float-chamber bowl, as is usual with Zenith carburettors.

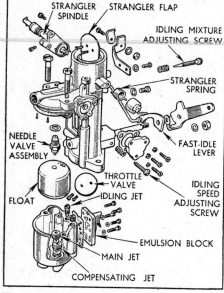

STRANGLER SPINDLE   STRANGLER FLAP

IDLING MIXTURE ADJUSTING SCREW

STRANGLER SPRING

NEEDLE VALVE ASSEMBLY

FAST-IDLE LEVER

THROTTLE VALVE

IDLING SPEED ADJUSTING SCREW

FLOAT

IDLING JET

EMULSION BLOCK

MAIN JET

COMPENSATING JET

FIG. 18. Zenith 30VI carburettor fitted to Hillman Minx, Mark VIII. This type is fitted with a flap-valve strangler for starting, an automatically operated spring allowing the valve to pulsate when the engine fires, thus weakening the mixture. It is not fitted with an economy device or an acceleration pump.

compensating jets are usually screwed into the base of the float chamber and are accessible only after the float has been removed. Apart from this difference, the more elaborate designs of Zenith carburettor shown in Figs. 18 and 19 will be seen to be modifications of this basic design.

The advanced type of carburettor shown in Fig. 19, is an excellent example of modern practice. Above the float chamber will be seen the spring-loaded economy valve that weakens the mixture when the engine is running under part-throttle conditions; under these circumstances a weaker mixture than normal can be burnt as the engine is lightly stressed and, moreover, the suction-operated ignition-timing control provides a degree of over-advance that prevents any lag in burning of the fuel which might otherwise cause burnt exhaust valves.

Built into the float-chamber casting is the acceleration pump that comes into action whenever the throttle is depressed, providing a spurt of fuel which ensures

FIG. 19. *The Zenith 42VIS carburettor fitted to the Austin A90 Westminster may be compared with the simpler carburettors shown in* FIGS. 17 *and* 18. *It incorporates an economy valve and an acceleration pump to ensure good petrol consumption combined with excellent acceleration. The economy valve operates under part-throttle cruising conditions; the acceleration pump provides an increase of fuel when the throttle is opened suddenly.*

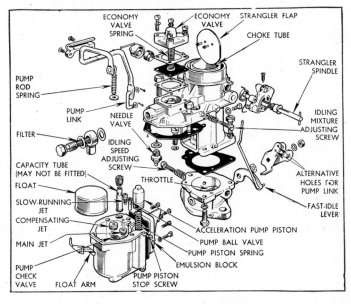

rapid acceleration, without the need for fitting an extravagantly large compensating jet or setting the slow-running mixture on the rich side, as must be done if good pick-up from low speeds is to be obtained from carburettors that do not incorporate acceleration pumps.

S.U. CARBURETTORS

As already explained, the mixture strength is automatically controlled by the tapered needle which varies the orifice of the jet. The base of the piston also varies the opening to the induction pipe, so that the amount of air which enters is also proportional to the throttle opening. This automatic control of

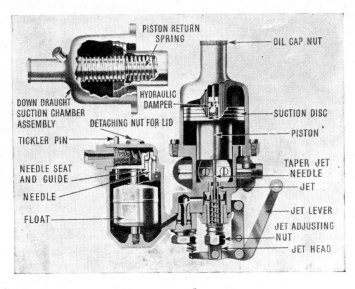

FIG. 20. *Construction of an S.U. carburettor. In the upper left-hand corner is shown the spring-loaded piston assembly on a down-draught version of the carburettor.*

petrol and air-flow thus provides a suitable mixture without the need for any correction or compensating devices. The efficiency of the S.U. carburettor, in fact, lies in its simplicity.

Adjustment of Mixture Strength. Tuning is equally simple. If a change in mixture strength is desired, it is only necessary to change the needle. The jet itself is a standard size. The needle, moreover, does not possess a constant taper, but is very accurately ground in what can best be described as a series of tapered steps. Thus it is possible to select a needle which will give the required degree of enrichment or weakening of the mixture at any given throttle opening, without affecting the remainder of the range. Alternatively, broad changes in overall mixture strength are possible by using other needles.

The manufacturer of the car or the carburettor can generally suggest two alternative needles to the standard one, giving a weak setting for maximum economy, or a rich setting for maximum performance. It is seldom that the average owner need experiment with other needles than these.

The method of removing the suction chamber has already been described. The new needle should be fitted with its shoulder flush with the face of the piston. The jet will now require centring, and the idling mixture strength adjusting, as described earlier in this chapter.

STROMBERG CARBURETTORS

In these carburettors the main jet delivers fuel over the whole of the speed range, but alteration in its size will mainly affect part-throttle running. High-speed operation is taken care of by the power jet, which is brought into operation by a spring-loaded plunger controlled by the inlet manifold depression. The acceleration pump is similarly operated on the earlier models, and is not adjustable,

although an alteration in the size of the restriction jet in the outlet from the pump will affect the rate at which the petrol is discharged and the period during which enrichment takes place.

On later Strombergs (Fig. 20) the acceleration pump is operated by the throttle; the amount of fuel discharged can be varied by adjusting the stroke of the pump, while the size of the discharge jet influences the period during which the fuel is sprayed into the airstream.

CLAUDEL-HOBSON CARBURETTORS

Like the Stromberg carburettor, most models of the Claudel-Hobson are fitted with a power jet which controls the mixture strength at wide throttle openings.

The larger downdraught carburettors are also fitted with an acceleration pump which is operated by the throttle linkage. In addition to downdraught models, updraught and horizontal carburettors are available, but the general principles are similar on the various types.

The idling mixture is adjusted by regulating the air supply by means of a screw in the vicinity of the float chamber; the screw is locked by a nut or spring. The carburettor is unusual in that the idling mixture passes through a transverse passage drilled in the body of the throttle valve, so that the mixture issues from the centre and from each edge of the butterfly.

Alteration in the size of the main jet will chiefly affect the power and consumption at medium throttle openings; the power jet must be changed to vary the mixture at maximum throttle openings. The power jet is brought into action by a spring-loaded valve which is depressed by a rocker arm on the throttle spindle. The operation of this valve should be checked if poor acceleration cannot be traced to a blocked power jet.

The diffuser tube, fitted above the main

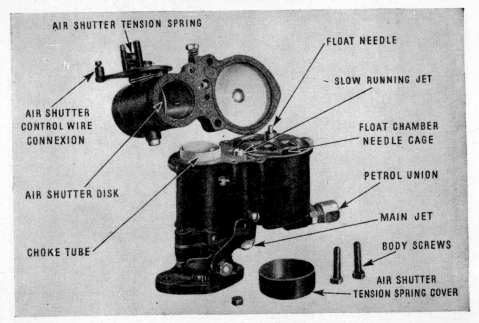

AIR SHUTTER TENSION SPRING

FLOAT NEEDLE

AIR SHUTTER
CONTROL WIRE
CONNEXION

SLOW RUNNING JET

FLOAT CHAMBER
NEEDLE CAGE

PETROL UNION

AIR SHUTTER DISK

MAIN JET

BODY SCREWS

CHOKE TUBE

AIR SHUTTER
TENSION SPRING COVER

FIG. 21. CLAUDEL-HOBSON CARBURETTOR. *The main feature of this design is the power jet which controls the mixture strength at wide throttle openings. It is brought into action by a spring-loaded valve which is depressed by a rocker arm on the throttle spindle. Slow running is adjusted on the adjustment screw located in the top of the slow running jet assembly.*

jet, should be removed for cleaning at approximately 8,000-mile intervals. It is accessible either by removing the main jet or the slow running jet plug, when a screwdriver having a blade ⅜-in. wide can be used to unscrew the tube. When reassembling, make sure that the washers are correctly positioned.

The position of the various jets and adjustments can be seen from the illustrations of typical downdraught carburettors.

CARTER CARBURETTORS

These carburettors, like the others described, are available in a number of different models, and are widely fitted on American cars. Fig. 22 shows, diagrammatically, a cross-section through a representative model. Carter carburettors employ a metering rod sliding in

a jet which controls the supply of fuel to the slip nozzle in the throat of the carburettor. The rod is graduated in three steps, and is linked with the throttle control so that it is progressively raised as the throttle is opened.

It will be obvious, therefore, that control of mixture strength will depend not only on the choice of a metering rod with steps of the correct diameter, but also on the correct adjustment of the rod in relation to the throttle opening. Enrichment during acceleration is also provided by a plunger pump which is coupled to the throttle lever, the stroke of the pump being adjustable by fitting the pump link to the appropriate hole in a pivoted plate attached to the throttle connecting rod. There are three positions: Winter, which gives the longest stroke; Normal; and Summer, which provides a

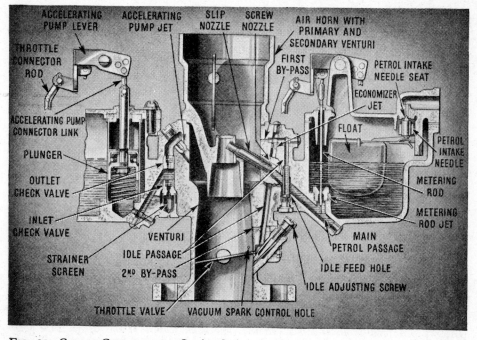

FIG. 22. CARTER CARBURETTOR. *Sectional view showing how the metering rod controls the supply of fuel to the slip nozzle in the carburettor throat. The rod is graduated in three steps and is linked to the throttle control so that it is slowly raised as the throttle opens.*

short stroke. Apart from this adjustment, the owner will be well advised to leave tuning in the hands of a service station familiar with the carburettor.

FORD CARBURETTORS

The Ford 8 h.p. and 10 h.p. engines are fitted with a downdraught carburettor of the static type. As can be seen from Fig. 23, the main and compensator jets are fitted in the base of the float chamber. The Ford company, however, discourage any attempt to alter the mixture strength, maintaining that the standard setting should prove the most satisfactory.

The Ford V-8 engines are provided with a carburettor which is, in effect, a twin instrument with a common float chamber. An acceleration pump is fitted, its fuel being divided between the two throttle barrels, one of which serves each

bank of cylinders. There is no adjustment for the volume of petrol delivered or the duration of the spray.

The main jets are screwed into passages closed by drain plugs beneath the float chamber. Since the size of the air bleed

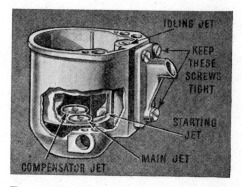

FIG. 23. *View showing the location of the main and compensator jets in a Ford carburettor.*

cannot be altered, the only tuning possible consists of an alteration in the size of the main jets, but as has been stated above, the manufacturer does not recommend such alterations being made.

STARTING MIXTURE CONTROLS

Starting from cold requires a very rich mixture in order to provide the initial explosions, but once the engine has fired, the mixture to the cylinder should be progressively weakened until the normal running temperature is obtained. To get the best possible results from the starting devices fitted to modern carburettors, and to diagnose the trouble should starting prove difficult, some knowledge of their construction and operation is desirable.

Stranglers or Chokes. The simplest method of providing a very rich mixture is to fit a strangler or air throttle valve in the air intake, so that the air supply is practically cut off when the engine is rotated to start it. The heavy suction on the slow-running jet will thus draw an excess of fuel from it. When the engine has fired, the strangler must be opened slightly to weaken the mixture.

Some years ago, this type of starting control, or choke, as it was often termed, was practically universal. The precise amount of enrichment for any given engine temperature was left to the discretion and experience of the driver. The amount of normal throttle opening was also critical in most cases, and often determined whether a start would be obtained.

Automatic Choke Controls. The basic strangler or choke is used on a number of modern carburettors, but with certain refinements to improve its efficiency. The valve is usually offset on its spindle, to which it is coupled by a spring, so that the suction of the engine tends to open it. Sometimes there is a spring-loaded flap in the choke. Both arrangements provide a semi-automatic mixture control, the choke opening as soon as the engine fires, and the degree of opening varying with engine speed.

Generally the choke control is interconnected with the throttle control, so that the throttle is opened to the correct position for starting and fast idling during the warming up period. For satisfactory starting, therefore, the accelerator pedal or hand throttle, when fitted, must not be used.

The modern development of the choke is a strangler which is opened or closed by the expansion or contraction of a thermostatic spring, influenced by the heat of the exhaust manifold. This

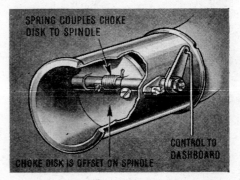

FIG. 24. *A semi-automatic choke or strangler starter fitted in the air-intake pipe.*

relieves the driver of any responsibility, the mixture strength being automatically determined according to the temperature of the engine. The choke is opened against the tension of the thermostat spring when the engine is running, due to suction acting on a small piston which is linked to the choke spindle.

STARTING CARBURETTORS

On several modern Solex and Zenith carburettors the starting mixture is produced by a small auxiliary carburettor which feeds into a port on the engine side of the throttle valve. When the starter

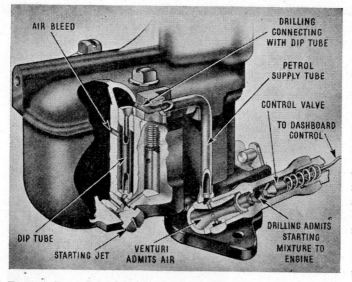

control is operated, a disk valve on Solex carburettors, or a spring-loaded plunger on Zenith models, puts this port in communication with a dip tube which draws petrol through a jet from the float chamber. The amount of air admitted is also controlled by a jet on Solex carburettors, or by the size of a venturi in Zenith carburettors. It will thus be seen that the mixture strength for starting depends on the size of

FIG. 25. *Part of the casing cut-away to show the automatic starting device on a Zenith carburettor controlled from the dashboard.*

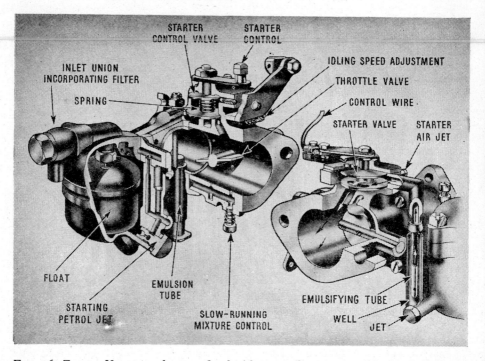

FIG. 26. ZENITH V-TYPE *carburettor fitted with an auxiliary starter. The detailed drawing on the right illustrates how the petrol and air are mixed and admitted to the engine.*

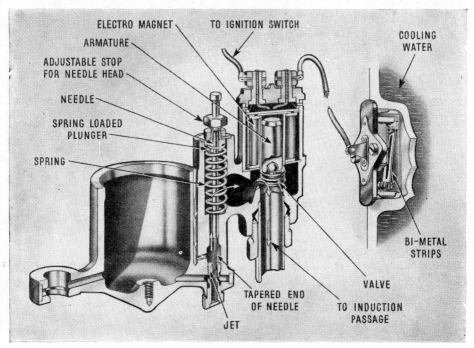

FIG. 27. S.U. THERMOSTATIC STARTER. *The device incorporated in this design of carburettor is controlled by an electro-magnet operated by a switch that opens and closes according to the temperature of the cooling water. Current for the electro-magnet is supplied from the starter battery. Adjustment of the needle's travel is made on the adjustable stop at its head.*

the petrol jet, while the engine speed during the warming up period depends on the size of the air jet. A rich mixture is only necessary during the initial firing, and the Zenith device is designed to supply a weakened mixture to ensure the correct engine speed and rapid warming up.

Since these starting carburettors depend for their efficiency on the depression present in the induction system when the throttle is closed, it follows that the accelerator pedal must not be depressed when starting. The dashboard control, moreover, must be either fully out or in. The only exception to this rule is the Solex A.I.P. type carburettor, on which an intermediate position is provided for the starter control, giving a less rich mixture during the warming up period.

THERMOSTATIC STARTING CARBURETTORS

As with automatic chokes, carburettor manufacturers have designed auxiliary starting carburettors which are brought into action by a thermostat operated by the heat of the exhaust manifold or the cooling water. In the Solex Thermostarter the fuel supply to the starting carburettor is controlled by a disk valve which is moved by a rod attached to a diaphragm in an airtight housing, as shown in Fig. 28. The outer side of the diaphragm is subject to engine suction, which will tend to deflect the diaphragm, and close the disk valve.

The suction chamber also communicates, through a tube, with a metal box attached to the exhaust manifold. This

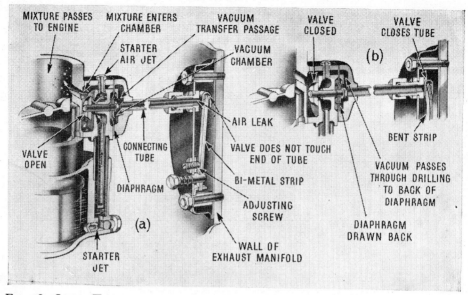

FIG. 28. SOLEX THERMOSTARTER. *A starting device in which the mixture is controlled by a disk valve operated by a diaphragm which is controlled by a bi-metal strip.*

box contains a bi-metal strip having at its free end a pad which is in contact with the end of the tube only when the engine is hot. The result is that, due to the air leakage through the tube when the engine is cold, the diaphragm is not deflected, and the starting carburettor is in operation. When the exhaust manifold warms up, the bi-metal strip bends, shuts off the air leak and the diaphragm is then deflected by suction and closes the starter valve. The adjustment of the bi-metal strip is carefully set, and should not need attention, but if the starter cuts out too soon, or stays in operation too long, a slight adjustment of the screw, not exceeding one complete turn, should put matters right.

Thermostatic Starting. The S.U. carburettor is sometimes fitted with a small starting carburettor, in which the valve is controlled by the solenoid of an electro-magnet. The windings of the magnet are energized from the battery through the ignition switch and a thermostatic switch operated by the temperature of the cooling water. Fig. 27 shows the arrangements clearly. When the engine is cold, the thermostatic switch contacts are together, so that

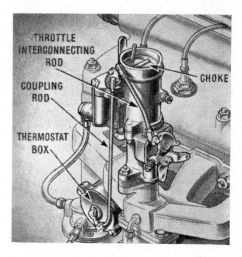

FIG. 29. *A modern thermostatically-operated choke fitted to a Stromberg carburettor.*

current flows through the magnet windings and opens the valve against spring pressure. Petrol is drawn past the needle valve, which fits into a jet supplied from the float chamber. This needle is carried by a small spring-loaded piston, and when the engine fires air is drawn into the carburettor past this piston, tending to force it downwards against the spring pressure. This moves the tapered needle into the jet, and weakens the mixture.

An adjusting screw limits the travel of the needle; screwing it inwards weakens the mixture, while screwing it outwards enriches it. This adjustment should be made with the engine idling at normal running temperature. The starting carburettor must first be brought back into operation by short-circuiting the terminal at the centre of the switch to the switch body. Next open the throttle momentarily, and then unscrew the adjustment until the mixture is as rich as possible, without causing the engine to idle irregularly or stall. If there is any difficulty in subsequently starting from cold, unscrew the adjustment by approximately another half turn.

CARBURETTOR FAULT TRACING

If the various maintenance operations described at the beginning of this chapter have been regularly carried out, the carburettor will seldom be found to be responsible for difficult starting, loss of power, or high petrol consumption. The section dealing with Systematic Fault Tracing in Chapter 5, should, therefore, be consulted in order to determine whether the trouble is due to an ignition, mechanical, or fuel feed fault, rather than a carburettor defect.

When the trouble can definitely be attributed to the carburettor, the fault must fall under one of two broad headings: too weak, or too rich a mixture. The following table will assist in analysing the trouble, but it is again emphasized that only carburation faults are quoted, and that other faults may be contributory.

WEAK MIXTURE OR STARVATION

Trouble	*Cause*
Fuel not reaching float chamber.	Filters clogged. Needle valve stuck in closed position. Jets choked.
Fuel not reaching cylinders.	Starting device not operating. Throttle not opening.
Insufficient fuel reaching cylinders.	Jets choked. Starting device incorrectly adjusted. Fuel level in float chamber too low. Wrong jet settings.
Idling mixture too weak.	Incorrect adjustment of mixture control. Petrol level too low. Slow-running jet obstructed.
Engine will start but will not keep running.	Insufficient fuel (see above). Starting control not remaining in action long enough.

Poor acceleration.	Compensating jet choked.
	Acceleration pump defective or in-correctly adjusted.
	Wrong jet settings.
Lack of power at all speeds.	Air filter dirty.
	Fuel supply restricted.
	Water or sediment in fuel.
	Wrong jet settings.
	Loose choke tube.
Lack of power at wide throttle openings.	Power jet obstructed.
	Air filter dirty.
	Throttle not opening fully.

OVER-RICH MIXTURE AND EXCESSIVE FUEL CONSUMPTION

Trouble	*Cause*
Carburettor flooding.	Grit on needle valve seating.
	Float punctured.
	Petrol level too high.
Fuel leakage.	Unions not tightened.
	Fibre washers defective or omitted.
	Leakage from emulsion block.
	Main jet cap loose.
Excessive fuel delivered.	Wrong size main or compensating jet.
	Economy device not functioning.
	Acceleration pump stroke too long.
	Starting carburettor does not cut out.
	Strangler does not open fully.
Engine "hunts" when idling.	Slow running adjustment too rich.
	Starting device not cutting out.
	Choke not fully open.
	Petrol level too high.
	Carburettor flooding.
Lack of power.	Air filter dirty.
	Main jet or compensating jet too large.
	Acceleration pump delivering too much fuel.

ELECTRIC PETROL PUMPS

The S.U. electric petrol pump is fitted to a large number of recent cars. Although it may appear from Fig. 21, Chapter 1 to be somewhat complicated, its construction is, in reality, quite simple, and seldom gives trouble. The majority of faults which do occasionally arise, in fact, can usually be traced to simple causes, such as choked filters, poor electrical con-nexions, or loose unions on the suction or delivery pipes.

Inspecting and Cleaning Filters. The petrol pump is provided with a filter of generous dimensions, but this should be removed and cleaned at regular intervals to forestall trouble. A large hexagonal nut will be seen on the underside of the base of the pump. When this has been unscrewed, the filter can be

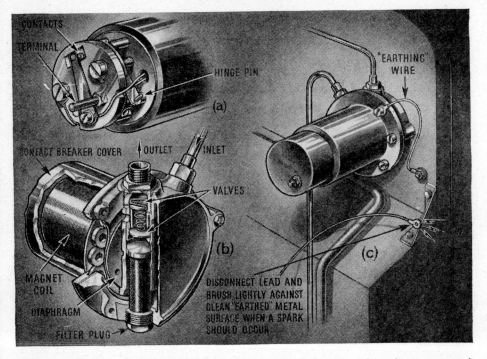

CONTACTS
TERMINAL
HINGE PIN
"EARTHING" WIRE
(a)
CONTACT BREAKER COVER   OUTLET   INLET
VALVES
(b)   (c)
MAGNET COIL
DIAPHRAGM
DISCONNECT LEAD AND BRUSH LIGHTLY AGAINST CLEAN "EARTHED" METAL SURFACE WHEN A SPARK SHOULD OCCUR
FILTER PLUG

FIG. 30. SERVICING AN S.U. PUMP. (*a*) *the front cover removed to show the contacts and terminal connexions;* (*b*) *location of the valves and filter, the latter requiring periodic cleaning;* (*c*) *a method of verifying that the current is reaching the pump.*

withdrawn. Swill the gauze in petrol to remove any sediment, and when replacing do not forget the fibre washer which fits under the nut, or leakage will take place.

Stoppage of Petrol Supply. If this filter is reasonably clean, and petrol is not reaching the carburettor, the small filter in the inlet union to the carburettor float chamber may be choked, or the needle valve may be jammed on its seating. The methods of dealing with these faults are described earlier in this chapter. It is unlikely that the pipe leading from the pump to the carburettor will be blocked, but it may be advisable to disconnect it at both ends and check it by blowing through it.

The pipe from the petrol tank to the pump does sometimes become choked,

however, so that it is well worth while checking it. The quickest method is to disconnect it from the pump, and to force air through it under pressure with the aid of a tyre pump. If the petrol filler cap is removed, and the services of an assistant are enlisted, it should be possible to hear the air bubbling into the tank on each stroke of the tyre pump. This treatment will usually clear a blocked pipe quite successfully.

Fuel Starvation. If the pump beats or clicks rapidly, the trouble can be traced to an air leak at some point, although similar symptoms occur when the carburettor needle valve sticks open and the float chamber is flooded. As we are concerned with lack of petrol rather than a surfeit of it, however, the tightness of the filter nut should be checked, as should the union nut on the inlet to the pump. If these appear to be in order disconnect the outlet pipe from the carburettor, and allow the pump to discharge into a clean tin or glass jar. If air leaks exist in the suction pipe, bubbles will be seen in the fuel. It will then be necessary to check each union in the pipe stage by stage until the petrol tank is reached. This is best carried out at a service station where a car lift is available.

An elusive cause of fuel starvation is local vaporization or boiling of the fuel at some point in the pipe line, usually where this passes too close to the exhaust pipe or silencer. The trouble is generally apparent only in hot weather, and may follow a burst of speed or hill climbing, when the exhaust system becomes hotter than normal. If the pipe cannot be re-positioned further away from the exhaust, the trouble can usually be cured by lagging the petrol pipe, or the exhaust pipe or silencer, with asbestos tape over the affected length.

The pump itself may become over-heated if too close to the exhaust manifold or pipe. The remedy in this case is to fit a metal shield, if necessary lined with asbestos, to screen the pump, or, better still, to move the pump to a cooler position.

When the Pump Clicks at Intervals. Sometimes the pump persists in clicking at intervals of five seconds or so when the ignition is switched on but the engine is not running. There are three possible causes :—evaporation of petrol from the float chamber, so that the pump restores the level; slight leakage of the carburettor needle valve, or a defective suction valve in the pump.

The first cause is quite often experienced during very hot weather in engines fitted with downdraught carburettors, since the float chamber is then placed in the heated air just beneath the bonnet, and over the exhaust manifold.

There is little that the owner can do, nor is the trouble very serious. The second cause, flooding of the carburettor, calls for immediate attention, however, due to the waste of fuel and detrimental effects of neat petrol in the cylinders.

The third possible fault, a suction valve in the pump which is not seating properly, is quite simply checked even by the novice, provided that a little care is taken. The outlet union, to which the pipe leading to the carburettor is attached, should be unscrewed from the base of the pump, when both the delivery valve and suction valve can be extracted. Both valves take the form of small fibre disks. The delivery valve fits into a cage, in which it is retained by a spring clip. When the cage has been lifted out, the suction valve, which is held down on its seating by a light spring, can be extracted.

The fit of this valve on its seating is very important. It may be found that a particle of grit or sediment has intruded between the valve and its seat; on the other hand, the valve may be slightly warped. A new valve is required, but a get-you-home dodge is to exchange the delivery valve for the suction valve, as the fit of the former is not so critical. When reassembling, make sure that the spring is in place above the suction valve, and that the two fibre washers are fitted, one above and one below the delivery valve cage.

Electrical Troubles. To operate at all, the pump depends, of course, on a supply of electricity. If it fails to show any signs of life when the ignition is switched on, therefore, first check the wire which is connected to the terminal on the end cover of the pump. If this connexion is clean and tight, unscrew the terminal, and, with the ignition switched on, brush the terminal on the end of the wire lightly against a bare metal part of the engine. A spark should occur. Do not press the terminal on the metal, or the heavy flow of current will burn out the fuse serving the pump. If no spark is obtained, check the fuse in any case, as explained in Chapter 7, and if this is in order look for a disconnexion at some point between the ignition switch and the petrol pump.

A point which is sometimes overlooked is that although current may reach the pump quite satisfactorily, it must eventually return to the battery through the pump body and the metal surface to which the pump is bolted. As the electrical contact at this point is not always perfect, most pumps are fitted with an earthing wire, which is connected between one of the screws in the base of the pump and a convenient chassis bolt. If this wire is not fitted it is always a good plan to provide an earth return, with bright, sound contacts. Fig. 30 (c) shows a typical example.

Examining the Contact Points. If current is reaching the pump, the trouble most likely lies in the contact points which are housed beneath the end cover. The suggestions which follow entail work which is rather beyond the scope of the novice, who would be well advised to leave any further attentions to a specialist. This sound advice cannot always be followed, however, so that the owner may of necessity have to try to rectify the trouble himself.

The end cover should be removed to expose the breaker points. One contact is attached to a strip which bridges the two arms of an outer rocker, which in turn fits over an inner rocker. The pair of rockers are mounted on a common pivot pin, and are connected by two small springs which give a toggle action, so that the contacts open and close quickly when the inner rocker is moved by the end of the rod, which is connected to the armature of the electro-magnet in the body of the pump, see Fig. 31.

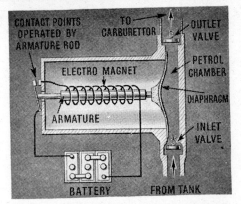

FIG. 31. *Wiring circuit of an S.U. fuel pump and arrangement of the diaphragm and valves.*

The two contacts should be together when the pump is not working. If so, a spark should be obtained when the electrical supply lead is touched against the terminal. If no spark occurs, separate the contacts carefully and clean their surfaces by passing a strip of fine glass-paper between them.

If the points have not closed, the inner rocker will not be in contact with the magnet housing, indicating that something is preventing the armature from returning to its full extent. If the armature is binding due to a particle of grit, flicking the contact points together with the finger, after reconnecting the electrical supply lead and switching on the ignition, will often start the pump working again. If the points are blackened and burnt, however, the most likely trouble is too great a tension on the diaphragm.

Excessive Diaphragm Tension. It should be realized that the armature rod passes through the body of the pump and is attached to the diaphragm. When the contact points are closed, the armature moves into the electro-magnet, drawing the diaphragm away from the base of the pump, so that fuel is drawn into the pump chamber. The outer end of the armature

121

rod moves the inner rocker, which, at the end of its travel, causes the outer rocker to flick over, opening the contact points.

This cuts off the current, so that the diaphragm is returned by a spring, forcing the petrol in the chamber through the delivery valve to the carburettor. If the diaphragm has shrunk, it does not return far enough to cause the armature rod to operate the rockers, so that the contacts remain open, and a fresh pumping stroke does not take place.

Easing the Diaphragm. To reduce the tension on the diaphragm, its edge must be freed at the point at which it is gripped between the base of the pump and the magnet housing. Remove the pump from the bulkhead and slacken the six screws which hold the two parts together. Invert the pump so that its base is upwards, and lift off the base. The diaphragm will probably be stuck to the flange of the magnet housing, from which it must be freed by carefully passing the blade of a knife between its surface and the flange. Eleven small brass rollers are fitted beneath the diaphragm, hence the need for inverting the magnet assembly, to prevent them falling out of place. Do not rotate the diaphragm.

Refit the base to the body of the pump, and screw home the nuts barely finger-tight. Re-connect the electric supply lead, switch on the ignition, and make sure that the contact points have closed. When the current is flowing, hold the contact points closed and tighten the screws in the flange firmly; as the diaphragm will be fully deflected by the armature during this process, the pump should now operate satisfactorily.

Diaphragm Replacement. If, during the preceding work, the diaphragm was found to be cracked or perforated, the fitting of a new diaphragm and armature assembly should be left to a service station, since some skill and experience is needed to obtain the correct adjustment of the contact-breaker rockers on assembly. Briefly, the procedure is to remove the diaphragm, complete with the armature rod, by rotating it anti-clockwise, thus unscrewing the threaded end of the armature rod from the inner rocker of the contact-breaker mechanism. The rollers referred to earlier must be placed on one side pending reassembly.

The new diaphragm is supplied assembled to an armature rod; the fabric itself is not obtainable separately. The new armature rod is passed through the body of the pump, engaged with the inner rocker, and the diaphragm rotated to screw it inwards until there is just space to slip the rollers into place in the groove between the armature and the diaphragm. The armature rod is then screwed into the rocker as far as possible; it is next unscrewed gradually, and pressed in and out at intervals, until the contact-breaker mechanism operates correctly. The armature is then unscrewed by an amount equal to four or five holes on the flange, when the base can be refitted, the diaphragm being tensioned while the screws are tightened as just described.

As the work will probably be carried out on the bench, however, an electric current may not be available, the pivot pin holding the two rockers should be pulled out, thus allowing the inner rocker to move further back as the return spring stretches the diaphragm. After the flange screws have been tightened the holes in the rockers can be re-alined, and the pivot pin refitted.

MECHANICAL PETROL PUMPS

The A.C. mechanical petrol pump shares the field with the S.U. electric pump just described. It has been manufactured in five different models, but basically the pumps are similar to that illustrated in Fig. 32.

Cleaning the Filters. The chief, and usually the only, routine attention re-

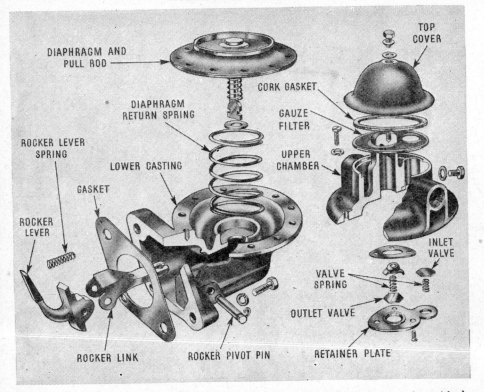

TOP COVER

DIAPHRAGM AND PULL ROD

CORK GASKET

GAUZE FILTER

DIAPHRAGM RETURN SPRING

ROCKER LEVER SPRING

UPPER CHAMBER

LOWER CASTING

GASKET

ROCKER LEVER

INLET VALVE

VALVE SPRING

OUTLET VALVE

ROCKER LINK

ROCKER PIVOT PIN

RETAINER PLATE

FIG. 32. A.C. PETROL PUMP. *There are several models of this type of pump, but with the exception of minor constructional features they are similar in principle and operation to that illustrated above and described in the text.*

quired is periodical cleaning of the filters, at regular intervals.

The earlier types of pump had a glass or metal filter bowl, held in place by a wire yoke and a thumbscrew. On slackening the screw, the yoke can be swung aside and the bowl, with a gauze filter disk above it, removed for cleaning.

The later pumps have a filter gauze beneath a domed metal cover on the top of the pump, secured by a nut. Again, removal of the filter is a simple matter. When replacing either type of filter, make sure that the cork washer against which the bowl or cover seats is in good condition, and do not overlook the fibre washer fitted beneath the top cover securing bolt on the later pumps.

Difficult Starting and Lack of Petrol. As has already been stressed when dealing with electric pumps, when petrol does not reach the carburettor, or the supply is insufficient, the pump should not necessarily be blamed. In most cases the trouble can be traced to choked filters, air leaks, or blocked petrol pipes. All the checks covering these aspects, dealt with in some detail in the preceding section under the headings "Stoppage of Petrol Supply" and "Fuel Starvation," should, therefore, be checked as they apply with equal emphasis to mechanical pumps.

If the filters, connexions and pipe lines appear to be in order, the suction or delivery valve may not be seating

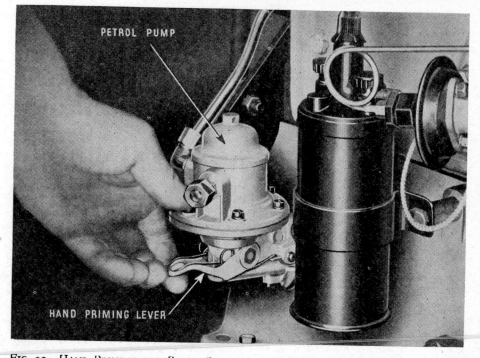

FIG 33. HAND PRIMING THE PUMP. *Due to normal wear and tear the movement of the diaphragm becomes reduced. As a result of this the pump is slow to prime when the engine is started. In these conditions the pump should be primed with the hand lever.*

properly. On the early pumps the valves may be removed by unscrewing the hexagonal plugs on the top of the pump, the outlet valve being beneath the plug in the pump body, and the inlet beneath that in the casting above the filter bowl. On the model M pumps the valves will be found beneath the screwed plugs revealed when the filter cover has been removed and the filter gauze lifted out. Notice that in this case the inlet valve is placed on top of its spring, whereas the outlet valve lies below its spring. The valves take the form of small disks of fibre, and should be renewed if they appear to be warped. The polished side should face the seat. When reassembling, fit new washers under the valve plugs unless the existing ones are in absolutely perfect condition.

The foregoing advice will, unfortunately, not be of any value to owners of recent cars, most of which are fitted with the model T pump, in which the valves are not accessible without dismantling the pump. As will be explained later, this is not, strictly speaking, within the scope of the average owner.

Mechanical Faults. Due to wear on the rocker arm which operates the pump, and an accumulation of slackness at the various joints and pivots which transmit this movement to the diaphragm, the movement of the diaphragm becomes reduced after a considerable mileage has been covered. The result is that the pump is slow to prime, or fill up with petrol, when first starting up the engine, resulting in prolonged use of the starter being necessary. Normally, about 25 strokes of the operating arm are necessary to prime an empty pump when the parts are in good condition; when insufficient diaphragm movement takes place, however, forty strokes will be required.

Under normal circumstances, of course, the pump is rarely entirely empty. Nevertheless, when the pump is worn an appreciable time elapses before the float chamber in the carburettor is filled, and it is well worth while priming the pump by means of the hand lever when this is fitted, especially in cold weather or when the car has not been in use for an appreciable time.

Testing the Efficiency of the Pump. The operating efficiency of the pump can be checked by disconnecting the suction pipe which leads to the petrol tank, and substituting a length of rubber tubing, ensuring that it makes an airtight joint where attached to the pump. When the engine is rotated or the hand priming lever operated, the pump should be able to draw petrol up the tube to a height of at least 30 inches.

If a second tube is attached to the outlet union and allowed to dip into a jar or tin, the presence of air bubbles in the fuel delivered will be readily detected, and will suggest that inefficiency is due to defective filter bowl or valve plug gaskets, insufficient tightening of the bowl retaining nuts, gasket plugs, or the ring of screws securing the two halves of the pump. Other possible causes are a cracked or perforated diaphragm, slackness in the unions on the suction side of the pump, or a fractured petrol pipe.

Testing by the Analyser. Better still, have the pump checked at a service station which is equipped with a portable tester specially designed for A.C. pumps. This enables the actual amount of fuel delivered in one minute to be measured, while a pressure of between $1\frac{3}{4}$ and 5 lb. per square inch, depending on the car, is recorded by a gauge.

Should the analyser, as it is called, reveal that the pump is below par, and attention to filters, unions and valves, when accessible, does not improve matters, an overhaul is indicated. When dismantling and reassembling the pump a special combined assembly and test stand is used, while a kit of service tools is also required if the work is to be carried out efficiently. Discretion suggests, therefore, that this work should be left to an authorized service station; a top overhaul, which consists of dismantling the pump, fitting a new diaphragm, valves, valve springs, gaskets, and so on, costs a very moderate amount, while a complete overhaul, which entails in addition the renewal of any worn parts of the operating linkage, is by no means expensive.

Excessive Operating Pressure. Occasionally flooding of the carburettor is attributed to a pump which generates too high a pressure. The pressure built up is determined by the strength of the diaphragm return spring, which is carefully calibrated for the particular car to which the pump is fitted. In nine cases out of ten, therefore, flooding is due to a defective needle valve in the carburettor float chamber, or to grit between the valve and its seating. Possibly a punctured float may be the culprit.

In some cases, however, flooding can be attributed to the pump, although such instances are infrequent on recent cars. One method of preventing the trouble is to have a weaker diaphragm return spring fitted; on some models a special air dome can be fitted to absorb the pulsations in the fuel flow from the pump, which tend to cause the carburettor needle valve to chatter on its seating.

The practically-minded owner may care to try the effect of fitting a thicker packing washer between the pump and the crankcase, thus displacing the operating arm further away from the cam, and reducing the length of stroke of the pump.

CHAPTER 5

ENGINE MAINTENANCE

IT is true to say that the ultimate life of an engine is determined during the first thousand miles of driving. No amount of conscientious maintenance after this period can compensate for neglect or mishandling during this critical stage. So important is careful running-in that even on the cheapest cars the initial stages are carried out at the factory, while more expensive models are given a fairly extensive run on the road before being handed over to the owner.

RUNNING-IN A NEW OR OVERHAULED ENGINE

Why, then, is further running-in required? The answer lies in the fact that however carefully the bearing surfaces in an engine may be finished, they are, technically speaking, still rough. Viewed under a microscope, the surfaces of the cylinder walls, crankshaft journals, and similar wearing parts appear to be made up of a series of hills and valleys. Some, it is true, are only several millionths of an inch high, while others may be more pronounced, perhaps measuring as much as a tenth of a thousandth of an inch. To normal sight and touch such surfaces appear mirror-smooth, but when working together in the engine, they generate appreciable friction.

Heavy Loading. During the running-in period, the projecting surfaces are gradually worn down, until a really smooth surface is obtained. During this process, it is obvious that if the bearings are heavily loaded, excessive friction and heat will be generated, so that there is a risk of the bearing metal melting or the pistons seizing in the cylinders.

Modern production methods produce excellent surface finishes, while the design of the bearings and pistons allows appreciable working clearances to exist even when the parts are new, so that the risk of seizure is much less than it was on cars built, say, fifteen or twenty years ago. Another factor, however, must be taken into account: the slight changes in shape which take place in various components as they become hot and expand when the engine is running. This can cause tight spots, and actual distortion sometimes takes place as the stresses which were induced in the various parts during manufacture are gradually released in the early life of the engine, under the influence of repeated heating and cooling.

However accurate modern machine tools may be, such parts as pistons, crankshafts and camshafts, or the cylinder block in which they are fitted, are bound to alter very slightly in shape: it is not unusual, for instance, for an engine, which rotates fairly freely when first delivered, to develop tight spots after the first two hundred miles of running.

Enough has been said to indicate that a certain amount of running-in, or lapping together of the parts, is required. The method of carrying this out is equally important. There are two schools of thought. One holds that a low engine speed must not be exceeded for at least the first 200–300 miles; the equivalent to about 30 miles per hour in top gear, and correspondingly lower speeds in the indirect gears, is usually the limit recommended. Many manufacturers specify this limitation, and often extend it to the first 500 miles. It must be admitted that it is probably the safest

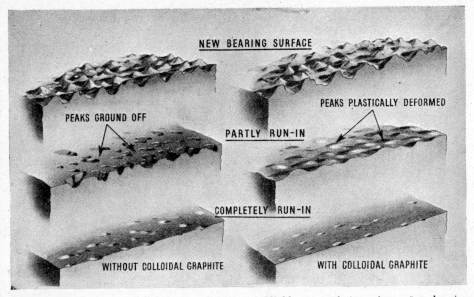

NEW BEARING SURFACE

PEAKS PLASTICALLY DEFORMED

PEAKS GROUND OFF

PARTLY RUN-IN

COMPLETELY RUN-IN

WITHOUT COLLOIDAL GRAPHITE

WITH COLLOIDAL GRAPHITE

FIG. I. RUNNING-IN AND BEARING SURFACES. *Highly magnified sections of a bearing surface in various stages of running-in. Of particular interest is the moulded bearing surface that is obtained by using a lubricant containing a proportion of colloidal graphite. With a normal lubricant, the high spots are simply rubbed away.*

counsel when the car is to be placed in the hands of a novice.

The engineer, however, will point out that the running-in is a grinding, lapping, or polishing process, and that the only way to obtain a satisfactory surface finish, is to employ a combination of high speed and light pressure: a fact which most owners will at some time have proved for themselves.

The polishing effect on the various rubbing surfaces of the engine when a car is driven at 30 miles per hour in top gear, then, is not very efficient; if the engine is allowed to slog up hill with top gear engaged, in fact, the process is a scoring, harsh friction instead of a polishing one.

Speed and Load. From this it is logical to assume that moderately high speeds are not harmful, but are actually beneficial, provided that the loads on the bearings are light. In other words, it is better to drive at 40–45 miles per hour,

with the throttle partly closed, than to restrict the speed to 30 miles per hour, with a wide throttle opening.

Delicate use of the throttle is more important than actual road speed, although this should not be excessive during the first hundred to two hundred miles, when, as already explained, a certain amount of distortion may be taking place. The conventional running-in instructions may, with advantage, be modified as follows:

First two hundred miles: Maximum speed in top gear, 35 miles per hour; in third, 25 miles per hour.

From 200 to 500 miles: Maximum in top, 40 miles per hour; third, 30 miles per hour.

From 500–1,000 miles: Maximum in top, 50 miles per hour; third, 35 miles per hour.

The maximum speeds quoted should not be held for more than a mile or so at a time, and should first be indulged in on downhill stretches, when a small throttle opening can be used. At frequent intervals the engine should be rotated with the starting handle, when hot, so that the general stiffness or tight spots will indicate how the running-in is progressing.

It must be remembered that the temperature of the rubbing surfaces is raised by the speed at which they move over one another, as well as by the degree of tightness; hence the undesirability of prolonged bursts of speed.

Lubrication is Vital. Lubrication is of prime importance during the running-in period. After the first 300 miles, the sump should be drained and flushed out with a flushing oil before it is refilled. Although scrupulous care is taken by the manufacturer to ensure that all the parts are clean before they are assembled, minute particles of foundry sand, abrasive and metallic dust are trapped in the pores of the metal, and are loosened during the first few hundred miles, to be carried away by the oil. The draining of the sump should be done immediately after a long run, when the oil is very warm and, consequently, flows freely.

To make sure that the pistons, rings and cylinders are adequately lubricated, an upper cylinder lubricant, in the form of a light oil, should be added to the petrol in the proportions specified by the makers of the compound. Since the cylinder bores are lubricated by oil flung from the connecting-rod bearings, lubrication is bound to be rather restricted at low engine speeds, until the bearing clearances increase. As soon as the car is taken over, therefore, the slow running adjustment on the carburettor should be set to give a really brisk idling speed, of 600–800 r.p.m. This can be judged by the fact that the ignition warning light goes out and the dynamo begins to charge at about this speed.

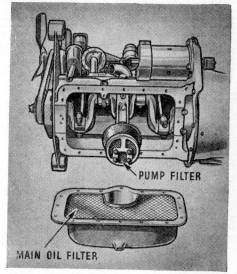

FIG. 2. *View of engine with sump removed showing the main oil filter and pump filter. These are of coarse mesh to prevent clogging and starvation of the pump.*

Colloidal Graphite. The addition of a running-in compound, consisting of a light oil containing colloidal graphite, to the oil in the sump is also advisable during running-in: it is also a wise precaution during the subsequent life of the engine. As explained in the section which follows, graphite has lubricating properties which enable a bearing to continue to run without damage even though the supply of oil may temporarily fail.

Its greatest advantage during the running-in period, however, is that it results in the formation of a different type of surface on the bearing faces from that obtained when ordinary lubricating oil is used. As illustrated in Fig. 1, the normal running-in process consists of wearing down the high spots and ridges on the surfaces in contact, until they are reduced from miniature hills and valleys to plateaux. When colloidal graphite is added to the oil, high spots are not rubbed away. Instead, they are moulded, or plastically deformed, so that the hills, as it were, fill up the valleys. This surface, which is known as the Beilby layer, forms an excellent bearing surface, while some of the microscopic particles of graphite actually become rolled into and beneath the surface of the metal, still further improving its bearing qualities.

Running-in Mileage. When is the engine fully run-in? When no tight spots can be felt when the starting handle is used, and smooth performace is obtained without any signs of overheating. It is impossible to state an actual mileage, which varies even between cars of the same model. From 750–1,500 miles is a rough estimate, although some manufacturers state that maximum performance is not obtained until 5,000 miles have been covered.

KEEPING THE ENGINE YOUNG

When an engine has been correctly run-in, many thousands of miles should be covered before any major repairs are required. This does not mean, however, that the care and consideration exercised during the running-in period can go by the board as soon as the first thousand miles have been covered. Routine servicing and attention are required if maximum efficiency is to be maintained, and expensive trouble avoided.

Lubrication. The importance of correct lubrication has already been stressed. It is logical to deal with this aspect of maintenance first. An owner may neglect to carry out mechanical adjustments, and

in most cases the result will be inefficient running, noise, or difficult starting; aggravating at the time, perhaps, but not necessarily disastrous. No such liberties can be taken with the lubrication system: neglect will almost certainly result in an expensive repair bill.

The first axiom is that the most expensive form of lubrication is the use of a cheap oil. First-class oils are blended and refined mineral oils, to which vegetable oils are sometimes added, together with chemicals such as oil-soluble compounds of chromium to prevent corrosion, and tin to prevent oxidation and the formation of sludge and gum.

Apart from the chemical properties of the oil, its physical properties are equally important: the fluidity when cold and its ability to maintain an effective film between heavily loaded surfaces at high temperatures. The car manufacturer and the lubrication specialists have taken all these factors into consideration, and their knowledge and experience is crystallized in the recommendations printed in the instruction book, or a lubrication chart which can be consulted at any garage.

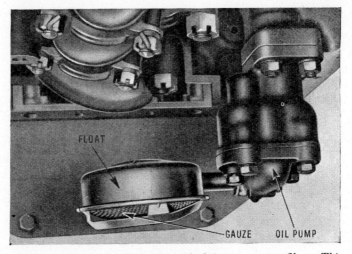

FLOAT

GAUZE   OIL PUMP

FIG. 3. *A floating oil intake embodying a gauze filter. This ensures that the intake is always just below the surface of the oil.*

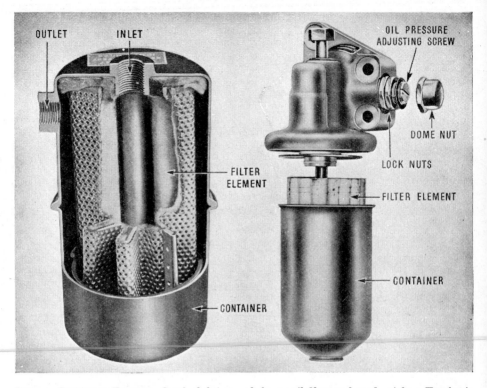

FIG. 4. EXTERNAL FILTERS. *On the left is a sealed type oil filter and on the right a Tecalemit type filter. The element in the latter can be removed and cleaned.*

During recent years there has been a tendency to use much lighter grades of oil than were once favoured; this is the result both of improvements in engine design and in oil specifications. Multigrade oils, whose viscosity is low when cold but high when hot, are advantageous if the engine is in good condition. They substantially reduce cylinder wear.

Oil Level. The level of the oil in the sump should be checked whenever the car is taken out, and on long trips, at intervals of not less than 250 miles. If the engine is worn, more frequent checks will have to be made; the appropriate interval will soon be learnt by the driver. Remember, however, that a higher consumption than usual will occur in very hot weather or when prolonged fast

driving is the order of the day, since the oil will become thinner, and will more easily pass the piston rings and be burnt. If the needle of the oil pressure gauge flickers or falls back when the car is driven fast round a corner, or the oil pressure warning light flashes momentarily under similar conditions, treat these signs as urgent danger signals. The inference is that the level of the oil in the sump is so low that when the oil surges to one side of the sump, the intake pipe or filter is temporarily starved.

When checking the oil level, the dipstick should always be wiped clean and re-inserted, as oil splashed onto it when the engine is running, will give a misleading reading. Often grit accumulates on the small ledge or boss on the side of the sump, in which the hole for the dipstick is drilled, and it is possible to push some of this dirt into the sump when re-inserting the dipstick. A useful tip is to bore a hole in a cork and fit this, widest end down, on the dip stick at such a height that it just rests on the ledge when the dip stick is pushed fully home, thus preventing the accumulation of grit around the hole, see Fig. 6.

Cleaning Filters. The lubrication system of the modern car is well protected against the entry of grit and sludge. In nearly every case there is a suction filter which surrounds the intake to the oil pump, or the suction pipe. Sometimes this is carried on a float, so that the intake is always just below the surface of the oil, thus preventing the gauze from being clogged by the heavier particles which fall to the bottom of the sump. Again, the filter may take the form of a gauze tray extending the full length of the sump, so that all the oil drains back through it before reaching the sump.

These filters are necessarily of rather coarse mesh, as the pump would be starved if a fine-mesh gauze, which quickly becomes clogged, were used.

FIG. 5. *Removing the filter cover to facilitate the cleaning or renewal of the element.*

Sometimes the filter can be removed by unscrewing a large nut on the side or base of the sump, or by taking off a plate secured by a ring of screws or nuts. It should preferably be cleaned at intervals of about 500 miles, by swilling it in petrol or paraffin, scrubbing it with a brush, and allowing it to dry before replacing it. On no account should it be wiped with a fluffy rag.

Internal filters can only be cleaned after the sump has been removed; as this is not always a simple matter, the job is best left to a service station. These filters are usually of fairly generous area, however, so that they need be cleaned only at infrequent intervals.

External Oil Filters. Most modern engines are equipped with an external filter through which oil is passed under pressure. The Tecalemit filter, for instance, consists of a casing in which a star-shaped filter element is fitted. This can be withdrawn after the filter cover has been removed. It should be cleaned in petrol at intervals of roughly 2,000 miles. When it has been cleaned in this manner about four times, it should be discarded, and a replacement element fitted. This recommendation is given point by the fact that above the element is a spring-loaded plate which acts as a safety-valve should the filter element become too choked to pass sufficient oil to the bearings. The plate then lifts, so that the oil passes directly from the filter body into the outlet pipe, instead of through the filter element. As this oil is not filtered, the advisability of regular cleaning and replacement of the element will be evident.

On many engines only a proportion of the engine oil passes through the filter at any one time; this is dictated by the fact that the filter elements capable of removing even microscopic particles from the lubricating oil are now used, and a filter for dealing with the whole of the oil would be of very large dimensions.

Renewing Filter Elements. The by-pass type of filter, as it is termed, cannot be cleaned. Instead, either the complete assembly or the internal element must be replaced by a new one at specified intervals, usually 5,000 or 10,000 miles. Since the rate at which the filter element becomes choked depends to a great extent on the mechanical condition of the engine and the conditions under which it is operating, an arbitrary figure is sometimes misleading. As a check on the condition of the filter, the outlet pipe union should be slackened off while the engine is hot, and running at a moderate speed. A steady flow of oil should be obtained from the outlet. If it is very sluggish or only a drip appears, the filter element is due for renewal.

Some filters, such as the Fram and Smith's designs, are provided with such effective filtering elements that the oil is maintained in virtually new condition, still having a golden appearance after many thousands of miles. When the oil begins to appear dark on the dipstick, the need for a change of filter element is indicated.

Draining the Sump. When modern high-efficiency filters are fitted, the need for draining the sump may not at first be apparent. It must be remembered, however, that the function of a filter is to remove solid particles from the oil; the small particles of carbon which are blown past the piston rings, the abrasive grit which enters through the breather pipe, oil filter, and dip stick orifice, and the carbon particles and sludge which form due to oxidation of the oil itself.

Oil Deterioration. The filter cannot, however, remove the unevaporated petrol which passes the piston rings when the engine is cold nor the water which is a by-product of combustion, and which finds its way past the rings; water also condenses from the air inside the crankcase and valve chamber, as the engine cools down. Petrol dilutes the oil, and water forms sludge, and often has acids, formed by the burnt gases, in solution.

It will be evident, then, that although oil does not wear out, its effectiveness as a lubricant is seriously reduced. Dilution by neat petrol is usually from 4–5 per cent by the time 1,000 miles have been covered, and may be as high as 10 per cent if the cylinders and piston rings are worn. Draining and refilling the sump at intervals of 1,000–2,000 miles, therefore, represents economy in the long run.

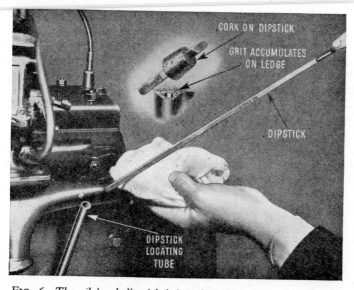

FIG. 6. *The oil level dipstick being cleaned prior to checking the oil level in the sump. The inset shows an ordinary bottle cork fitted to the end of the dipstick to prevent grit entering the sump.*

The drain plug should be removed when the engine is really hot, preferably after a fairly long run, so that any impurities are thoroughly mixed with the oil, instead of lying in pockets in the crankcase or on the bottom of the sump. When the oil has drained away, the drain plug should be replaced and about a quart of a proprietary flushing oil poured into the sump. Large-capacity sumps will require about half a gallon. The engine should then be run at a moderate speed to circulate the flushing oil, thus cleaning out the oilways. Paraffin should never be used for this purpose. Not only will it have insufficient lubricating power when the engine is run, but it may accumulate in pockets or oilways and seriously dilute the fresh oil.

On most modern engines some form of crankcase ventilation is provided to prevent both condensation of moisture within the sump and the formation of sludge; it also serves to extract oil fumes. A fume pipe may be taken into the carburettor air cleaner, or the engine may be sealed and a depression created in the crankcase by suction from the induction manifold. Fresh air is then drawn into the crankcase through a pipe communicating with the air cleaner. At the suction connexion to the induction manifold a small calibrated restrictor is fitted; this frequently contains a small pin. At fairly long intervals the restrictor should be removed and cleaned out.

Removing the Sump. If the oil is drained at regular intervals and a good flushing oil used, the sump need be removed only at very infrequent intervals, since there will be little tendency for sludge and gum to accumulate. Nevertheless, it is a wise precaution to remove the sump at 15,000-mile intervals, so that the sump, suction filter, and the inside of the crankcase may be thoroughly cleaned.

When this job is tackled by the owner, access to the various bolts will be easier if the front of the car is first jacked up as high as possible, and the chassis supported on really substantial blocks so that there is no risk of its becoming dislodged when working beneath it. Since the nuts securing the sump are sometimes difficult to reach, a socket spanner fitted with a long extension will be an advantage; alternatively, by fitting one box spanner into another, the same effect can be obtained. It is sometimes necessary to remove other components, such as the starter motor or oil filter, which may obstruct some of the sump retaining nuts.

Refitting the Sump. Considerable care must be used when refitting the sump, especially in the case of pressed steel sumps, on which the flanges are easily distorted. If possible, use a new gasket, and smear both sides with grease before assembly. Gasket cement should not be required, although it may enable a doubtful gasket to be reused if a replacement is not available. Gasket cement, however, will entail laborious scraping when the sump is next removed.

Colloidal Graphite. The beneficial effect of colloidal graphite during the running-in period has already been stressed. It is well worth while adding about half the quantity used during running-in whenever the oil is changed. Half-a-pint of graphited oil to the gallon of oil in the sump will prove adequate.

Colloidal graphite consists of highly-refined graphite, in such a superfine state of division that the particles cannot be distinguished under a microscope. These particles consist of tiny scales which slide over one another, thus conferring on the graphite its unique property of slipperiness. The particles permeate the surface pores of the metal of the bearings or cylinders, and form what is known as a graphoid surface, which will resist the action of petrol and the heat of the combustion flame. Not only does the graphoid surface possess

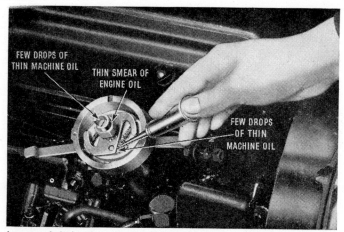

FEW DROPS OF
THIN MACHINE OIL

THIN SMEAR OF
ENGINE OIL

FEW DROPS
OF THIN
MACHINE OIL

FIG. 7. *The distributor should be lubricated at intervals of about 3,000 miles. This necessitates removing the cover and rotor: do not remove the hollow screw which is exposed when the rotor is removed. It should be noted that the contact breaker base plate has been removed for lubrication purposes.*

its own lubricating properties, but it also encourages the flow of oil over its surface.

Upper Cylinder Lubricants. It will be evident, then, that the building up of a graphoid surface on the working parts of the engine is an excellent means of prolonging the life of the power unit. The upper parts of the cylinder bores and pistons, and the piston rings, valves and valve guides, can be given this surface by adding graphited upper cylinder lubricant to the petrol, although the graphite is deposited more slowly than in the case of the parts lubricated by the oil in the sump. Any attempt to speed up the process by over-dosing the petrol with oil will simply lead to a dirty combustion chamber and fouled plugs.

When a graphited upper cylinder lubricant cannot be obtained, one of the many proprietary oils sold for this purpose will have beneficial results, particularly during the first few minutes after starting from cold.

Lubricating Accessories. Many owners conscientiously check the level of the oil in the sump, have the oil drained at the appropriate intervals, and clean or renew the filters, yet overlook the smaller items which need periodical attention, such as the distributor, dynamo, water pump, fan bearing, and

starter motor. The lubrication required by each of these is comparatively infrequent, yet is important.

The distributor, for instance, requires a few drops of thin oil in the lubricator, which serves the spindle bearing; this lubricator has a dust-excluding sleeve, and is fitted just below the body of the distributor. Rotating the sleeve exposes the oil hole. Sometimes a small screwdown greaser is fitted; when this cannot be screwed up any further, it should be unscrewed and refilled with grease.

On removing the rotor from the top of the spindle beneath the moulded cap, a screw or a felt pad will be seen in the end of the spindle, see Fig. 7. A few drops of thin oil, placed on this screw or on the pad, will lubricate the cam bearing and the automatic advance mechanism in the base of the distributor. Do not remove the screw. About every 3,000 miles is sufficient for this attention.

The dynamo and starter motor sometimes have lubricators or greasers fitted, when thin oil or high-melting point grease should be added as necessary at about 1,000-mile intervals. Modern dynamos often have a small lubricator, in which is cut a slot to take a screwdriver, at the commutator end. This should be unscrewed every 10,000 miles and refilled with petroleum jelly if the wick is dry.

The water pump spindle may be lubricated by means of a greasing nipple or a screw-down greaser. In either case, only a high-melting point grease should be used; special grades are available for this application. As this type of grease does not pass easily through nipples, it is a good plan to substitute a screw-down greaser if one is not already fitted. A suitable size can be obtained from most accessory dealers. Over-lubrication of the water pump must be avoided, since excess grease will find its way into the cooling system, and may clog the radiator.

The fan pulley spindle may be lubricated with a normal grade of grease, but here again discretion should be used, since an excess of grease will be flung out by centrifugal force and splash over the inside of the bonnet.

Mechanical Adjustments. So far the emphasis has been on lubrication. Some minor mechanical adjustments will also be required if the engine is to be kept in tune: the sparking plugs will require cleaning and the gaps re-setting, say, at 5,000-mile intervals, while the contact breaker points in the ignition distributor should be checked at the same time.

Cleaning Plugs. Removing the sparking plugs from the engine is a fairly straightforward operation on most cars, yet it often results in damage to the plug when the novice tries his hand at it. Most modern engines use small sparking plugs having a 14 mm. diameter threaded portion, as compared with the 18 mm. plugs previously used.

A box spanner should always be used to unscrew the plug from the engine; to employ an open-ended spanner or, worse still, an adjustable wrench, is asking for trouble. The box spanner, moreover,

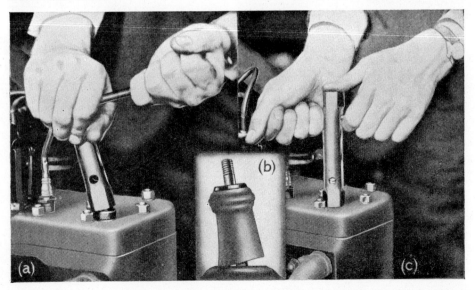

FIG. 8. REMOVING SPARKING PLUGS. *This operation appears to be very simple, but can, if awkwardly carried out, result in damage to the plugs. View (a) shows the box spanner tilted while the plug is being unscrewed, and (b) what generally happens to the insulator when the spanner is held in this position. The correct method is to hold the box spanner square with the top of the cylinder head as shown in (c).*

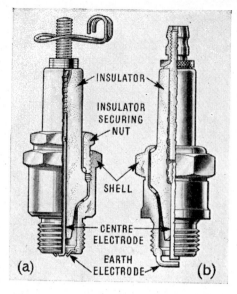

and the body of the plug gastight. This should be placed on one side until the plug is reassembled.

Carbon should first be scraped from inside the body of the plug, finally cleaning out the recess with a petrol-soaked rag. The insulator should not be scraped unless the carbon is too hard to remove otherwise. If mica is used as an insulating medium, although this is unusual today, it should on no account be scraped. A rag soaked in petrol, or metal polish, is the safest means of cleaning any type of insulator. The central contact point, and those in the body, should be rubbed with fine emery cloth until clean and bright.

FIG. 9. *Part section showing the construction of two designs of sparking plug: (a) is the detachable type plug which can be dismantled for cleaning, and (b) the non-detachable type.*

should be held squarely on the plug, and the tommy bar turned with both hands. If the spanner is allowed to tilt, the insulator of the plug will probably be fractured, see Fig. 8.

There are two main types of plug: the detachable and the non-detachable designs. These terms refer to the fact that the plug can, or cannot be dismantled for cleaning, and do not imply that the plug is or is not a permanent fitting in the engine. A detachable plug has an hexagonal ring nut screwed into the main body, and this retains the central insulator in place. To dismantle the plug, grip the hexagonal part of the body in a vice, and unscrew the insulator securing nut with a box spanner. This nut is comparatively easily distorted, so care is necessary.

The central insulator can now be lifted out. A small copper washer is used to render the joint between the insulator

Adjusting the Gap. The small copper sealing washer should be cleaned and placed in position before the insulator is refitted and the gland nut lightly tightened down. With the body of the plug gripped in the vice, tighten the gland nut with a box spanner, until it is firmly home, but avoid being heavy-handed. Distortion will cause a gas leak which will reduce compression in the cylinder to which the plug is fitted, besides causing the plug to become excessively hot.

The correct gap between the central electrode and the electrode, or electrodes, on the body of the plug depends on the particular engine. On most cars a gap of from 20–25 thousandths of an inch is about right. Some modern engines, however, need a gap of 35–45 thousandths of an inch; in this case a special high-voltage ignition coil is fitted. If a manufacturer's handbook is not available, the local agents for the car, or the manufacturers themselves, will furnish the information.

The gap must always be adjusted by bending the outer electrodes. Never bend the central one as this will result in the insulator being cracked or fractured. The gap should be measured by a feeler gauge, see Fig. 10, or by a wire gauge, made from a short length of wire of the correct diameter. The advantage of this type of gauge is that the wire will fit into any slight pit on the electrode, which would be bridged by a feeler gauge; an accurate measurement of the gap is thus obtained.

For guidance, the following are Standard Wire Gauge sizes: 25 SWG, 20 thousandths of an inch; 24 SWG, 22 thousandths; 23 SWG, 24 thousandths; 22 SWG, 28 thousandths; 21 SWG, 32 thousandths; 20 SWG, 36 thousandths; 19 SWG, 40 thousandths, and 18 SWG, 48 thousandths.

Non-detachable Plugs. Many types of sparking plug cannot be dismantled for cleaning, and these can be effectively dealt with only by subjecting the internal insulator to a blast of fine grit in a special cleaning machine operated by compressed air. Most service stations possess one of these cleaners, but the owner who entrusts his plugs to one for cleaning should verify that the work has been properly carried out. Sometimes too low an air pressure is used, with the result that the insulator is imperfectly cleaned, especially high up inside the plug, so that misfiring will quickly recur. A quantity of the fine abrasive compound is sometimes trapped, too, in the upper part of the plug, particularly if the insulator is oily, with the result that this sandy

FIG. 10. *Measuring the gap between the centre and earth electrodes with a feeler gauge. The gap is usually specified by the manufacturer in the instruction handbook.*

substance subsequently finds its way into the combustion chamber.

When it is necessary to clean a non-detachable plug quickly and the services of a garage are not available, it is possible to obtain a reasonable result by inserting the threaded portion of the plug in the neck of a metal-polish tin of a suitable size. The tin should be half-filled with petrol and shaken vigorously.

Refitting the Plugs. When refitting the plugs, the same precautions against distortion or damage to the insulator should be taken as when removing them. Make sure, too, that the copper-asbestos sealing washer is in place before the plug is screwed home. If the washer is badly flattened, fit a new one. If no spares are available, the washers can be annealed and given a new lease of life by heating them to red heat over a clean flame, and then plunging them into cold water. Finally, take care that the sparking plug leads are connected to the correct terminals, and that the terminals are securely screwed down, clipped in place, or pushed home into their sockets.

Routine Adjustments. The valve tappets may require adjustment if noisy, although if properly adjusted after decarbonization has been carried out as described below, they should not need further attention until the engine is again due for decarbonizing. On some modern cars no provision is made for adjustment once the engine has been assembled. The petrol pump and carburettor filters will require examination and cleaning every 5,000 miles. The fan and dynamo driving belt will require occasional adjustment as slackness develops, as will the camshaft driving chain in some instances.

This completes the routine attention necessary to maintain the engine in good condition, and to restore its efficiency. The mechanical adjustments just mentioned are fully described in the appropriate sections of this book.

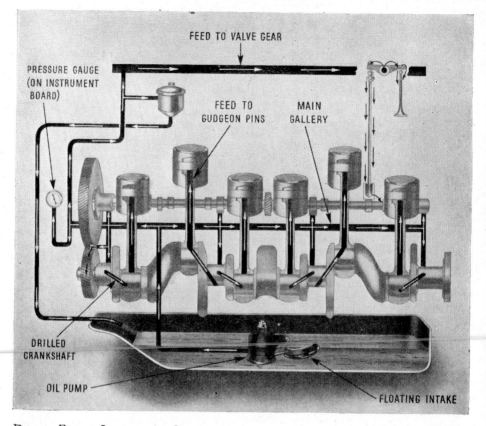

FEED TO VALVE GEAR

PRESSURE GAUGE
(ON INSTRUMENT
BOARD)

FEED TO
GUDGEON PINS

MAIN
GALLERY

DRILLED
CRANKSHAFT

OIL PUMP

FLOATING INTAKE

FIG. 11. ENGINE LUBRICATION SYSTEM. *Diagrammatic view showing how the moving parts of an o.h.v. six-cylinder engine are lubricated. The oil is pumped to the various parts by the pump situated in the sump. The oil is filtered before returning to the sump.*

CURING LUBRICATION TROUBLES

Most lubrication troubles are attributable to low oil pressure. Under "Keeping the Engine Young", we discussed the importance of using the correct grade of oil, periodical cleaning of filters, and changing the oil in the sump at prescribed intervals. If the advice given is followed, lubrication troubles should not normally be experienced.

When Oil Pressure is Low. The most usual case of low oil pressure is wear of the main and connecting rod bearings; as the mileage mounts up, so the oil pressure reading gradually falls,

owing to the reduced resistance to the escape of oil from the various bearings. The oil pressure shown by the gauge, in fact, is one of the most important indications of the general state of the bearings, and a low pressure is regarded with suspicion by the experienced motorist who may be contemplating the purchase of a second-hand car.

Choked Suction Filters. Like most generalizations, however, this is by no means always true. A choked filter surrounding the intake to the oil pump, for instance, will cause a low reading on the oil-pressure gauge, owing to the pump being starved; this is generally most pronounced when the oil is cold and viscous. A filter gauze which surrounds the pump intake can sometimes be crushed when the sump is refitted, and will offer considerable resistance to the flow of oil. A wise precaution is to refit such a filter after the sump has been bolted into place; the hole in its upper plate can then be guided over the oil intake pipe.

When the suction filter is mounted externally, it will be evident that a loose union on the suction line, or a badly fitting gasket or washer under the filter cover, will allow air to enter the pump, and so reduce the pressure.

Relief Valve. When a sudden drop in oil pressure is experienced, with no other symptoms that anything is amiss with the engine, the trouble can often be traced to a small particle of carbon or grit lodging between the ball or plunger of the oil pressure relief valve and its seating. The purpose of this valve, as explained in Chapter 1, is to allow excess oil pressure

to escape. If it is held off its seating when the oil is thoroughly warmed up, a low pressure will be recorded.

The valve may be fitted in a variety of positions: sometimes it is incorporated in the oil pump itself, which may mean that the sump must be dropped to gain access; in other cases it is fitted in a boss or housing on the crankcase. The spring that holds the ball or plunger in its seating may be retained by an adjustable set-screw, with a locking nut, or may be kept in place by a cap or plug.

Once the valve has been located it is a simple matter to dismantle it when it is accessible from the outside of the engine. When the adjusting screw, plug, or cap has been unscrewed, the spring can be withdrawn, if it does not fly out of its own accord, and the ball or plunger may be inspected. Carefully clean the seating with a non-fluffy rag, and syringe the seating and the passage leading to it with thin oil to wash out any grit or carbon. Then reassemble the

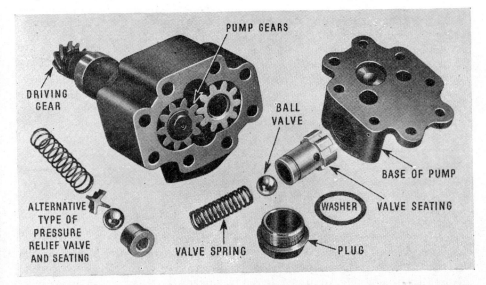

PUMP GEARS

DRIVING GEAR

BALL VALVE

BASE OF PUMP

ALTERNATIVE TYPE OF PRESSURE RELIEF VALVE AND SEATING

VALVE SPRING

WASHER

VALVE SEATING

PLUG

FIG. 12. ENGINE OIL PUMP. *Components that comprise a gear-type oil pump. The pressure is created by the oil being carried round between the teeth. A pressure relief valve is incorporated to prevent the pump being damaged should the oil channels get blocked up.*

parts, not forgetting the sealing washers.

Adjusting Oil Pressure. When an adjustable screw is fitted, it should be screwed home to approximately the position that it occupied before removal, and should be locked with the nut. If the oil pressure registered when the engine is started is too low, screw the adjuster inwards a quarter of a turn at a time to increase the pressure. Too high a pressure can be rectified by unscrewing the adjuster slightly.

The non-adjustable type of valve depends on the correct spring tension. Fitting a new spring may restore the pressure if the remainder of the system is in order. Some manufacturers recommend that the spring be stretched slightly to increase its length, or that one or more washers of suitable diameter and thickness be placed behind it to increase the pressure.

It is seldom advisable to depart from the standard setting of the valve, however, in an attempt to increase the oil pressure: the cause of a low oil gauge reading should be sought elsewhere, not forgetting that the oil pressure gauge itself may not be above suspicion, a point often overlooked by the amateur mechanic.

Overhead Valve Gear. On overhead valve engines the oil supply to the rocker shaft or camshaft is generally restricted or metered by an adjustable screw or by a resistance pin fitted in the oil passage. Should the metering screw be incorrectly adjusted, or the pin have been omitted during assembly, a low oil pressure, coupled with too copious a supply to the rockers, will result. When no metering device is fitted, the oil pressure will drop as wear of the rocker bushes and rocker shaft takes place. It is sometimes possible to obtain from the manufacturer of the engine a small adjustable restrictor, see Fig. 11, Chapter 6, which can be inserted in the feed pipes to the overhead valves, thus preventing the trouble.

High Oil Pressure. This is a less common fault. It may be due to an incorrectly adjusted relief valve, or to a blockage in one of the oil feed pipes or oilways; similarly, a choked overhead valve restrictor will cause a higher pressure. In any case, an abnormally high pressure when the engine is warm should be regarded as a danger signal. It probably indicates that one or more bearings are being starved of oil.

SYSTEMATIC FAULT TRACING

Before carrying out any haphazard tests, the experienced driver will attempt to diagnose engine trouble logically, first considering the symptoms, if any, which preceded the misfiring, loss of power, or sudden stoppage, and then analysing the probable causes of the trouble. Similarly, a fault-finding chart, such as that which accompanies this chapter, cannot be of full value unless it is used systematically.

Refusal to Start. When the engine refuses to start from cold, diagnosis may be hampered by the fact that there are no preliminary symptoms on which to base an estimate of the cause of the trouble. The starting controls must, of course, be correctly set, since modern carburettors are usually fitted with a special starting device, and often incorporate a thermostatically-operated strangler or choke. If the car refuses to start when the normal setting which has hitherto proved effective is used, however, a process of elimination must be adopted. The tests which follow can be applied equally effectively when an engine stops suddenly on the road.

Is Petrol Flowing? The first step is to make sure that petrol is reaching the carburettor. It is not wise to accept the reading of the petrol gauge as an indication that there is petrol in the tank. The best plan is to flood the carburettor by means of the plunger on the float chamber, Fig. 13; the ignition must be switched on when an electric pump is fitted, or the engine must be rotated by means of the starter if the pump is of the mechanical type.

Many modern carburettors cannot be flooded in this manner, however, and it will then be necessary to undo the bolt or bolts securing the float chamber to the body of the carburettor. This course is also advisable when working single-handed, as it will be easy to observe whether there is a flow of petrol from the small valve in the body of the carburettor above the float chamber when the pump is operating.

If petrol is flowing, the trouble may possibly be due to a choked jet, although this is not a frequent occurrence nowadays, and while it can cause difficult starting, is unlikely to result in a complete stoppage on the road. To dismantle some modern types of carburettor, moreover, is a somewhat complicated operation best left to a service station that has the necessary facilities.

If petrol is not available at the carburettor, check that the pump and carburettor filters are clean, and that the fuel pipes are free from obstruction.

Ignition System. Assuming that adequate petrol is available at the carburettor, attention should be turned to the ignition system. If the starter spins the engine at its normal speed, it can be taken that the battery is adequately charged. A sudden cut-out on the road, combined with lack of response to the starter button, can be caused by a battery connexion breaking adrift or one of the cables may be loose or have become disconnected from the battery terminal. Sometimes the cable fractures inside the rubber or other insulating sleeve close to the terminal, due to corrosion by acid; this can prove a very elusive fault. Although the connexions may appear sound, it is wise to give each lead a tug as a precaution.

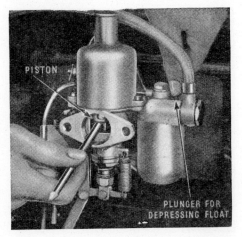

FIG. 13. *When it is necessary to observe the flow of petrol from the jet in an S.U. carburettor, the piston should be lifted with a small implement and the plunger on the top of the float chamber depressed, as shown above.*

Simple Ignition Check. If all appears to be in order, the next operation is a simple test which at once checks the low-tension and high-tension ignition circuits, including the contact-breaker, coil and condenser. A high-tension cable will be seen running from the central terminal on the ignition coil to the central terminal on the moulded cap of the distributor. The lead should be disconnected from the distributor cap, which should be removed, exposing the contact-breaker points. Make sure these are closed, rotating the engine if necessary until they are, and switch on the ignition.

The high-tension lead should then be held with its metal end about a quarter of an inch from a bare metal part of the engine, while the contact breaker points are flicked apart with the finger. No shock will be experienced from the points, but the high-tension lead should be handled with discretion, since a blue spark should jump the quarter-inch gap to the metal of the engine whenever the contact points are separated.

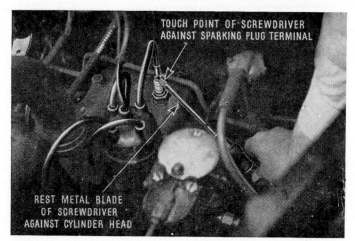

TOUCH POINT OF SCREWDRIVER AGAINST SPARKING PLUG TERMINAL

REST METAL BLADE OF SCREWDRIVER AGAINST CYLINDER HEAD

FIG. 14. *A quick and simple method of checking whether the current from the ignition coil is reaching the sparking plugs. To avoid an electric shock when carrying out this operation it is advisable to use a screwdriver fitted with an insulated handle.*

If no spark is obtained, see that all connections are clean and secure, and that the plug points are not oiled or the insulators cracked. Refer also to Chapter 7.

The tests just described will already have ensured that the contact-breaker points open and close when the engine is rotated. If the pivot arm is stiff in operation due to the fibre bush binding on the pivot, a complete stoppage can occur. The bore of the bush can be slightly enlarged by means of a small roll of emery paper, or preferably sand-paper, if it is tight. A similar fault can be caused by the spring which operates the arm fracturing. A get-you-home dodge is to wedge a section of rubber tube or piece of pencil eraser between the arm and the distributor case so as to close the contact points. To complete the electrical circuit a short length of wire must be connected between the rocking arm and the peg on which the broken spring was fitted.

Sparking Plugs. If a good spark was obtained in the test described earlier, it

only remains to make sure that the high-tension current is actually reaching the sparking plugs. At the centre of the distributor cap is a contact which conveys the current to the rotor arm which passes in turn each of the electrodes to which the sparking plug leads are connected. This is usually a spring-loaded carbon contact, and may be stuck up in its housing. An alternative is a spring-loaded contact on the rotor itself, which should make contact with a carbon pip at the centre of the distributor cap. The spring may be cracked or fractured in this case.

If all appears to be in order, remove a sparking plug from the engine and rest it on the nearest bare metal with its lead connected to it so that only its body is in contact with the metal, the terminal

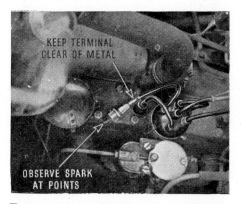

KEEP TERMINAL CLEAR OF METAL

OBSERVE SPARK AT POINTS

FIG. 15. *A test to ensure that sparks are jumping across the points. This test follows when it is found that although current is reaching the plug it does not jump the gap.*

being well clear. When the engine is rotated with the ignition switched on, a good spark should jump the plug points. If the insulator is covered with oil or moisture, of course, a good spark, or any spark at all, cannot be expected. Remember, too, that although a spark may jump the gap between the points when in the open air, it will find it much more difficult to do so when under compression in the engine.

Mechanical Faults. As a result of the foregoing tests it should have been possible to localize the fault in either the carburation or ignition systems. If both systems appear to be in order, it only remains to suspect a mechanical fault. Since such possible defects as failure of the distributor drive, or of the operating linkage of a mechanical petrol pump, will have already been revealed during the test just described, the only likely cause is breakage of the chain which drives the camshaft, or fracture of the driving key which connects the sprocket wheel or gear to the camshaft or crankshaft. Sometimes a camshaft driving chain which has become too slack, due to wear or the failure of a tensioning device, will jump one or more teeth on the sprockets, thus completely upsetting the timing. This is a comparatively rare occurrence, however.

Such a fault can be detected if the engine is rotated by the starting handle, partial or complete loss of compression being evident. Unfortunately, the threading of a long starting handle through the radiator grille of the average modern car is often by no means as simple a matter as it should be, while, once engaged with the starting dog on the crankshaft, the handle is often so flexible, and subject to such friction, that the compression of the engine cannot be checked effectively. Sometimes an engine will sink on its flexible mounting to such an extent that the handle cannot be en-

gaged with the end of the crankshaft. It is due to this retrograde aspect of the modern car that it has not been recommended that the engine should be rotated by the starting handle in the first place. On some larger cars, chiefly of American origin, no starting handle is provided.

Loss of Compression. It is worth while to go to a little trouble to make sure that the starting handle can be easily fitted, and that it does not bind at any point, since it is one of the best guides to engine condition. When a four-cylinder engine is fitted, the compression of each cylinder can be felt in turn as the handle is rotated; the resistance of each should be equal, and there should be a springy feel at the point of maximum compression. Should the compression be poor, or die away after a few seconds, leaking valves, gasket, or worn cylinder bores and piston rings can be diagnosed. The test should preferably be made with the throttle held wide open.

Measuring Compression. The most satisfactory method of checking the compression is to measure the actual pressure in the cylinder with a gauge which screws into the sparking-plug hole; many service garages possess such a gauge.

The mechanically-minded owner can improvise quite an effective gauge by soldering a tyre pressure gauge, of the type intended for high-pressure tyres, into the body of a discarded sparking plug, from which the electrode has been removed.

The engine should be rotated by the starter, with the throttle held wide open, If the ignition must be switched on before the starter can be used, the low-tension wire connected to the terminal marked S.W. on the coil should be temporarily disconnected.

If the engine has a compression ratio of about 5 : 1 or 6 : 1, a pressure of between 110 and 150 lb. per square inch should be recorded by the gauge. These

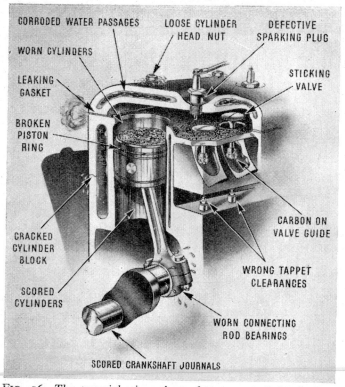

CORRODED WATER PASSAGES

LOOSE CYLINDER HEAD NUT

DEFECTIVE SPARKING PLUG

WORN CYLINDERS

LEAKING GASKET

STICKING VALVE

BROKEN PISTON RING

CRACKED CYLINDER BLOCK

CARBON ON VALVE GUIDE

SCORED CYLINDERS

WRONG TAPPET CLEARANCES

WORN CONNECTING ROD BEARINGS

SCORED CRANKSHAFT JOURNALS

FIG. 16. *The pictorial view above shows some of the leading mechanical faults that can develop in an engine. Although some of these faults are the result of simple wear and tear, many are due directly to the lack of regular and careful servicing and maintenance as recommended by the manufacturer.*

Leaking exhaust valves are more difficult to detect, although the hissing caused by this fault can sometimes be heard by listening at the exhaust tail pipe while an assistant turns the engine. A more positive check can be obtained by slackening the bolts securing the exhaust pipe to the exhaust manifold, and allowing the pipe to drop slightly, when the hissing will be more clearly heard.

Leaking Gasket. A leaking . cylinder head gasket can best be detected by applying thin oil to the junction of the cylinder head and block, around each cylinder head securing nut, and the base of each sparking plug, while the engine is

figures, however, are seldom reached in practice; possibly 70–80 lb. per square inch will be recorded on the average engine which has a fair mileage to its credit. A low pressure, or a variation in pressure between individual cylinders, indicates leakage past the valves, piston rings, or possibly the gasket.

Leaking Valves. Leakage past the inlet valves can be detected by listening at the carburettor air intake while the engine is rotated slowly with the throttle open. A pronounced hissing reveals leakage from this source. The air cleaner or silencer, if fitted, should, of course, be removed during this test.

running. If any leakage is taking place, froth and bubbles will be formed. Unfortunately, one of the most likely points of leakage is between adjacent cylinders, where the gasket is often very narrow, and this cannot be detected by an external test; it is revealed when the cylinder head is removed, by the discoloured or burnt appearance of the gasket at the point of leakage. The trouble may be suspected if two adjacent cylinders show an equal loss of compression.

Cylinders and Piston Rings. Decarbonizing, grinding-in of the valves, and fitting a new gasket, will cure the leakages just discussed. Provided that the cylinder bores and piston rings are in good condition, this is all that is usually required to restore good compression. Worn bores and rings will generally be revealed in any case by an increase in oil consumption, blue smoke from the exhaust, and a tendency to oil-up the sparking plugs. Leakage past the rings can be detected by listening at the crankcase breather, or the oil filler orifice, when the characteristic hissing will be heard.

Even though a compression gauge may not be available, it is a simple matter to detect any individual cylinder in which the compression is low by rotating the engine until the compression in that cylinder is as high as possible. If the cap is now removed from the ignition distributor, the rotor will be pointing in the direction of one of the electrodes in the cap, to which a sparking plug lead is connected. By tracing this lead to its plug, the cylinder which is the culprit is indicated.

Misfiring. The falling-off in power which takes place as the car covers a considerable mileage is often such a gradual process that the average owner remains unaware of it. Since the efficiency of the engine depends on the compression in the cylinders, it will be obvious that the first cause of lost power and performance is leakage from the combustion chamber, due to any of the causes just dealt with.

Misfiring is, of course, often caused by sparking plugs in which the insulators are dirty, or the gaps incorrectly set. Misfiring at one sparking plug is very easily detected when the engine has been running for a few minutes. Simply switch off the ignition and feel each plug in turn. The faulty plug will be appreciably cooler than the others. An alternative method is to short-circuit each plug in turn by resting the tip of a screwdriver on the cylinder head and touching the plug terminal with the blade. When

an efficient plug is short-circuited the engine speed will drop, whereas short-circuiting a faulty plug will cause little or no difference in the running of the engine.

Other Ignition Faults. There are, however, several points which are frequently overlooked even by the conscientious owner who normally carries out routine engine maintenance in an exemplary manner. However carefully the ignition contact breaker points may be cleaned and adjusted, for instance, it still remains for the current to find its way to earth, and so back to the battery, through the distributor body and its mounting. These parts are generally partly insulated from one another by a film of oil or grease; moreover, in the case of cars fitted with a manual ignition control, the distributor body must be free to rotate slightly in its mounting. It is not surprising that quite a considerable resistance to the flow of current often exists, leading to misfiring. The remedy is to fit a separate earth-return wire, one end being gripped under the head of the bolt which tightens the split clamp holding the distributor, and the other being taken to a convenient nut on the chassis; needless to say, all contact surfaces at each point of attachment should be bright and clean.

Another elusive source of misfiring is looseness of one of the two small screws in the rim of the distributor body which hold the contact breaker base plate in position. One of these screws generally forms part of the low-tension circuit, although there is no external evidence of the fact. Both should, therefore, be checked for tightness from time to time.

Loss of power, amounting to serious misfiring at speed, can also be traced to lack of lubrication of the centrifugally operated advance mechanism which is housed in the distributor body, see heading, "Lubricating Accessories" above.

Causes of Spitting Back. Spitting back in the carburettor is sometimes attributed to too weak a mixture, when it is, in fact, due to a sticking valve. When asked which valve is likely to be the culprit, the average owner will unhesitatingly answer: "The inlet, of course." In practice, inlet valves very seldom stick; the exhaust valve is almost invariably to blame. When this valve sticks open, some of the mixture in the exhaust manifold is drawn back into the cylinder as the piston descends on the suction stroke. This pollutes the fresh mixture, and leads to a very slow rate of burning, so that a flame is still present in the cylinder when the inlet valve opens again. This ignites the gas in the inlet manifold, and causes the popping back in the carburettor usually associated with a weak mixture or retarded ignition.

Explosions in the Silencer. A sticking exhaust valve will also cause explosions in the silencer. The trouble is usually due, however, to intermittent misfiring in the ignition system, with the result that unburnt gas reaches the silencer, where it may be ignited by a particle of incandescent carbon, or by the flame of a succeeding explosion.

Here again a pitfall awaits the unwary owner, for explosions in the silencer can be caused by nothing more serious than an air leak in the exhaust system. The backfiring occurs when the throttle is closed with the engine running fast, and the car is driving the engine. Under these conditions a rich, partially burnt mixture passes into the silencer. This mixture is quite capable of further combustion if extra oxygen is available, and an air leak in the exhaust system supplies that added incentive. The mixture therefore explodes. It will be found that a richer idling mixture will often cure the backfiring, since still more oxygen will be required to enable it to burn in the silencer, but this is obviously an extravagant alternative to tightening up the various joints in the exhaust system, and renewing any defective gaskets.

Choked Silencer. While on the subject of silencers, this component can be the cause of power loss, since it gradually becomes choked with carbon. When internal baffles are fitted, a loose baffle, probably dislodged as a result of backfiring, will aggravate the trouble. An exhaust which is suspiciously quiet, and has a hissing note, should be suspect. If the engine refuses to start or dies out after reversing towards an earth bank or slope, the most likely, and often overlooked, cause is a clod of earth wedged in the exhaust tail pipe. This can be removed with a bent wire or other similar device.

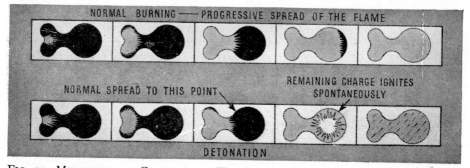

FIG. 17. MECHANISM OF COMBUSTION. *The upper sequence shows the progressive spread of a flame during normal combustion, while below is the process that results in a part of the charge igniting spontaneously and causing detonation or pinking.*

146

Engine Noises.
Accurate diagnosis of the various knocks, taps, rattles and other noises which may develop in a worn engine is by no means a simple matter. Even the experienced mechanic is often led astray. Locating the source of the noise is rendered easier by using some form of stethoscope. Service stations often use the type employed by doctors, but a more primitive form, such as a length of wood fitted with an ear-

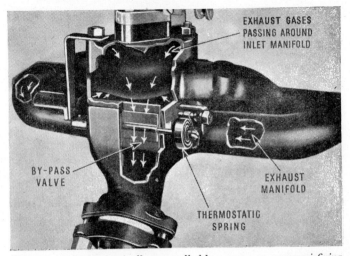

EXHAUST GASES PASSING AROUND INLET MANIFOLD

BY-PASS VALVE

EXHAUST MANIFOLD

THERMOSTATIC SPRING

FIG. 18. *A thermostatically-controlled hot spot may cause misfiring when the engine is cold, and if the by-pass valve sticks in the open position, or a loss of power due to overheating of the charge if the spring does not open up the valve when the engine warms up.*

piece, or even a long screwdriver, the handle of which is held to the ear, is better than nothing.

Piston Slap. The first noise which usually becomes apparent is the metallic slapping or tapping sound caused by the piston slapping against the cylinder wall at the beginning of the power stroke. The cause is wear of the cylinder bore, piston and rings, and only an overhaul will remedy the trouble. If the sound is only noticeable for a short time after starting from cold, disappearing as the engine warms up and the piston expands to a better fit in the cylinder, the noise need not be regarded too seriously.

Light Tapping in the Cylinder. A light metallic tapping can be due to wear of the gudgeon pin; the noise will often cease if the sparking plug in that cylinder is short-circuited.

A very light tapping or clicking noise can sometimes be caused by loose piston rings being forced against the top and bottom surfaces of the grooves alternately as the piston moves up and down.

Metallic Clatter from Base of Engine. This noise is usually an indication of worn or run connecting rod bearings, commonly known as big ends. The noise is evident when the engine is speeded up without load, and at moderately high speeds on the road, but often disappears when the engine is pulling hard at low speeds. Abnormally low oil pressure confirms the diagnosis.

Thumping or Pounding Noise. This can usually be detected only when the car is being driven, and is a symptom of worn main crankshaft bearings. Again low oil pressure is apparent, while oil will probably leak from the clutch housing and from around the fan pulley.

A loose flywheel, i.e. the type fitted to the crankshaft by a taper, will cause a dull thumping noise, particularly when the engine is accelerated from idling speed.

Rumbling and Vibration. This symptom is again a sign of main bearing wear, in this case when the crankshaft is carried in ball or roller bearings. This arrangement is unusual in modern cars.

Chatter from Clutch. Usually a sign of something amiss internally, the noise can also be caused by a ball thrust bearing which requires lubrication, although this often causes a whirring or ringing sound. On modern clutches fitted with self-lubricating release bearings the noise is a sign that the graphite thrust ring is badly worn.

Tapping in Valve Gear. Generally a sign that one or more tappets have excess clearance and require adjustment. If the noise persists when the tappet clearance is correct, worn tappet plungers or valve rocker bushes, bent push rods, or worn overhead camshaft bearings can be suspected, depending on the type of valve gear fitted.

Whine or Chatter from Front of Engine. In this case the camshaft driving gears or chain is usually the culprit. Gears must be renewed, but some form of tensioner is often provided for a chain, unless this is too short to require one, in which case renewal of the chain, and possibly the sprockets, also, is the only cure.

Whistle or Creaking Noise from Front of Engine. The rubber belt which drives the fan and often the dynamo as well is usually the offender. The sides of the belt should be dusted with French chalk, and its tension adjusted if necessary, Fig. 19. A high-pitched squeak may be traced to an unlubricated fan bearing, or to a dynamo-brush which requires re-bedding on the commutator. If a lubricator is fitted to the dynamo, attention at this point may cure the noise.

FAULT-TRACING

Before carrying out any tests, verify that the ignition is switched on, and that petrol is reaching the carburettor.

FIG. 19. *Noises coming from the front of the engine can sometimes be traced to the belt that drives the fan and dynamo. Above is shown the method of adjusting the tension of the belt.*

ENGINE WILL NOT START
Starter does not turn engine.
  Battery discharged.
  Starter switch or cables faulty.
  Water pump frozen.
Starter spins but does not turn engine.
  Battery discharged.
  Dirt or oil on starter motor shaft.
Starter turns engine sluggishly.
  Battery discharged.
  Grade of engine oil too heavy.
  Starter switch contacts pitted.
  Loose connexions in starter circuit.
  Starter motor brushes dirty or worn.
Starter turns engine briskly.
  Fuel not reaching carburettor, due to fuel pump, filter and petrol pipe faults.
  Carburettor faults.
  Current not reaching coil and distributor; disconnexion or short circuit.
  Ignition circuit faults.
  Moisture on internal or external insulation of sparking plugs.

Air leaks in induction system.
Valves sticking open.
Incorrect valve or ignition timing.

ENGINE STARTS, BUT WILL NOT CONTINUE TO RUN

Mixture too rich.
Incorrect mixture control setting.
Carburettor flooding.
Piston or automatic control in carburettor sticking.

Mixture too weak.
Incorrect mixture control setting.
Faulty petrol pump.
Choked filters.
Partially choked petrol pipe.
Air leaks in fuel pipe from tank to pump.
Choked carburettor jet.

Ignition Faults.
Loose electrical connexions.
Condensation on sparking plug internal insulators.

Mechanical Faults.
Broken valve spring.
Exhaust tail pipe collapsed or clogged.

ENGINE STOPS WHEN THROTTLE IS CLOSED

Carburation Faults.
Idling mixture incorrectly adjusted.
Idling jet choked.
Air leaks in induction system.
Air leaks past valves or piston rings.

Ignition Faults.
Sparking plugs fouled.
Sparking plug gaps too narrow.
Ignition timing too advanced.

ENGINE MISFIRES

At Low Speeds.
Engine not fully warmed up.
Valves not seating properly.
Air leaks in induction system.
Carburettor jet choked.
Sparking plugs dirty or incorrect gap.

At High Speeds.
Weak valve springs.
Sticking valves.
Tappet clearances incorrect.
Broken valve spring.
Fuel starvation: faulty petrol pump, pipes, choked filters, fuel vaporizing in pipe.
Ignition retarded.
Sparking plugs dirty or incorrect gap.

When Pulling Hard.
Weak mixture or petrol starvation.
Pre-ignition due to incandescent particles in combustion chamber or wrong type of plug.
Ignition too far advanced.
Sparking plugs dirty or incorrect gap.

Loss of Power.
Poor compression.
Choked exhaust system.
Petrol starvation.
Ignition or carburation faults.

WINTER PRECAUTIONS

Cold weather brings fresh lubrication problems, over-cooled engines, new chances for excessive wear, and run-down batteries. Most of us realize that with the advent of winter, an engine's duties grow more difficult, but unfortunately do nothing about it until freezing weather suddenly sets in. The wise motorist will save time, money and worry by preparing his car in the autumn.

His first duty should be to the engine. The old contaminated Summer oil should be drained off and the engine flushed and refilled with the recommended grade of Winter oil. Quite apart from its condition after being in use for some time, Summer oil is unsuitable for winter conditions. Manufacturers definitely specify the use of a Winter Grade for engine lubrication, with the knowledge that only by this means can the modern car give efficient performance.

Light Oils. Research carried out by the Institution of Automobile Engineers has disclosed that a period as long as 6 minutes elapses before efficient oil circulation is secured when a Summer oil is used at freezing temperatures; with a suitable Winter oil, however, this delay in efficient oil circulation can be cut down to a few seconds. Efficient oil circulation also has a considerable bearing on the problem of the reduction of engine wear. Unless oil circulates quickly after starting from cold, cylinder wear is bound to occur.

There are other important factors which emphasize the importance of using the correct Winter grade of oil. One of these is oil drag. The close working clearances of modern engines accentuate the drag caused by a cold, stiff oil. In new engines particularly, it is important to ensure quick starting from cold, rapid oil circulation, and reduction of oil drag to the minimum.

Laboratory Tests. A convincing proof of this is revealed in a report issued by the National Physical Laboratory, which showed that in a bench test conducted on a Morris Eight engine run under conditions equivalent to 30 m.p.h. on the road, an increase of thirteen per cent in power was obtained when a lighter oil was used, as compared with a thicker grade.

Much of the sluggish running caused by using too heavy a grade of oil is frequently attributed to bad carburation, faulty fuel, over-cooled engines and similar reasons. It can be demonstrated, however, that the use of Winter oil in cold weather as compared with a Summer oil, enables the engine to respond much more quickly on the road during the warming-up period.

It is a common belief that the warming up of the engine is merely the time taken for the cooling water to reach its working temperature. The truth is that the lubricating oil in the oil sump warms up much more slowly, and until it is thoroughly warm the engine cannot produce its normal working efficiency. This has an important effect on both power output and fuel economy.

Winter Starting Difficulties. Obviously, mechanical, electrical, or carburation faults will render an engine difficult or impossible to start. The section dealing with systematic fault-tracing and the table on page 144 should enable the trouble to be traced, while the method of rectifying the defect will be covered by the appropriate section in this book, whether it lies in the engine, ignition, carburettor, fuel feed or electrical system. Difficult starting, however, is often experienced even when the engine, carburettor, and ignition appear to be in order and the controls are correctly set. The trouble usually appears as the weather becomes colder, and is generally due to a combination of factors.

Overnight Precautions. The routine for easy starting begins overnight, when the car is put away. Most drivers already make a habit of revving up just before the engine is switched off, but some of them neglect the most important point of this procedure, which consists of holding the accelerator open until the engine stops, so that a weak mixture is sucked into the cylinders. If this is not done it is a rich mixture which enters, and being wet, it will deposit moisture on the plug points and insulator with bad effect next morning. The weak mixture, on the other hand, is dry, and leaves the plug points in the right condition for easy starting.

If difficulty is experienced in starting, switch on the ignition and leave it on until the electric petrol pump stops beating; then switch off and pull out the easy-starting control. Turn the engine a few revolutions with the starting handle, switch on the ignition and then either operate the starting motor or manually start with the starting handle.

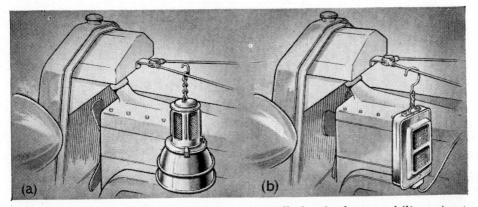

Fig. 20. Protection From Freezing. (a) *is a paraffin-burning heater and* (b) *an electric heater. In most cases the current for the latter design is supplied from the mains.*

When a mechanical pump is fitted, it is well worth while to prime by means of the small hand lever which is often fitted. If no priming lever is available, rotate the engine by the starting handle for about a dozen times, so that the float-chamber will be filled. If this is not done, the initial few seconds of starter operation will be wasted, as the engine will not fire until the float chamber is full, and a needless drain is imposed on the battery.

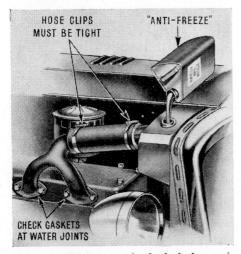

HOSE CLIPS MUST BE TIGHT

"ANTI-FREEZE"

CHECK GASKETS AT WATER JOINTS

Fig. 21. *All joints must be checked when anti-freeze compound is added to the cooling water.*

Cranking Speed. The average engine must be rotated at from 40 to 60 r.p.m. to ensure an easy start. Even when the battery is fully charged, the starter motor in good condition, and the correct grade of oil in use, the starter rarely turns the engine at more than 60 r.p.m. on a freezing morning, although a warm garage may enable a speed of 100–120 r.p.m. to be reached.

When the starter is turning a stiff engine slowly, a very high current is taken from the battery, often reaching 400 amps. This means that the voltage is reduced to half the normal figure, so that the ignition coil is unable to generate a high enough secondary voltage to produce an adequate spark at the plugs. It will often be found in these circumstances, that the engine will fire or spit back once just as the starter control is released, due to the increased current which momentarily reaches the ignition coil. This is the cue for a quick pull-up on the starting handle, when, with the full battery voltage available for the ignition, and the cylinders filled with mixture, a start will usually be obtained.

Warmth will Help. Sometimes, when all efforts to start the engine have proved unavailing, and it has been allowed to stand for five or ten minutes, an apparently inexplicable start will be obtained at the first touch of the starter button, or the first pull-up on the handle. This can be partly attributed to the fact that the battery will have recuperated a little during the interval, but the main reason is that petrol which had condensed on the inner surfaces of the induction manifold and cylinder head, has had time to re-evaporate. To speed up this process, it is well worth while draining the radiator and refilling with hot water. If this cannot be done, a cloth, wrung out in boiling water, should be laid on the inlet manifold. It is surprising how little additional heat is required to evaporate the condensed petrol.

Often, if the sparking plugs are removed after several efforts to start the engine, the points and insulators will be found to be covered with globules of moisture. This may be condensed petrol or water, the

latter being the more likely if the engine has fired once or twice but failed to run. If the plugs are heated, either over a stove, or by pouring petrol into each and igniting it, and are replaced while still hot, a start is usually obtained.

Low-grade Fuel. Sometimes starting troubles are due to a low-grade fuel in the float chamber which will not vaporize at low temperatures. When the engine is switched off, the heat from the exhaust manifold and cylinder block is often sufficient to vaporize the more volatile constituents in the petrol, leaving only the heavier fractions available when the engine is next started. Some considerable time must elapse before the stale petrol in the float chamber has been replaced by fresh fuel from the tank. If a really volatile fuel is poured into the float chamber, that already in it having first been removed, the engine will often start without experiencing any difficulty.

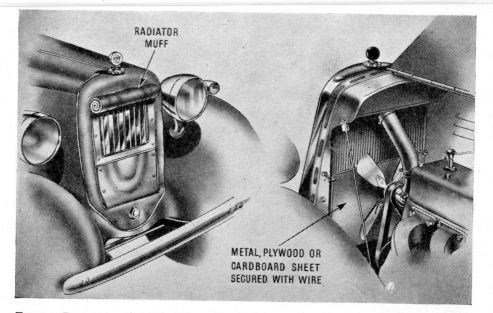

Fig. 22. Protecting the Radiator. *On the left is shown a radiator fitted with a muff. This is used to prevent the bottom of the radiator freezing in severe cold weather. A method of achieving the same result should it not be possible to fit a muff is shown on the right.*

152

Undoubtedly the best plan, however, is to use some form of heater which will keep the engine as a whole reasonably warm; suitable types are described in this section. A trickle charger, which will maintain the battery in good condition, is also a useful winter adjunct. A warm engine and a fully charged battery will compensate for a number of minor faults which would otherwise render starting difficult.

Rapid Warming up. It is often advised that when the engine has been started it should be left running at idling speed for a little time to warm up. Technical experts have now discredited this theory, however, as it has been proved that considerable engine corrosion takes place during the idling period. Instead, it is recommended that the engine should not be started until just before the car is to be driven off. It will then reach running temperature in the shortest possible time.

The engine should not be heavily loaded, but should be driven in third or second gear for a short distance until it is warm. Often the oil pressure gauge gives a useful indication of the temperature of the oil, the pressure remaining higher than usual until the lubricant has warmed up. Until the pressure returns to normal, the engine should be treated with respect.

In very cold weather, it may be advisable to warm up the engine at a very fast idling speed before leaving the garage, since, as explained later, there is a risk of the radiator freezing at the base if the car is driven before the cooling water is warm enough for the thermostat to open. A radiator muff, however, will overcome this difficulty; alternatively, the base of the radiator may be blanked off.

Heaters. A number of different types of heater are obtainable, the choice lying between electrical and paraffin models. When electric current is available in the garage, the electric type of heater, see Fig. 20, is very useful. A convenient and very useful type of electric heater is that designed for fitting into the lower radiator hose. The supply leads are led to a socket on the dash, so that it is a simple matter to plug in the mains lead before leaving the driving seat. One or two modern cars are fitted with a heater of this type.

In most cases, however, a small heater which can be hung under the bonnet against the radiator will provide adequate protection against freezing, besides conferring some benefit on starting from cold, although it cannot keep the engine as a whole very warm. It does, however, prevent condensation on the external insulators of the sparking plugs, and on other items of the ignition system. In an emergency a 60-watt electric bulb will prevent the engine or radiator from freezing if hung under the bonnet. Some heaters take advantage of this fact by combining the heater with an inspection lamp. A sliding metal panel encloses the lamp when in use as a heater, thus raising the temperature of the bulb.

Under-sump Heating. For really good starting, combined with protection from frost, a heater which is placed beneath the sump is strongly advocated, since it keeps the oil from becoming congealed. Tubular types are available which have a very moderate current consumption. A heater of this type has a number of domestic uses during the summer, such as heating a linen or airing cupboard, so that its cost is well repaid.

When electric current is not available, a paraffin heater will give very effective protection. In these the burner is surrounded by copper or brass gauze, on the principle of a miner's lamp, so that there is no fire risk even when the heater is used in a petrol-laden atmosphere. Paraffin heaters can be obtained in under-bonnet or under-sump designs, while larger units are also available to heat the garage as a whole. Most modern types will burn for about 250 hours on one filling, so that only infrequent attention is required.

Anti-freeze Solutions. Even an efficient heater does not altogether banish the risk of a frozen radiator or cylinder block, however. Frost strikes quickly and often without warning, so that if there is the slightest risk that the car may be left for some time without heat, a reliable anti-freezing compound should be added to the cooling water.

A number of different chemicals can be added to water in order to lower its freezing point, but most have one or more disadvantages, such as a tendency to corrode the water passages, or the thermostat, or have a low-boiling point, with the result that they boil away or evaporate quickly at quite low water temperatures, steadily reducing the degree of protection afforded.

Of the possible anti-freezing compounds, then, the choice can be narrowed down to three: ethylene glycol, glycerine, and alcohol, although the latter does suffer from the disadvantages of a low boiling-point. Most proprietary anti-freezing mixtures employ either ethylene glycol or glycerine and provided that a reputable brand is used, no risk of corrosion is likely.

Degree of Protection Afforded. Add the anti-freeze in the correct proportion to the cooling water; most firms supply a chart which indicates the appropriate quantity for each car. This depends on the capacity of the cooling system, and not on the size of the engine. The cooling system of a large engine fitted with a water pump may contain less water than that of a small engine in which the water is circulated by thermo-syphon action only.

Fortunately, there is a considerable measure of latitude in temperature when an anti-freezing compound is mixed with the cooling water. If the proportion is such that the solution will freeze at, say, 20 degrees Centigrade, no damage will be done to the radiator or cylinder block, even though 50 degrees of frost may be experienced. This is due to the fact that, unlike plain water, the solution does not turn solid at its freezing point; instead it begins to form small crystals, and becomes increasingly mushy, but does not solidify until a temperature equivalent to $2\frac{1}{2}$ times below freezing point is reached. A slushy mixture in the radiator on a freezing morning, therefore, need not cause undue alarm, although the engine should be run slowly until it has warmed up, if a water pump is fitted, as this will find difficulty in circulating the crystals.

Sound Joints. One point which must be watched even with the best anti-freezing compounds, is the uncanny knack that they have of finding the most minute point of leakage in the cooling system. All radiator hose connexions must be tightened up, and perished hoses replaced. Since the compounds also tend to loosen scale or dirt in the system, the radiator should be drained and thoroughly flushed out before the fresh water and compound are added.

Draining the Radiator. When it is necessary to run the car without an anti-freezing compound, it is a wise precaution to drain the radiator whenever the car is to be left overnight, and there is any possibility of frost. The drain tap will be found at the lowest point of the radiator, water off-take pipe, or cylinder block. Sometimes a second tap or a drain plug is fitted to the cylinder block or the water pump, if the design of the cooling system is such that these cannot be completely drained by the normal tap. If this is overlooked, there is still a chance of damage due to the freezing of water trapped in the pump or in pockets at the base of the cylinder block.

When the Radiator Freezes. Another trouble which is apt to baffle the novice is the engine which, having been kept warm all night in a heated garage, or by means of a suitable engine heater, begins to boil furiously within a few minutes of being driven on the road. The explanation lies in the fact that the car is probably fitted with a thermostat, and has been driven in a freezing atmosphere before the water in the cylinder block has had a chance to warm up. Since the thermostat cuts off the circulation of water to the radiator in these circumstances, the result is that the water at the base of the radiator freezes. When the thermostat does open, circulation still cannot take place, hence the violent boiling.

The same thing can happen with thermo-syphon cooling systems even when a thermostat is not fitted. Thermo-syphon circulation is slow until the cylinder block and head have warmed up, so that the water at the base of the radiator or in the area in front of the fan will freeze. The engine should be switched off and the car allowed to stand with a rug or a coat completely enveloping the radiator until the system thaws out.

The moral, obviously, is to fit a radiator muff, and to keep this closed for the first few miles. Modern radiator grilles, however, often render it difficult to fit a muff, while they may be so far ahead of the radiator itself that the muff loses most of its value. In this case the base of the radiator should be blanked off with a piece of metal, cardboard, or even brown paper, although this process may present some difficulty on certain models.

SIMPLE DECARBONIZING

Sooner or later even the most carefully maintained engine begins to lose power, although the process may be so gradual that the owner fails to notice it at first. After about 10,000 miles have been covered, decarbonizing will probably be required, although it is impossible to quote an arbitrary figure. Many engines will run 15,000–20,000 miles before this attention is necessary, whereas a high-compression engine may need attention at 5,000 miles. The cylinder head should not be disturbed until pinking becomes evident at moderate throttle openings, or lack of compression can be detected in one or more cylinders when the engine is rotated by the starting handle, indicating that the valves or gasket are no longer fully effective.

Tools Required. Decarbonizing is a job which can be tackled quite successfully by the owner, although modern engine, chassis and body design does render some of the vital parts of the engine inaccessible. It is possible to carry out the work with the normal tool kit furnished with the car in some cases, but one or two additional items, if not essential, are very desirable.

A valve spring compressor, adapted to the particular design of valve gear, is the first; often this is included in the tool kit, or the manufacturer's service station sells a suitable type. Next comes a set of good socket spanners, preferably with an extension and a ratchet action handle. Such sets are apt to be expensive, however, and an inexpensive set of sockets, with a hexagonal handle, or a good set of box spanners, will usually fill the bill.

A small tin of valve-grinding paste, containing both coarse and fine grades, a plentiful supply of clean, non-fluffy rags, and some jam jars, tins and boxes to hold the various bits and pieces as they are removed, complete the items required in the majority of cases, although one or two special tools are required for certain engines, as will be seen later. To save time on the job, a new cylinder head gasket, a set of manifold nuts, a couple of valve springs, one or two valve cotters, and possibly a spare inlet and an exhaust valve should be available, so that a hold-up will not occur if an item is found to require replacement.

Preliminary Dismantling. A survey of the engine before starting work will indicate which items must be removed to give access to the cylinder head nuts. On side valve engines these usually include the dynamo, distributor, and carburettor. On overhead valve engines the first two components can often be left in place, but the valve cover must be removed.

The first step will be to drain the radiator. While this is in progress, the bonnet must be removed, and, on recent models, the side-plates which are attached to the mudguards and scuttle. On side valve engines a fair-sized inspection plate is sometimes fitted to the inner side of one front mudguard, to give access to the valve chamber; this should be removed after hosing down the inside of the mudguard and removing the wheel. The upper water hose can now be disconnected. As the rubber generally sticks to the metal, it may be necessary to insert a thin, flexible blade between the hose and the pipe in order to free it; a sharp implement should not be used, due to the risk of cutting the rubber. If the hose is perished it should be renewed on reassembly.

The battery should be disconnected as a precaution before the leads are removed from the dynamo and distributor. When the dynamo driving belt has been slackened, this unit can be unbolted from the cylinder head. The ignition distributor is generally retained by a set-screw which passes through a hole in the locking plate beneath its body. Do not slacken the split clamp. Sometimes a second set-screw engages with a groove in the spindle of the distributor.

After disconnecting the leads from the sparking plugs and the high-tension lead from the coil, the distributor can be lifted

away. If a vacuum-operated ignition control is fitted, the pipe-line should be uncoupled at the distributor and carburettor ends.

Removing Carburettor. After the petrol pipe, throttle and starting controls have been disconnected, the carburettor can be unbolted from the manifold. Sometimes the manifold retaining nuts can be reached without removing the carburettor, but as this should in any case be detached from the manifold later, there is no great advantage in deferring the operation. On overhead valve engines the manifolds can often be left on the cylinder head, and subsequently dismantled on the bench. They may, however, mask one or more cylinder head studs.

The manifold retaining nuts are usually made from brass, to prevent them binding on the studs. If they are difficult to remove, penetrating oil should be applied and allowed to soak in while other jobs are tackled.

Lifting Cylinder Head. On side valve engines the cylinder head can now be removed. The cylinder head nuts should be unscrewed a little at a time in rotation, following a sequence similar to that recommended in Fig. 23, thus avoiding distortion of the head.

The head may be difficult to free, but by tapping it lightly with a mallet the joint will generally be broken. Sometimes lugs are cast on the head and cylinder block so that the head may be levered up with a pair of screwdrivers or tyre levers. Never be tempted, however, to drive a screwdriver or other tool between the head and the block to break the joint. An obstinate cylinder head can often be freed by replacing the sparking plugs and rotating the engine sharply with the starting handle or the starter motor. On overhead valve engines, however, as will be seen later, the valve gear must be partly dismantled, and this useful dodge

FIG. 23. *This view shows the order in which the cylinder head retaining nuts should be removed to prevent distortion of the cylinder head.*

cannot then be used to break the joint.

Similarly, when removable cylinder barrels are fitted to the engine the crankshaft should not be rotated when the cylinder head nuts have been removed owing to the risk of the barrels being lifted. The cylinder head must be carefully withdrawn and small clamps, in the form of short lengths of tube or even several large nuts, should be fitted to studs adjacent to the edges of the barrels in order to retain the barrels in place.

The head must be lifted squarely, to prevent it binding on the studs.

Overhead Camshaft. When an overhead camshaft is used, for instance, it will be necessary to detach the chain from the sprocket on the camshaft, or to remove the sprocket, leaving the chain in place on it when the cylinder head is lifted away. As either process will disturb the valve timing, a manufacturer's instruction book should be consulted whenever possible; alternatively, the local agents may be willing to advise on the correct procedure.

Keeping the Chain Taut. When no information is available, examine the chain and the teeth of the sprocket for markings which indicate the timing. A spring-clip fastener on the chain may

register with a marked tooth. If the clip is carefully sprung off, a link can be pressed out of the chain, and the two ends held up by attaching lengths of wire or string to them while the cylinder head is raised. This is generally a two-man job, as it is important to keep the chain from dropping into the timing case, or becoming disengaged from the sprocket on the crankshaft.

On engines on which the sprocket must be removed from the crankshaft, the chain tensioner should be slackened if this is adjustable, and the bolts securing the sprocket removed. The sprocket is then levered until it rests on the tensioner or on a special bracket supplied by the manufacturers.

When the camshaft is driven by bevel gears, these should be cleaned and examined for timing marks. If none are visible, adjacent teeth should be marked with a centre pop before the parts are dismantled, see Fig. 36, Chapter 6.

Push Rod Operated Valves. Push rods can usually be withdrawn after each rocker has been depressed sufficiently to lift the ball out of the cup, using a special tool or by obtaining leverage against the underside of the rocker shaft. Alternatively, the rocker shaft as a whole can be unbolted from the cylinder head and lifted off the push rods. These should, however, be temporarily linked together with string before the rocker shaft is lifted, so that there is no possibility of them dropping into the sump. After removal, the push rods should be laid out in sequence on the bench, so that each will subsequently be refitted in its original position. It is as well to check each push rod with a straight-edge to detect any which may be bent, and any that are should be straightened.

After uncoupling any oil pipes which supply the valve gear, the cylinder head can be lifted, the procedure being similar to that described for side valve engines.

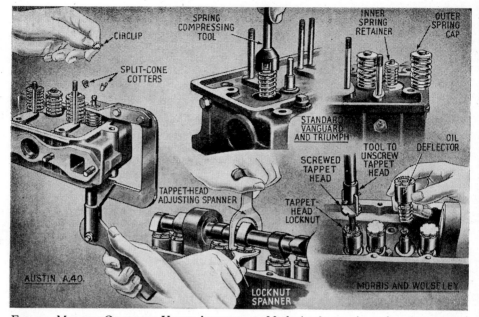

FIG. 24. MODERN OVERHEAD VALVE ASSEMBLIES. *Methods of removing valves from typical modern o.h.v. engines. The lower central drawing illustrates tappet adjustment on recent Morris and Wolseley six-cylinder engines.*

Gasket. The gas-tight and water-tight joint between the cylinder head and block is formed by the gasket, which generally consists of a layer of asbestos sandwiched between two sheets of copper. Unfortunately, this all-important item does not always receive the attention it deserves. It is often damaged during removal, put on one side, and refitted without further thought when the engine is reassembled.

A golden rule is always to fit a new gasket. If a replacement is not available, however, the existing gasket must be removed very carefully, cleaned, and placed out of harm's way until required. If the surface is dented by contact with components, or tools on the bench, leakage will be likely. In any case, carefully examine the narrow sections between the cylinder openings, and if these show signs of burning or are badly carboned, as a result of leakage between adjacent cylinders, obtain a new gasket.

Removing Valves. In this case it is the side valve engine which presents the most difficulty. The valve springs are retained on the valve stems by collars, which in turn rest on a pair of small conical cotters, which fit into a groove at the base of the valve stem. Sometimes a flat steel cotter passes through a slot in the stem, or a horseshoe shaped cotter is fitted to a groove on the stem, but these arrangements are not common nowadays.

In any case, the valve spring must be compressed so that the collar can be lifted and the cotter extracted. This is achieved with the aid of a C shaped valve spring compressing tool, similar to that shown in Fig. 25, which will explain its action clearly. It is often a good plan to engage the claws of the tool with the lowest coil of the spring, instead of beneath the collar. The collar can then be eased up with the fingers, and the cotters removed. As the cotters have a habit of dropping into the valve chamber, any openings from the chamber into the sump should be blocked with a non-fluffy rag before commencing operations.

As the valves are removed, each should be placed in a numbered space or box, complete with its spring, collar, and cotters, so that it will be assembled in its original position. The heads of the valves are often numbered to ensure that they are correctly replaced.

Ford engines deserve a word of explanation, as the valves cannot be lifted out of the valve guides, owing to the stems being of larger diameter at the base. The valve guides are made in two halves, and may be driven downwards by inserting a short length of wood beneath the valve head, when this is raised as high as possible after removal of the spring. Better still, a special tool can be obtained from Ford dealers which simplifies removal of the valves.

Removing Overhead Valves. The overhead valves are retained in the same manner as side valves, but the owner scores in this case, as removal of the valves is a very much simpler operation with the cylinder head on the bench, as compared with the restricted working space and cramped quarters afforded by most modern cars fitted with side valve engines.

The simplest method of compressing the valve springs is to shape a block of wood to fit inside the combustion chamber, and to place the cylinder head on the bench with this block beneath the heads of a pair of valves. The springs can then be compressed by downward pressure exerted by a short length of slotted tube, fitted with a pad. Again, the manufacturers can generally supply a suitable tool, if it is not included in the kit. Such a tool is illustrated in Fig. 24.

Valve Springs. At this stage the valve springs should be examined to see whether they have weakened. If a new

spring is available, stand it on a level surface and compare each of the used springs with it. Any marked variation in height indicates that a spring has weakened. A reliable test is to compare the length of the spring with a new one in a jig similar to that illustrated in Fig. 12, Chapter 6. Alternatively, the tension of the spring can be checked with a spring balance; the tension is usually specified by the manufacturer. Double valve springs, consisting of an inner and outer coil, are sometimes used. If one of the springs has weakened or fractured, always renew the pair.

It is worth while fitting a new set of valve springs whenever the engine is decarbonized, say, at 10,000-mile intervals. The cost is not high, and considerably increased efficiency will be obtained.

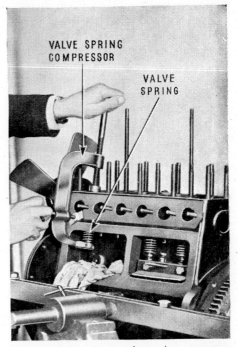

FIG. 25. *A screw-type valve spring compressor used for removing the cotters in a side valve engine. A good plan is to engage the claws of the tool with the lowest coil of the spring.*

Decarbonizing. We now come to the main object of the work, the removal of carbon deposits from the piston crowns, combustion chambers, and manifolds. The carbon may be scraped off with suitably shaped tools, followed by a wire brush. Particular care must be taken not to scratch or score the relatively soft surfaces of the aluminium pistons, and of the combustion chambers when an aluminium cylinder head is fitted. The cylinders on which work is not proceeding must be plugged with clean rags, so that carbon chips do not find their way into them; the water openings in the cylinder block and head should be plugged.

It is always a good plan to leave a ring of carbon about $\frac{1}{4}$ in. in width around the circumference of each piston crown, as this will act as an oil seal and will prevent an increase in oil consumption for the first few hundred miles following decarbonizing. If an old piston ring is available, this should be laid on the piston crown, to maintain an untouched ring of carbon.

Cleaning. Careful cleaning of the valves is well repaid. The exhaust valves will be found to have a deposit of hard, scaly carbon, which is sometimes difficult to remove, whereas that on the inlet valves is generally soft and oily or sooty. A quick method of cleaning a valve is to grip the stem in the chuck of a breast drill; the stationary handle of the drill is then gripped in a vice, and the drill rotated at high speed while a wire brush is pressed against the various portions of the valve head as illustrated in Fig. 29.

Do not clean the stem of the valve with emery cloth, as the diameter may be reduced; make sure, however, that all carbon is removed by careful scraping, and that the stem is perfectly clean. The valve guides will also need cleaning out, although carbon will only accumulate at the necks of the guides; the bores may be cleared of gummy oil by drawing a petrol-soaked rag through them.

Valve and Seating Overhaul. The condition of the valves should be carefully checked. If the seatings are badly eroded or deeply pitted, there is little object in attempting to obtain a satisfactory seal by grinding them onto their seatings in the cylinder block or head. They should be taken to a service station for reconditioning; most garages possess special valve-grinding machines which restore the seating surface quickly and with a high degree of accuracy, so that only light grinding-in is required.

If the seatings in the cylinder block or head are in bad condition, there is little that the owner can do, as it will be necessary to regrind the seats with a special power tool, or, if the seatings are badly worn so that the valve is pocketed, to build them up by welding or to machine them out and fit new seatings; this work is covered later in Chapter 6.

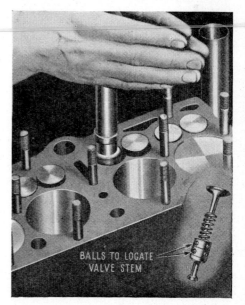

FIG. 26. *When the valve head is not slotted, a suction cap can be used as illustrated above. The inset shows the special valve guide which should be used when grinding-in Ford valves.*

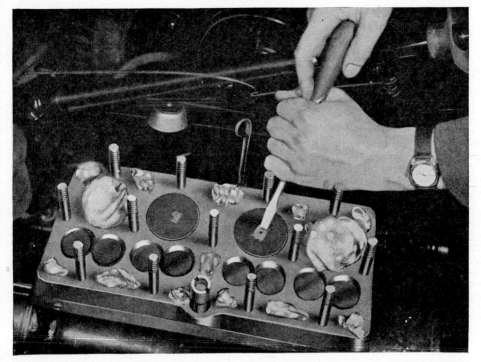

FIG. 27. DECARBONIZING. *The carbon on the head of the piston can be scraped off with a tool similar to that shown above. A ring of carbon should be left round the edge to act as an oil seal. Plug all openings with rags to prevent dirt entering the interior of the engine.*

Grinding-in Valves. Assuming that the valves and seatings are in reasonably good condition, each valve must be matched to its seating by the use of an abrasive valve-grinding paste. Smear a little of the fine grade of paste, or the coarse grade if the valve is pitted, on the seating, and insert the valve in its guide with a light spring beneath its head. The valve must then be rotated a dozen or so times, half a turn in each direction, while light pressure is applied. If the valve head has a slot cut across it, a screwdriver may be used to rotate it. If the head is plain, a tool consisting of a small rubber suction cap attached to a handle will be required, see Fig. 26.

At frequent intervals the valve must be raised from its seating and turned through part of a revolution to distribute the grinding paste evenly; the light spring beneath the valve head facilitates this. When a reasonably good surface has been obtained, grinding should be continued with the fine grade of paste until an even, matt grey ring exists on the valve and seating. Clean both the valve and seating and make a series of pencil marks across one face. Replace the valve, and rotate it once. All pencil lines should now have been erased at the centre. If lines are still visible, grinding must be continued.

Prolonged grinding, however, is both a waste of energy and detrimental to the seatings. If good results cannot be obtained with light grinding-in, the valves, and possibly the seats, will require reconditioning.

It is worth mentioning that on Ford engines some method of supporting the split valve guides must be devised while grinding is in progress. A suitable tool is illustrated in Fig. 26.

Reassembling Valves. This is a reversal of the dismantling process. The chief difficulty, particularly on side valve engines, is to persuade the split cotters to remain in place on the valve stem as the collar is lowered. A useful tip is to coat the groove on the valve stem liberally with a thick grease, which will hold the cotters in position. A further point is that some engines are fitted with special valve springs, which give a progressive resistance when compressed; in these, the coils are noticeably closer together at one end. The spring should be fitted so that the closely-spaced coils are nearest to the valve head, i.e. uppermost on side valve engines, and downwards on overhead valve units.

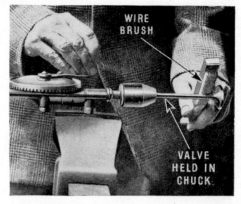

FIG. 29. *A rapid method of cleaning a valve by rotating it in a breast drill while a wire brush is held against the underside of the head.*

If a power operated decarbonizing wire brush such as is used for cleaning valve ports is available it should be used.

After the head has been cleaned make sure that it is a sliding fit over the studs. If it does not fit freely then inspect the holes in the head for obstructive deposits due to corrosion. Another reason for the head not fitting freely is bent studs. If the studs are bent only slightly then they should be squared-up. If, however, the bend is too much, they should be replaced. This operation must be carefully carried out, especially if the stud is screwed into an aluminium block, as it is so simple to strip the threads in the block. Should this happen, the hole must be re-threaded and an oversized stud fitted.

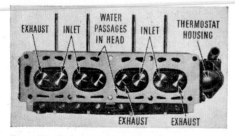

FIG. 28. *It is important to replace the valves in their correct order after decarbonizing; a typical order is shown above.*

When a metal shroud is fitted to overhead valves to prevent excessive oil from finding its way down the valve guides into the combustion chambers, see that the parts are reassembled in the correct manner.

Cleaning Cylinder Head. Before replacing the cylinder head the accumulated carbon on the inside surfaces should be removed. When an aluminium head is fitted every care must be taken not to damage the surfaces with scratches, etc.

Refitting Cylinder Head. When all is ready for the fitting of the cylinder head, the gasket should be eased down over the studs. If a new gasket is being fitted compare it with the one being replaced to make quite sure that it is the correct type and is being fitted the right way. Care must be taken that the edges of the stud holes are not buckled. It is often a good plan to press the gasket over the studs with two box spanners. See that it lies perfectly flat on the cylinder block. The use of a jointing compound on the gasket is not advisable; if both sides are smeared with a thin film of high-melting-point grease a good seal will be obtained.

The cylinder head should slide down easily on to the gasket, see above.

The cylinder head nuts should be tightened progressively in the order shown in Fig. 23, and it is advisable to carry out the tightening in at least three or four stages, beginning with the nuts finger-tight, and ending with them pulled down as tightly as is possible with a spanner of normal length for the particular size of nut. Never use a spanner extension piece to obtain additional leverage as you may easily shear the studs.

Retiming Engine. At this stage it will probably be necessary to check the valve and ignition timing, although on side valve engines only the distributor will have been disturbed, and the spindle generally has an offset driving key so that it cannot be incorrectly coupled up to its drive. When the camshaft drive has been disturbed on overhead valve engines, care must be taken on reassembly to obtain the correct timing. Practical aspects of valve

FIG. 31. *After the gap has been adjusted it should be measured with a feeler gauge. The gap is usually specified by the manufacturer.*

and ignition timing are dealt with in Chapter 6.

Valve Clearances. Before the manifolds are refitted on a side valve engine, the valve clearances should be adjusted, as considerably more space is available at this stage. On overhead valve engines the tappet adjustment can be left until later if preferred. Again, the method of adjusting various types of valve gear is dealt with fully later.

Final Assembly. It only remains to complete the assembly of the engine, the operations being a reversal of the dismantling process. Do not forget to fill the radiator before the engine is started. The engine should be allowed to warm up gently, until normal running temperature is attained, as the cylinder head and manifold nuts, valve cover nuts and similar items can usually be further tightened down to an appreciable extent when the engine is hot. Remember that tightening the cylinder head nuts on a push rod operated, overhead valve engine will alter the valve clearances. If the valve clearance quoted by the manufacturers is applicable to a hot engine, it will be necessary to reset the clearances at this stage. If any case, the clearances should be checked when the car has covered about 100 miles, since the valves tend to bed down onto their seatings, thus reducing the clearance.

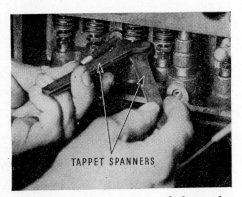

FIG. 30. *Tightening the tappet lock nut after adjusting the tappet clearance. Check the clearance again to ensure that the setting has not been upset when the lock nut was tightened.*

CHAPTER 6

ENGINE REPAIRS AND OVERHAULS

T HE owner who proposes to undertake more ambitious work than that described in the previous chapter will require a more comprehensive tool kit, although a large number of specialized and expensive tools are not necessarily required. What is needed is a basic kit of hand tools with which normal dismantling, fitting and assembly work can be carried out, supplemented, where necessary, by one or two special tools which may be required for certain jobs.

Before dealing with repair and overhaul, therefore, a brief outline of the essential equipment will not be out of place, while mention will be made of some general aspects of workshop practice.

The Workbench. The first requirement is a robust bench, placed where there is sufficient space to work in comfort, and adequately illuminated. To this must be bolted a heavy vice, with jaws not less than 4 in. wide. A cheap vice is a false economy. To prevent machined surfaces or parts made from soft metal being damaged by the serrated jaws of the vice, clamps made from brass, zinc, or even lead will be necessary, while a pair of V-blocks will enable cylindrical parts to be securely held without damage.

At the back of the workbench several boards attached to the wall will enable the various tools to be held in clips or hung from hooks, so that they are readily available and quickly checked over from time to time. It is an excellent idea to outline each tool in pencil or chalk, and to paint in this outline. Any missing tool will thus be immediately evident, and quickly identified. If a tool is missing it is a good policy to find and replace it.

Most owners gradually accumulate a varied stock of nuts, bolts, washers, and other small items. Such useful oddments are best kept in a series of glass jars, partly filled with paraffin, so that they will be protected from rust and can be identified immediately.

Spanners. The most used tools in the class of work under consideration are the various types of spanner illustrated in Fig. 1. Set spanners, with open jaws, should be made from good quality steel, otherwise the jaws may spread or fracture. A set of ring spanners is invaluable, while a range of box spanners, or socket spanners, will be required for heavy-duty work. The latter may be an inexpensive set costing only a few shillings, or a comprehensive kit which includes several different lengths of extension, universal coupling joints, and that most useful item, a ratchet handle. Again, the maxim is to buy the best that can be afforded.

One or two different sizes of adjustable spanner will be useful, although the engineer regards this tool as a necessary evil, to be used only when a normal spanner cannot be applied.

Hammers. The ball-peen type, weighing about 2 lb. and a second of about 4 lb. weight, will be found most useful. In addition a copper hammer will be required for those jobs which would be marked or damaged by a steel hammer; for use on soft metals a rawhide or plastic-faced hammer is invaluable.

Drills. The breast drill or hand drill is capable of carrying out most of the work covered in this chapter. When used with a wire brush gripped in the chuck, it is a useful decarbonizing and cleaning tool. Better still, of course, is an electric drill, with, as an added luxury, a flexible cable drive and a set of wire brushes, buffing heads, and a selection of small grinding stones. With the drill clamped in a bench stand, the polishing and grinding equipment can save hours of tedious hard work on many jobs.

Miscellaneous Tools. Both the large, side-cutting, and small, pointed nose types of pliers will be necessary, preferably in two sizes of each type. A centre-punch, and two or three pin punches of different diameters will often be called for, while a strong extractor for drawing off bearings, gears, or hubs will prevent damage to the components. An internal extractor for dealing with races or bushes in blind holes may also be required. Several different sizes of screw-driver, including the insulated variety for electrical work, a set of feeler gauges as used to measure valve, sparking plug and contact breaker clearances, and a good steel rule or straight-edge will complete the basic kit of tools required for the average job.

Specialized Tools. In the following pages the various specialized tools which are required to carry out some operations are described under the appropriate headings. Since a certain degree of skill is required to use, say, a micrometer or a bearing scraper, the novice will be well advised to leave such jobs as require the use of these and other special tools in the hands of the expert.

An owner of moderate ability will, however, undoubtedly find use for such items as files, cold chisels, hacksaws, drills, taps and dies, and soldering and brazing equipment. Generally such items are added from time to time as the work in hand dictates and the owner's skill improves. A discussion of their uses, and the technique of using them is rather outside the scope of this book.

Nuts and Bolts. By long custom the Whitworth standard sizes of screw threads have been accepted in general engineering to denote the various sizes of bolts and the nuts which fit them. The hexagon head of a bolt, and the hexagonal nut, bear a definite relationship to the diameter of the threaded portion. A $\frac{1}{4}$-inch spanner is one which will fit the flats on the head or the nut of a $\frac{1}{4}$-inch diameter bolt.

This is apt to be a little confusing when dealing with the nuts and bolts on cars, since in this case a B.S.F., or British Standard Fine thread, is used. A B.S.F. nut or bolt has more threads to the inch and is stronger than the equivalent Whitworth size: a $\frac{1}{4}$-inch B.S.F. bolt, has 26 threads per inch, for instance, as compared with the 20 threads per inch of a $\frac{1}{4}$-inch Whitworth bolt. A B.S.F. nut cannot, therefore, be screwed onto a Whitworth bolt of the same size. A further difference lies in the fact that the bolt heads and nuts in the B.S.F. range are one size smaller than the Whitworth sizes. Thus a $\frac{3}{16}$-inch Whitworth spanner must be used to turn a $\frac{1}{4}$-inch B.S.F. bolt.

For small-diameter nuts and bolts, chiefly used on electrical and instrument parts, the B.A., or British Association, thread is used, the size of the screw or nut being denoted by a number instead of being quoted in fractions of an inch. On American cars the American thread is used, while Continental cars use the metric thread.

High-tensile Bolts. Special bolts and nuts made from high-tensile steel are used on some engine components, among them being the connecting rod and main bearing securing bolts, flywheel bolts, and similar applications where the bolts are severely stressed. Such bolts are twice as strong as those made from mild steel, and are sometimes identified by small nicks cut in the vertical edges of each hexagon. Often, however, they are not identified, and as a precaution any bolts, studs or set-screws in highly stressed components should be replaced only by the manufacturer's spares.

Tightening Nuts. The locking effect of a bolt or nut depends on the friction between the screw threads in the two parts, and, to some extent, friction between the underside of the bolt head or nut and the surface against which it is tightened. The more firmly a nut or bolt is screwed down, therefore, the less likelihood there will be of it slackening off in service.

This axiom, however, is open to abuse in the hands of the novice. The standard sizes of spanner just described are of such a length that the correct leverage is applied to tighten the appropriate size of bolt or nut fully. Unfortunately, additional leverage is often exerted by lengthening a set spanner by fitting a length of tube over its free end; when a box spanner or a socket spanner is used, increased leverage may be provided by using a longer than normal tommy bar or handle. In either case the result is that the bolt, stud or set-screw is stretched and rendered dangerously weak, or is twisted so that it shears off. Alternatively the thread is stripped.

The use of brute force in this manner, then, defeats its object. It is now becoming usual to employ a special type of spanner which incorporates a dial or similar device to measure the actual turning effort, or torque, applied; each and every nut will thus be tightened to a specified figure which depends on its diameter and the design of the parts which it secures. Such a spanner is an expensive luxury for the average owner, but with the use of an ordinary open-ended spanner of the correct length and providing reasonable care is taken when tightening down, quite satisfactory results can be obtained.

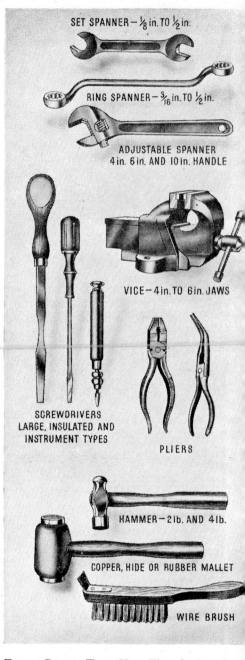

SET SPANNER—⅛ in. TO ½ in.

RING SPANNER—³⁄₁₆ in. TO ½ in.

ADJUSTABLE SPANNER
4 in. 6 in. AND 10 in. HANDLE

VICE—4 in. TO 6 in. JAWS

SCREWDRIVERS
LARGE, INSULATED AND
INSTRUMENT TYPES

PLIERS

HAMMER—2 lb. AND 4 lb.

COPPER, HIDE OR RUBBER MALLET

WIRE BRUSH

FIG. 1. REPAIR TOOL KIT. *The selection of tools illustrated above are those most likely to be required during the normal maintenance and*

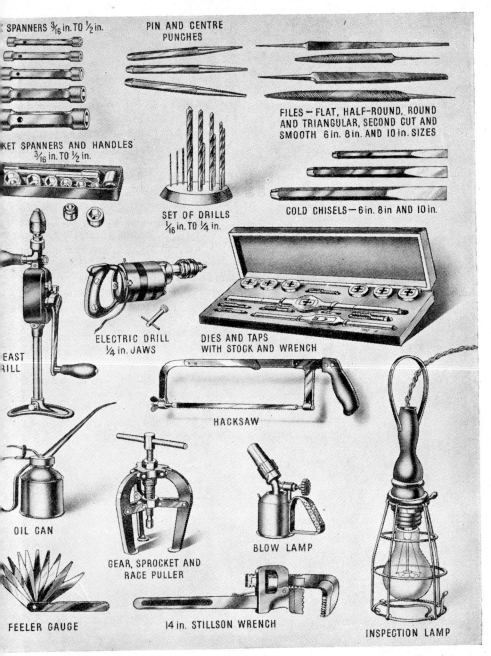

SPANNERS ³⁄₁₆ in. TO ½ in.

PIN AND CENTRE PUNCHES

FILES — FLAT, HALF-ROUND, ROUND AND TRIANGULAR, SECOND CUT AND SMOOTH 6 in. 8 in. AND 10 in. SIZES

KET SPANNERS AND HANDLES ³⁄₁₆ in. TO ½ in.

SET OF DRILLS ¹⁄₁₆ in. TO ¼ in.

COLD CHISELS — 6 in. 8 in AND 10 in.

ELECTRIC DRILL ¼ in. JAWS

DIES AND TAPS WITH STOCK AND WRENCH

EAST RILL

HACKSAW

OIL CAN

GEAR, SPROCKET AND RACE PULLER

BLOW LAMP

FEELER GAUGE

14 in. STILLSON WRENCH

INSPECTION LAMP

repair of a car. Such items as the electric drill and inspection lamp depend on electric power being available in the garage or workshop. When buying tools it is advisable to purchase the best that can be obtained as they will not only prove more reliable, but last much longer.

167

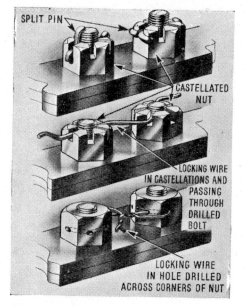

FIG. 2. *The correct method of locking plain and castellated nuts with split pins or wire.*

Locking Nuts and Bolts. When it is essential to prevent a nut from slackening off, there are three main methods of locking it. The first is the locking washer, either the split spring steel variety, or the star washer which has a number of small projections. Then we have the tab washer, which has two tabs, one of which is bent down against a fixed surface or into a groove or hole, while the other is bent up against a flat on the nut or the head of the bolt. The third scheme is to fit a locking nut above or beneath the nut which is to be locked, or on the thread of a bolt or set-screw: a common example is the lock-nut on the valve clearance adjusting screws. The fourth, and most positive method is to drill a hole through the end of the nut or stud, and to fit a split-pin through this hole so that it passes through the slots in a slotted or castellated nut. Fig. 2 shows the correct method of fitting split-pins and bending back the ends.

Among the less common locking devices found in various engine components are the cotter pin and the self-locking nut. The former is a means of locking a bolt or a shaft in its hole, and consists of a tapered pin which engages with a flat or a groove on the shaft. As the pin is pulled into place by a nut, its taper causes it to bind more firmly against the shaft, which is thus rigidly locked against both end-wise movement and rotation. The self-locking nut is a special type which has a fibre or a spring steel insert at the outer end of its thread; this grips the thread on the bolt, and friction prevents the nut from unscrewing.

When a number of adjacent nuts must be locked, as in the case of those around the edge of a cover plate, a hole is sometimes drilled diagonally from one flat to another, so that a locking wire can be inserted; the wire is then taken to the next nut, and so on in succession. Care must be taken to lead the wire in such a manner that it tends to keep the nuts tight. Fig. 2 should make this clear. A wire can also be passed through a series of drilled bolts or studs and the slots in castellated nuts in a similar manner, instead of using split-pins.

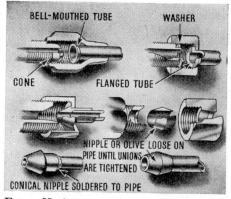

FIG. 3. *Various types of union connexion. The conical nipple type which was once universal is now being replaced by the bell-mouthed type.*

Pipe Unions. Four common unions used on petrol and oil pipes are illustrated in Fig. 3. The type in which a conical nipple is soldered to the end of the pipe was once almost universal, but is now being replaced by the design in which the end of the copper pipe itself is opened out into a cone which matches a cone on the other half of the union. While this is cheaper to produce, fitting a new pipe is not such an easy proposition for the owner, since to form a reasonably accurate bell-mouth on the pipe is more difficult than soldering the earlier type of nipple in place. The simplest method is to use a short length of steel rod, bent into the form of a crank, and rotated by a drill brace. This will swage a bell-mouth in the end of the pipe.

Alternatively, the loose-nipple type of union can often be substituted. The two internal cones have the effect of squeezing the tapered edges of the nipple onto the pipe when the union is screwed up. The fourth type of union, with a flanged end on the pipe which is tightened against a fibre or cork washer, is not so common as the three just described.

With any of the types of union just described, scrupulous cleanliness of the mating surfaces is essential to prevent leakage, while any surface damage or distortion of the cones will render it almost impossible to obtain a sound joint.

RE-CONDITIONING THE VALVE GEAR

In the previous chapter it was emphasized that satisfactory valve seatings cannot be obtained by grinding-in if the seating faces of the valve and the cylinder block or head are not in good condition. The first step, however, should be to examine the valves carefully after cleaning them. Check each stem with a straight-edge for any sign of bending or distortion. Normally a bent valve should be renewed,

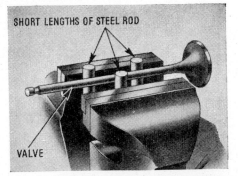

FIG. 4. *A bent valve stem can be straightened as illustrated above, but this should only be done if a replacement valve is not available.*

but when a replacement is not available the stem can often be straightened by clamping it between the jaws of a vice, with three packing pieces arranged as shown in Fig. 4. The valve should be straightened a little at a time, testing it frequently for truth.

Renewing Valve Guides. If the valve stem is worn, so that a ridge can be detected just below the head, renewal will be the only satisfactory course. Since the guide will also be worn, this too should be renewed. The guides are a tight press fit, and must be drawn out by means of a long bolt, washer and distance piece, as shown in Fig. 5. The new guides may be tapped into place with a suitable stepped mandrel inserted in the bore, or pulled into position by reversing the bolt and distance piece arrangement used to extract them. If locating flanges are not machined on the guides, make sure that each projects into the port to the same extent as the original guides. If one end of the guide is tapered off or counter-bored to prevent carbon accumulating, this end must naturally be nearest to the valve seating.

Re-cutting Seatings. The seating should be checked to make sure that it is truly circular. The average owner will not possess a sensitive dial gauge of the

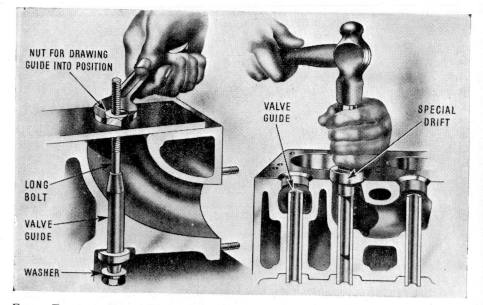

NUT FOR DRAWING
GUIDE INTO POSITION

VALVE
GUIDE

SPECIAL
DRIFT

LONG
BOLT

VALVE
GUIDE

WASHER

FIG. 5. FITTING A VALVE GUIDE. *On the left is a simple fixture for drawing a valve guide into position. Guides such as that illustrated on the right are driven into position with a special drift that prevents the open end of the guide getting burred over.*

type used by service stations when making this check, but a fairly accurate test is to smear the seating on the valve lightly and evenly with Prussian blue oil-colour, or mechanic's marking blue, and turn the valve several times on its seating. The marking should be transferred evenly over the full circumference of the seating in the block or head.

When new guides have been fitted, it will be necessary to recut the seatings in the cylinder block or head. As already indicated, this work is best left to a garage equipped with special power-driven grinding equipment, but a reasonable result can be obtained with care by the use of a cutter of the type shown in Fig. 6. The tool must be rotated lightly but firmly, so that it does not chatter on the seating. A worn valve guide will prejudice a good finish, as the tool must be accurately located. A similar tool is used to recut the seatings on the valves.

Make sure that the tool purchased is designed to cut the seating at the correct angle; the seatings on some valves differ from the usual 45 degree angle.

Replacement Rings. If an overhead valve cylinder head is being dealt with, by far the best plan is to take the head to a service station so that all the necessary work can be done with proper workshop equipment. If the seatings in the head are so worn that the valve sinks below the level of the seating, and is pocketed, the assistance of a service station will in any case be necessary, as the usual procedure is to machine away the existing seating so that a new seating, in the form of a replacement ring, can be pressed into place. On side valve engines symptoms which indicate the need for specialized assistance can generally be temporarily allayed by carefully grinding-in the valves, with the reservation that the car should be put in the hands of a garage as soon as possible so that a really effective job can be done.

Tappet Faults. On side valve engines the next step is to examine the tappet screws, as these generally become worn by the foot of the valve. The resulting depression prevents accurate measurement of the valve clearance, as the feeler gauge bridges the gap. The screws can be screwed out of the tappets; in some cases the tappets are held in detachable blocks bolted to the crankcase. When such blocks are fitted the work is very much simplified. New screws should be fitted where necessary, or, if replacements are not available, the existing screws may be faced up on the side of a grinding wheel. It is not an easy matter, however, to ensure that the faces are ground truly flat and at right-angles to the screw.

If any tappets appear to be slack in their guides, they should be renewed if possible, as side-clearance on a tappet

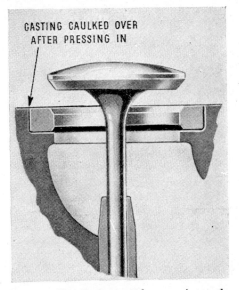

FIG. 7. *After fitting a valve seat insert the casting surrounding it should be caulked over.*

can cause an elusive tap which cannot be cured by adjustment of the valve clearance. When detachable tappet blocks are not fitted, it may be possible to lift the tappets out of their guides. Sometimes they are located by spring-loaded plungers, which are retained by a bar bolted to the crankcase. If the tappets have mushroom-shaped feet, however, it will be necessary to remove the camshaft and withdraw them from below. As this is an involved job, it is as well to get the advice of the manufacturer or local agent.

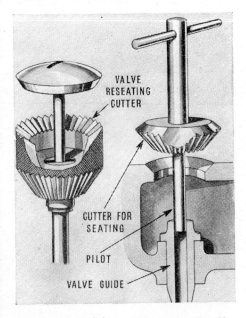

FIG. 6. *Hand cutters used for truing the valve face and valve seating. After this operation the surfaces must be lapped, see* FIG. 9

FIG. 8. *Types of valve seat insert used when reconditioning a valve seat.*

On push rod operated overhead valve engines, the tappets will be similar to those described, except that the adjusting screw is replaced by a well or socket into which the push rod fits. Check the push rods for straightness. If they are slightly bent they may be carefully straightened, but any badly bent rods should be renewed.

Rocker Gear. The rockers which operate the valves should next receive attention: the details which follow below apply equally to push-rod and overhead camshaft engines. The main fault will be wear on the underside of the rocker shaft, and on the lower half of the bush;

consequently, fitting new bushes alone will not necessarily restore the new clearances. Since the valve gear is bound to be noisy if excessive clearance exists, it is generally necessary to renew the shaft if the car has covered a considerable mileage.

The bushes themselves may be a press fit in the rockers, or may be a light push fit. If they are pressed in tightly, it may be necessary to ream them slightly after fitting, as this operation tends to compress them. It is a simple matter to press a bush into a rocker by clamping the two parts in the vice, but the jaws must be padded with brass, copper or

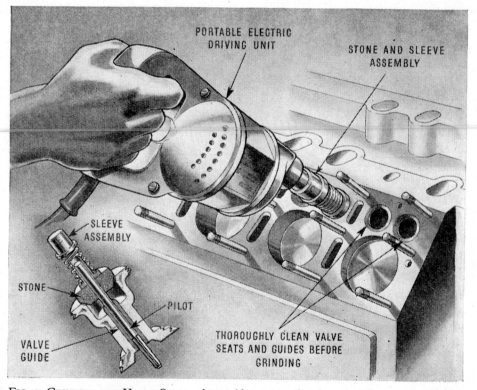

FIG. 9. GRINDING THE VALVE SEATS. *A portable power tool such as that illustrated above can be used for accurately grinding the valve seatings after they have been cut. The inset shows a section through the stone and sleeve assembly. To ensure that the stone is perfectly square with the seating, a pilot locates in the bore of the valve guide. The spring on the sleeve assembly allows slight movement of the power tool without affecting the position of the stone.*

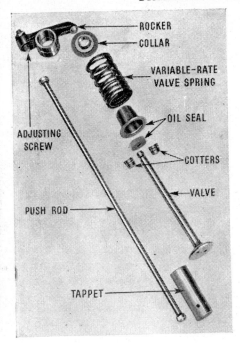

FIG. 10. *Exploded view of the parts in a valve assembly operated by an overhead camshaft.*

12; this enables the condition of the spring to be checked by comparing its length with a new spring, which should be kept for reference purposes. The same principle can, of course, be applied by compressing the two springs in the vice with a washer between them, and comparing their respective lengths. In any case, a new set of springs is a worthwhile investment whenever the engine is decarbonized.

Timing Chain. So far the work described has been within the scope of the owner of average mechanical ability. If the timing chain or camshafts require attention on side valve and push rod overhead valve engines, however, the dismantling required is more extensive, and the work should preferably be left to an expert. On most modern side valve and push rod engines a short timing

tin to prevent damage to the parts. After fitting, do not forget to drill an oil hole in the bush, i.e. if a passage is drilled in the rocker to supply oil to the valve contact face and the push rod cup. It may be possible to pass the drill through an existing hole in the rocker, which is generally sealed at its outer end with solder.

If the tips of the rockers have been indented by the valve stems, they should be trued up with an emery stone, or by grinding. As these surfaces are case-hardened, it may be that the hardened skin has been worn through, in which case a new rocker should be fitted.

Valve Springs. The importance of checking the condition of the valve springs has already been stressed when dealing with decarbonizing in Chapter 5. A useful jig which can be made up mainly from scrap materials is illustrated in Fig.

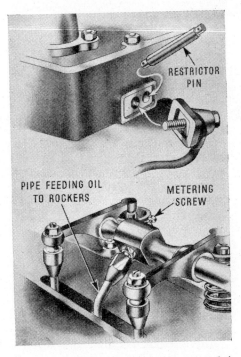

FIG. 11. *Two methods of metering the lubricating oil supply to an overhead valve gear.*

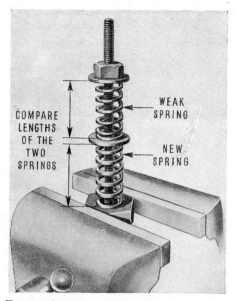

WEAK
SPRING

COMPARE
LENGTHS
OF THE
TWO
SPRINGS

NEW
SPRING

FIG. 12. *A simple jig for checking the tension of valve springs by comparing their length, when compressed, with that of a new valve spring.*

without causing it to whine when the engine is speeded up. When the chain also drives the dynamo, tensioning is often effected by slackening the dynamo mounting bolts and swinging it outwards slightly.

Fitting Timing Chain. In order to renew the chain it will be necessary in most cases to take off the timing cover at the front of the engine. This will entail removing the radiator shell, radiator, starter dog and fan pulley. The starter dog is generally very tightly screwed on to the nose of the crankshaft, and a really robust spanner is needed to unscrew it. The makers can generally supply a special tool. Having unscrewed the dog, the fan pulley must be drawn off, preferably by using an extractor.

Having removed the timing cover, the chain should be examined for a detachable link, which is usually brighter than the remainder. It is generally held in place by a small U-shaped clip, which must be sprung off the pins. Before doing this, however, examine the sprockets for timing marks, to facilitate reassembly. The most widely used methods of indicating timing are described under the heading "Timing the Engine" later in this chapter.

If no spring clip can be found, it may be necessary to draw off the camshaft chainwheel without separating the chain; the chainwheel will then be secured by a central setscrew and tab washer. Sometimes it is necessary to draw off both sprockets together. Again, if the sprocket is shrunk onto the camshaft, this must be withdrawn after removing a locking plate behind it. In this case the valve gear must also be dismantled, and the tappets held up clear of the cams, as described in a later paragraph.

chain is used and no adjustment for tension, whether automatic or manual, is provided. Such chains, however, will operate for very long periods before excessive wear develops. When a slapping or rattling noise is evident, the chain must be renewed.

On some engines, mainly the overhead camshaft type, the use of a longer chain calls for the provision of some form of adjustment to compensate for wear. One form of tension comprises a sprocket, carried on a hub into which is fitted a spring which tends to force the sprocket towards the chain. A ratchet device prevents the sprocket from moving back. In other cases the tensioner sprocket is carried on a pivoted arm, which can be moved by an adjusting screw which projects on the outside of the timing case, as shown in Fig. 14.

After slackening the lock-nut the adjuster should be screwed in just sufficiently to take up the slack in the chain,

When a long chain is fitted, slackening off the tensioner to its full extent will generally allow the chain to be freed from the sprocket teeth. The method of dis-

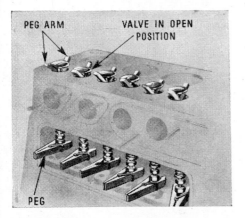

FIG. 13. *A method of holding the tappets clear of the camshaft without removing the valves.*

It should seldom, if at all, be necessary to remove the camshaft from the engine, except when this is essential to renew the timing chain. The camshaft bearings are of generous area, and, owing to the copious lubrication which they receive, wear very slowly. Moreover, camshafts will run efficiently with quite large bearing clearances, so that the maxim is to leave well alone if possible.

Among the extra dismantling required will be removal of the sump so that the oil pump and its drive, which is usually taken from the camshaft, can be disconnected. This will often disturb the drive to the ignition distributor. A

connecting the spring on the various forms of spring-loaded tensioner will be evident on inspection, but it is always advisable to consult the manufacturer as to the correct procedure, as reassembly is not always such a simple matter as it may at first appear.

Before fitting a new chain, examine the sprocket teeth for wear. As the drive is taken on one side of each tooth, this gradually becomes undercut and develops a hooked shape. New sprockets should be fitted when wear reaches this stage. If this is not done in good time trouble will be experienced with the timing of the engine.

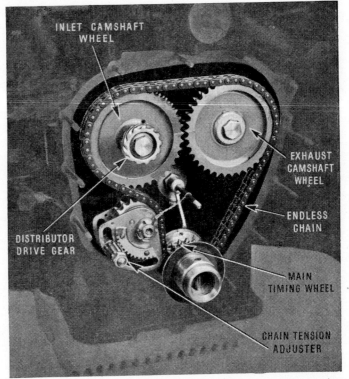

FIG. 14. *With long timing chains some form of adjustment is necessary to compensate for the slackness that develops as a result of wear. The view above shows the location and arrangement of the chain tension adjuster fitted to a Riley engine.*

mechanical petrol pump must be removed, and its short push rod, if fitted, extracted. Sometimes the front or centre bearing of the camshaft must be free to move forward as the camshaft is extracted; the bearing locating setscrew must be removed in these cases.

Next the tappets must be removed or held up clear of the cams, after removal of the valves and springs, or the push rods as the case may be. The makers sometimes supply a service tool which can be fitted to the valve chamber to hold up the tappets. Otherwise, the tappets may be held by a number of spring clothes pegs, as shown in Fig. 13. It should then be possible to withdraw the camshaft. If it is decided to remove the bearings, the manufacturer's advice should be sought, as the methods of removal, refitting, reaming to size, and the drilling of oilways, hold pitfalls for the unwary.

Renewing Timing Gears. When the camshaft is driven by gears, excessive backlash between the gear teeth will cause noisy operation. The clearance between the teeth may be measured with a feeler gauge, and should seldom exceed 4–5 thousandths of an inch. If both gears are of steel, it will be necessary to fit a replacement pair, as it is usual to

lap these together during manufacture to ensure silent operation. When one gear is of bronze or compressed fibre, it may be sufficient to renew this. Since the gears are a tight fit on their shafts, a suitable extractor should be used. It is often necessary to fit a fibre gear to the camshaft with the aid of an arbor press, so that the average owner will require professional assistance for this job.

ADJUSTING VALVE CLEARANCES

Because the valves expand when hot, a small clearance must be left between the tip of the valve stem and the tappet or rocker; since the exhaust valve reaches a much higher temperature than the inlet, this valve will require a greater clearance when cold. If an adequate clearance does not exist, there will be a risk of the tappet or rocker holding the valve slightly off its seating when the engine is hot, leading to loss of compression and rapid burning of the seating faces. The clearance will affect the valve timing, too: a smaller clearance than normal will result in the valves opening too early, while too great a clearance will cause late valve timing.

Valve Clearances. No general rule can be given regarding the correct clearance, since this will depend on the

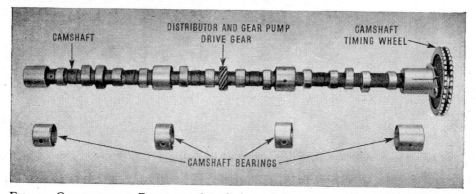

FIG. 15. CAMSHAFT AND BEARINGS. *A typical camshaft used in a six-cylinder, four-stroke engine. After the camshaft has been removed from the engine, the front, intermediate and rear bearings should be examined and if worn or scored they should be replaced.*

FIG. 16. REMOVING THE CAMSHAFT. *The view above shows the camshaft being withdrawn. During this operation every care must be exercised to prevent damage to the white metal bearings.*

design of the cams and the operating gear. On one engine the exhaust valves may require 6 thousandths of an inch clearance, and the inlets 4 thousandths; yet a later model of the same engine may have a special design of cam which will allow clearances of 20 thousandths of an inch to be used without rendering the valve gear noisy. The only safe plan is to ascertain the correct figure, and to work to it.

Do not be tempted to use a smaller clearance because the engine runs a little more quietly than with the correct gap. Immediately after an overhaul, in fact, it is better to allow a slightly larger gap than normal as the valves will bed down on their seatings during the first few hundred miles of running. It is this bedding down which gives point to the recommendation that the valve clearances should be checked when the car has covered about 200 miles after an engine overhaul, or when new.

Some years ago, when engine and body design did not render the valves as inaccessible as they are on many cars today, particularly in side valve engines, the conscientious owner would check the valve clearances at 500 or 1,000 mile intervals. Since valve adjustment on side valve engines generally entails removal of the manifolds and one or more panels or valances, however, the valve clearances seldom receive attention between decarbonizing periods. In practice, this does no harm, since modern engine design and improved materials have resulted in the valve clearances remaining fairly constant over long periods.

On Ford engines, for instance, the valve clearances cannot be adjusted in the normal manner, but are obtained by grinding sufficient metal from the foot of the valve to provide the required clearance. If, on assembly, the clearance is too great, the valve must be ground-in a little more until the correct clearance is obtained. Ford dealers possess the correct type of grinder which ensures that the foot of the valve is perfectly flat and at a right-angle to the stem.

Methods of Adjustment. On most side valve engines, however, the adjustment almost invariably takes the form of an adjusting screw in the tappet, which is locked by a nut. Thin, good-quality spanners are required to carry out the adjustment, as the locking nut must be firmly tightened. When the tappets are free to rotate, or are positioned by spring-loaded plungers, a third spanner is required to hold the tappet stationary; this engages with flats on the head of the tappet.

The manipulation of the three spanners in a confined space is apt to be difficult, however, so that it is a good plan to file a strip of sheet metal to fit snugly between the flats on an adjacent pair of tappets, thus preventing them from rotating while adjustment is being carried out. It will be found that when the locknut is tightened, the tappet clearance will be altered slightly, so several attempts will probably be necessary before the correct clearance is achieved.

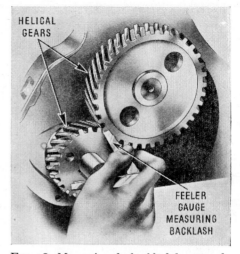

FIG. 18. *Measuring the backlash between the teeth of the helical timing gears with a feeler gauge. The backlash for particular designs of car is usually specified by the manufacturer.*

Clearance Gauge. On overhead valve engines with push rod operation, the clearance is generally adjusted by means of a ball-ended set-screw which fits into the upper end of the push rod. This is locked by a nut, and once the nut has been slackened the screw can be turned with a screwdriver, while a feeler gauge is inserted between the other end of the rocker and the tip of the valve. This method of adjustment, with small variations in detail, applies to the great majority of push rod engines.

When an overhead camshaft is used, the adjusting screw is generally in the end of the rocker which bears on the valve. On one or two

FIG. 17. *Checking the float between the end of the camshaft and the thrust flange with a feeler gauge. The tolerance for a given design of car is usually specified by the maker.*

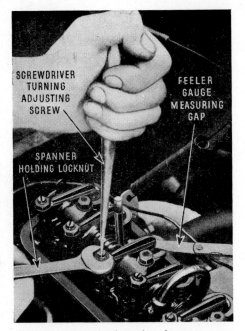

FIG. 19. *Adjusting the valve clearance on an overhead valve engine. Before this is done it should be determined whether the gap is to be adjusted when the engine is hot or cold.*

engines the rocker is carried on an eccentric bush, and adjustment is effected by slackening a steel locknut and rotating a bronze adjusting nut which moves the rocker outwards over the valve, thus reducing the clearance. Another scheme is to fit hardened steel caps, carried on threaded spindles, to the valve stems. By rotating the cap the effective length of the valve stem is altered.

Correct Measurement. When adjusting any of the types of valve gear just described, the blade, or blades, of the feeler gauge should just be lightly gripped, but free to slide between the valve and the tappet screw or rocker. As a check, try to insert a blade one thousandth of an inch larger. If it slides in easily the clearance is too great. Conversely, if a blade one thousandth of an

inch smaller than the correct clearance cannot be inserted, the gap is too small. It is essential to set the clearance when the tappet or rocker is on the base of the cam. On overhead camshaft engines this is a simple matter since the cams are visible. On side valve engines the safest plan is to adjust the clearance on one valve when another is fully open, as the point of maximum lift is easily judged. On a four-cylinder engine, for instance, numbers 1 and 4 cylinders, and numbers 2 and 3 move up and down in unison. When a valve in one cylinder of a pair is fully open, the corresponding valve in the other is fully closed.

A similar principle applies to six and eight-cylinder engines. It is not difficult to work out the correct sequence, but the manufacturer or agent will usually be able to supply the correct sequence. Otherwise, rotate the engine until the valve to be adjusted closes, and then give the starting handle a further half-revolution.

Hot or Cold? Some manufacturers recommend that the gaps should be checked when the engine is hot, but there is a growing tendency to specify clearances with the engine cold. In one or two instances on overhead valve engines the clearances must be adjusted while the

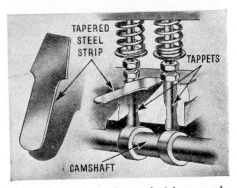

FIG. 20. *A steel wedge pushed between the flats on the tappets will stop them rotating during adjustment.*

engine is running. The idling speed should be set to a slow tick-over, and the spanner and screwdriver must be allowed to ride up and down with the rocker while adjusting the clearance. Although this may sound difficult, the knack of synchronizing the movements is not difficult to acquire. After setting and locking the tappet adjusting screws, it is essential to reset the idling speed to what it was before the adjustment of the tappets was carried out.

Finally, remember that when push-rods are used, tightening the cylinder head nuts will upset the valve clearances, as the rockers will be brought closer to the ends of the rods. A further point to be watched on this type of engine is that the valve clearances will increase slightly when the engine begins to warm up, since the cylinder block expands and lifts the rockers away from the push-rods. As the valves become hot, and the rods also warm up and expand, the clearances decrease again. Adjustment must, therefore, be carried out with the engine cold or thoroughly hot: never when warm.

THE PISTONS, RINGS AND CYLINDERS

After 20,000 miles, engine oil consumption often begins to increase. Sometimes symptoms of cylinder and piston ring wear appear at an earlier mileage; on the other hand, many engines will run for 30,000 miles or more before poor compression and excessive oil consumption indicate that attention is required. When it is considered that during 25,000 miles the crankshaft in the engine of a medium-sized car will have revolved about 100 million times, while each piston will have travelled about 13,000 miles up and down the cylinder walls, the amount of surface wear which takes place on the various moving parts is really infinitesimally small.

Removing Pistons. The method of removing the pistons and connecting rods varies with different engines. In some cases it is possible to withdraw them from below, after removing the sump and unbolting the connecting rod bearing caps. Sometimes some skill is necessary to persuade the pistons to pass through the restricted space between the crankshaft and the wall of the crankcase, especially when balance weights are fitted to the crankshaft. For instance,

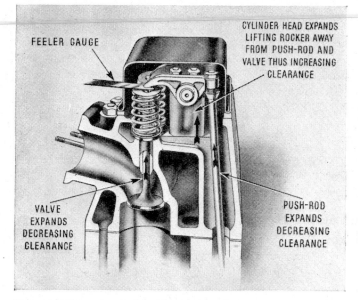

FEELER GAUGE

CYLINDER HEAD EXPANDS LIFTING ROCKER AWAY FROM PUSH-ROD AND VALVE THUS INCREASING CLEARANCE

VALVE EXPANDS DECREASING CLEARANCE

PUSH-ROD EXPANDS DECREASING CLEARANCE

FIG. 21. *This sectional view shows how the cylinder head, push rods and valve stem expand when the engine is heated up, and explains why it is essential that a small clearance must exist between the rocker and the end of the valve stem.*

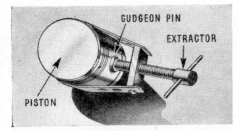

FIG. 22. *A tool for extracting the gudgeon pin before removing the connecting rod.*

it may be necessary to hold the piston against the crankshaft, which must be rotated until the piston is clear of the crankcase.

Extracting the Gudgeon Pin. An alternative scheme is to withdraw the pistons from the top of the cylinders, the connecting rods passing through the bores: care must be taken that the big ends do not score the cylinder walls. If the connecting rods will not pass through the bores, the piston must first be pushed up above the cylinder block, when the gudgeon pin can be removed, allowing the

connecting rod to be withdrawn from below.

It will be seen, therefore, that there is everything to be said for obtaining expert advice before beginning work. Every part should be examined for marks or numbers as it is removed, so that it can be reassembled in its correct position. Each connecting rod bearing cap, for instance, must be matched to its rod, and must be replaced the same way round as before; the numbers on the caps and rods must, therefore, be on the same side, and a note should be made of whether this is on the near side or the off side of the engine.

Removing Pistons. The gudgeon pin may be securely held in the connecting rod by means of some form of split clamp, tightened by a bolt, or may be carried in a bearing in the connecting rod, in which case it is positioned by small spring steel circlips fitted to grooves in the piston. Alternatively, end pads of soft metal may be fitted to position it.

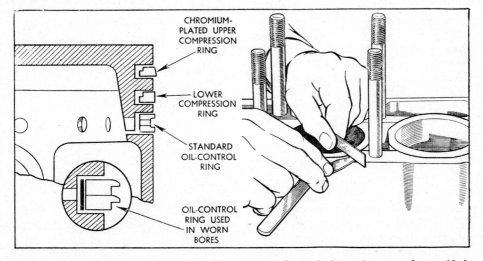

FIG. 23. *Points to watch on modern engines. A special set of piston rings may be specified, such as the arrangement used on Vauxhall engines (left). When detachable cylinder barrels are fitted, as on the Standard Vanguard (right) it is necessary for the barrels to protrude above the cylinder block by a specified amount to obtain the correct 'nip'. The manufacturers' repair schedule should always be consulted.*

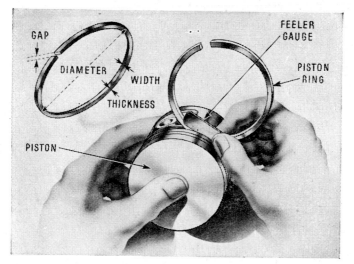

FIG. 24. *Measuring the side clearance of a piston ring. Other vital piston ring measurements are shown on the ring to the left.*

rings, the degree of cylinder wear must be determined. When the car has covered about 20,000 miles the cylinders are generally worn to a perceptible degree. This wear takes two forms; the cylinders become oval, and are also worn more at the top than at the bottom of the bores, i.e., they become tapered.

The cause of the first type of wear is easily understood, since the piston exerts a thrust against the side of the cylinder on the power stroke, resulting in this side of the bore being worn to a greater extent than the other. The fact that the cylinder is worn to a greater extent at the top than at the bottom, and that this wear is greatest over the first third of the distance travelled by the piston rings, is more difficult to explain.

As the gudgeon pin is often a tight fit in the piston, even when the parts are worn, an inexpensive extracting tool similar to that shown in Fig. 22 should be used to remove it. To attempt to drive it out generally entails the risk of distorting the piston or connecting rod or both. Similarly, the piston rings are easily broken if an attempt is made to remove them by makeshift methods. A ring-expanding tool is not expensive, and it is essential when dealing with the latest types of high-pressure rings.

Piston Ring Wear. After the pistons and rings have been cleaned, the rings should be checked for fit in their grooves, as excessive vertical clearance will allow the rings to pump oil up to the combustion chamber. Usually a clearance of from $1\frac{1}{2}$–3 thousandths of an inch is specified for the upper compression rings, and from 1–2 thousandths for lower compression and oil control rings. The correct clearance, however, depends on the type of ring.

Wear on Cylinder Walls. Before any decision is made regarding the piston

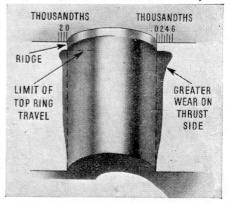

FIG. 25. *Diagram showing how a cylinder bore wears due to corrosion of the cylinder wall and the thrust of the piston. The greatest amount of wear takes place at the upper end of the cylinder bore.*

Among the factors responsible are the comparative lack of lubrication of the area swept by the piston rings; the leakage of hot gases past the upper compression ring, which is accentuated by ring flutter or chattering; and corrosion of the bore due to the deposition of moisture, containing acids from the products of combustion, as the engine cools down. The latter theory has a sound scientific basis as the main cause of upper cylinder wear. It has been found that railway lines in tunnels wear out three times more quickly than those in the open air, due to the corrosion caused by the smoke fumes.

The uneven wear of the cylinder bore renders it impossible to restore compression and normal oil consumption simply by fitting oversize piston rings

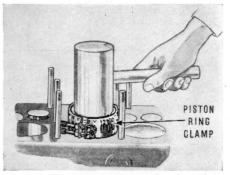
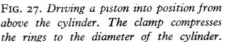

FIG. 27. *Driving a piston into position from above the cylinder. The clamp compresses the rings to the diameter of the cylinder.*

if the wear has exceeded a certain figure. New, standard-size, compression and oil control rings will give satisfactory results if oval or taper wear does not exceed about 2–3 thousandths of an inch. If the wear exceeds these figures, several special types of piston ring are available which will compensate for ovality up to about 15 thousandths of an inch, and taper wear in the region of 7 thousandths. When the wear exceeds these limits, the cylinders should be rebored and fitted with a set of oversize pistons and rings.

Measuring cylinder wear. Accurate measurements of the cylinders calls for the use of a special type of micrometer, but a fairly good idea of the amount of wear can be obtained by measuring the clearance between the piston and the cylinder wall, with long tapering feeler gauges which are sold for this purpose. First measure the clearance at the top of the bore, in line with the gudgeon pin; this will be the point of least wear. Then measure at right angles to the gudgeon pin, on the thrust side, where wear is greatest. The difference will indicate the amount of ovality. Measurements at the bottom of the bore can now be made, and compared with those at the top to ascertain the amount of taper. Another method of assessing taper wear is to

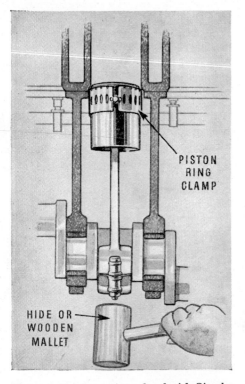

FIG. 26. *Driving a piston fitted with Simplex rings into position from below the cylinder.*

measure the gap in a piston ring at the top and at the bottom of the bore, and to divide the difference between the two measurements by three. When using either method, remember that wear of the piston or the ring itself will contribute to the figure obtained, although the greater part of the wear takes place in the cylinder wall.

Oversize Rings. When it is proposed to fit oversize rings to moderately worn bores, it is essential that the pistons should be placed in expert hands for machining, since successful results depend on the correct clearances of the piston rings, while in some cases oil drainage holes must be drilled in one or more of the grooves. When a set of special rings is purchased, such as Wellworthy Simplex or Cord rings, to quote two well-known examples, it is possible to have the pistons machined and the rings fitted to them for a very moderate charge.

Removing the Ridge. Before the pistons can be refitted to the cylinders, the ridge at the top of the cylinder bore, which forms at the upper limit of the travel of the top compression ring, must be removed. Otherwise the oversize ring will strike the ridge, causing an audible tap, and the ring will probably fracture. Service stations use a special cutter to remove the ridge, but the owner who is carrying out the work himself must resort to careful use of a scraper, until the ridge

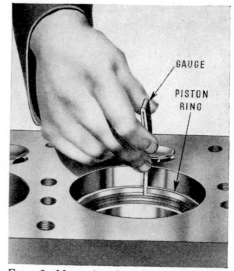

FIG. 28. *Measuring the gap of a piston ring which is resting on an inverted piston to keep it square in the bore of the cylinder.*

is removed and the surface is just flush with the worn portion of the bore.

The next important step is to ensure that the correct gap exists between the ends of the piston rings when inserted in the cylinder. When the bore is worn the gap must be measured with the ring at the lowest point of its travel; it should be pushed down the bore with a piston in order to keep it square. The gap recommended by the manufacturers of the ring should be adhered to. As a general rule, about 2 thousandths for each inch of the cylinder diameter is

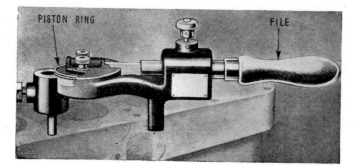

FIG. 29. *A jig used for filing the ends of a piston ring to obtain the correct clearance, i.e. after measuring the gap, see FIG. 28. The movement of the file is guided to ensure that the gap is parallel.*

TOOL BIT SHARPENER

BORING BAR

¼ — ½ H.P.
ELECTRIC
MOTOR

ANCHOR CLAMP

FIG. 30. PORTABLE BORING BAR. *The electrically operated boring bar illustrated here enables worn cylinders to be rebored without removing the engine from its mounting in the chassis.*

about right, although air-cooled engines require twice this gap.

If the gap is too small, the ends of the ring must be filed to give the correct clearance. Simple jigs are available which enable the filing to be done accurately. A typical example is illustrated in Fig. 29.

When reassembling the pistons and connecting rods, the gudgeon pin should be inserted by using a tool of the type already described, rather than driving it into place. Similarly, the piston rings should be expanded with a properly designed tool. They should then be compressed into their grooves with an adjustable clamp so that there is no risk of

fracturing them as the piston is inserted in the cylinder. The rings should be so arranged that the gaps are equally spaced around the circumference of the piston; two gaps in line with one another will afford a leakage path for gas.

The rings, piston and cylinder should be lubricated with engine oil, and the piston crown or skirt, depending on whether the piston is fitted from below or above, should be squarely alined with the bore. It may be necessary to tap the connecting rod or the piston crown lightly with the handle of a hammer to push the rings through the clamp, but once they have entered the bore they should slide freely. If the piston appears to jam, it is probable that one or more rings has sprung out of its groove and is wedged on the land. This will lead to fracture of the ring and scoring of the bore if the piston is forced into the cylinder.

REBORING THE CYLINDERS

When the degree of cylinder wear calls for a rebore, the work will, of course, be beyond the scope of the average owner. Three courses are open to him; to have the engine stripped completely, and the cylinders rebored or ground oversize in a rigid machine tool; to strip the engine himself, if the necessary tackle is available to lift it from the chassis, and to send the cylinder block and crankcase assembly away, for reboring; or to have the work carried out while the engine is installed in the chassis, by means of a portable boring machine.

The choice will naturally depend on individual circumstances. Undoubtedly the best work is performed by a rigid machine, to which the dismantled cylinder block can be firmly clamped. Many garages, on the other hand, produce satisfactory bores by the use of portable machines, which work to a high degree of accuracy. Provided that adequate precautions are taken to clean all foreign matter from the crankcase, rebores "in situ" combine efficiency with economy.

If the engine has already been rebored one or more times, the degree of wear may be such that a further rebore is impossible, due to too little thickness of

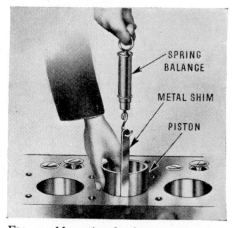

FIG. 32. *Measuring the clearance of a piston in a rebored cylinder. The spring balance measures the effort required to pull the shim.*

metal remaining in the cylinder walls. The remedy in this case is to have the cylinders bored out to accommodate a set of steel liners, which are honed after fitting to the original size of the cylinders when new. This gives the engine a very long lease of life, since the steel liners have better wearing qualities than the original cast iron bores.

Honing the Bores. On modern engines on which piston rings which exert a high pressure on the cylinder walls are used, it is essential to hone the bores after reboring. Worn cylinders cannot be satisfactorily reconditioned by the use of a honing tool alone, as this will follow the contours of the worn cylinder and produce a bore which is not at right-angles to the crankshaft. A light honing operation after the bores have been trued up by boring, however, is an advantage, as it provides a better working surface.

CONNECTING ROD AND MAIN BEARINGS

The life of the connecting rod and crankshaft bearings of the modern car is from four to five times as long as that of the bearings fitted to cars some years ago.

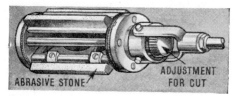

FIG. 31. *A hone used to remove the boring or grinding marks in the cylinders after they have been rebored.*

If the advice regarding lubrication given in Chapter 5 is followed, the main and connecting rod bearings should show very little wear even after a considerable mileage. The connecting rod bearings lead a more exacting life, and wear rather more quickly than the main bearings, it is true, but they seldom give trouble nowadays.

When attention is required, it may be due either to general accumulation of wear, as evidenced by low oil pressure and possibly a clatter when the engine is speeded up without load, or may be the result of one connecting rod bearing failing due to oil starvation, usually as the result of blockage of the oil passage which supplies it.

Whenever the connecting rods and pistons are removed, the bearings should be examined carefully for signs of cracking or flaking. The fitting of replacement bearings or rods at this stage will prevent a more expensive failure subsequently. At the same time, the crankpins should be checked for ovality, i.e. if a micrometer is available; in any case, signs of scoring or ridges should not be disregarded, or they will take their toll in the near future.

FIG. 33. *The condition of various engine and rear axle components as a result of insufficient lubrication. Of particular interest here are the connecting rod big-end bearing, piston and bearing shells.*

Types of Bearing. The amount of work which can be undertaken by the average owner to rectify the trouble depends on several factors. In the first place, the design of the bearing must be taken into consideration. Three types are in use. The first consists of separate brass bearing shells lined with white metal, which are fitted to the connecting rod and cap. Alternatively, the white metal may be cast directly into the connecting rod and cap. The third arrangement is the most recent, and consists of thin steel bearing shells, faced with white metal, which are fitted to the rod and cap. The main bearings in which the crankshaft rotates may similarly be one of the three types described. Sometimes, however, ball or roller bearings are used, although these are not very common today.

Renewing Bearings. The thin-shell bearing is the simplest proposition for the owner, since replacement shells can be fitted to the connecting rods without the necessity for any filing of the caps or scraping of the bearing metal, and the engine may be run at normal speeds immediately.

The directly-metalled type should be renewed by returning the connecting rods containing the defective bearings to the manufacturer or agent, in exchange for remetalled rods. These bearings are accurately bored to size, and are assembled without fitting, so that the work is fairly straightforward.

The earlier types of bearing, whether directly-metalled or fitted with detachable shells, often need fitting to the journals after the bearings have been remetalled. Sometimes a number of thin metal shims are placed between the two halves of the bearing. By removing the requisite number of shims, the diameter of the bearing can be decreased to give the required fit. If shims are not fitted, the bearing cap must be carefully filed or rubbed down with emery cloth to take up any excessive clearance. This process naturally destroys the true circularity of the white metal linings, so that they have to be carefully scraped to ensure that they bed evenly over the surface of the crankpin or journal.

This calls for skill and experience, and is best left in expert hands. An incorrectly fitted bearing will fail again after a comparatively small mileage.

Hand fitting, moreover, should be adopted only when absolutely essential. A more effective and lasting result will be obtained if the remetalled bearings are accurately bored to size.

Renewing Main Bearings. This is, in fact, the only reliable method of dealing with the main bearings, as perfect alinement can be assured, so that main bearing replacements are beyond the scope of the owner unless the thin-shell type of bearing is fitted. The upper halves of main bearings of this type are removed by fitting a split pin in the oil hole of the crankpin, as shown in Fig. 34, and rotating the crankshaft so that the bearing is pushed round until it is free. The new bearing shell is fitted in a similar manner. Each bearing should, of course, be dealt with in turn, while the crankshaft is held in place by the other bearings.

Bearing Clearances. Connecting rod bearings are given fairly generous clearances nowadays, a radial clearance of two thousandths of an inch being common, while the end-float is usually from three to five thousandths. This end-float, or clearance between the bearing and the sides of the crankpin, is an important factor in controlling oil consumption and pressure. The end-float of the crankshaft, which is generally controlled by the rear main bearing, exercises a similar influence on oil pressure, while wear of the front or rear bearings will cause oil leakage.

Crankshaft Condition. Attention should not be concentrated solely on the bearings, however. The condition of the crankpins and journals is a vital factor. If the engine has seen considerable service, these will be worn oval, to a considerable extent in the case of the crankpins, and to a lesser degree where the journals are concerned.

To fit new bearings to journals in this state is a waste of time. The crankshaft journals should be reground, and undersize bearings fitted.

If only one connecting rod bearing has failed, it is essential to clean out the oilways in the crankshaft in order to remove the cause of oil starvation. The remaining connecting rods should, therefore, be removed, and air or oil should be forced through the main oil supply pipe under high pressure. Sometimes even this treatment fails to dislodge the obstruction, and it is necessary to pass a drill through the passages. When plugs are fitted to the oilways, these should be removed so that the passages may be thoroughly cleaned. Neglect to take these precautions will lead to a succession of bearing failures.

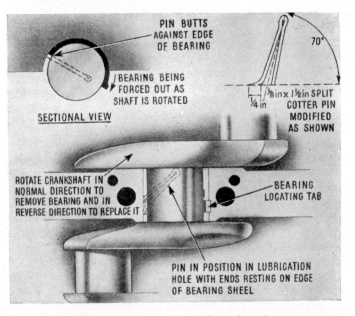

FIG. 34. *This diagram shows a very simple method of removing or replacing the main upper bearing shells with the crankshaft in position.*

TIMING THE ENGINE

When the time comes to reassemble the engine, the method of obtaining the correct valve and ignition timing often baffles the novice. Retiming an engine should not present any difficulty, however, if the principles are understood.

Fig. 36 shows a typical valve timing diagram of a modern engine. From the description of the four stroke cycle in Chapter I, it might reasonably be assumed that the inlet valve should open at the beginning of the inlet stroke, when

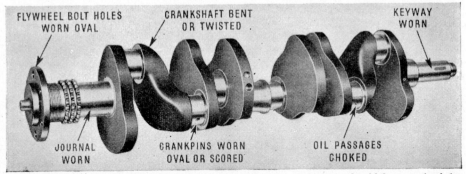

FIG. 35. CRANKSHAFT DEFECTS. *After removing the crankshaft it should be examined for the defects indicated above. If one or more of these faults exist, then the crankshaft should be removed and reconditioned or replaced.*

189

the piston is at the top of the cylinder or at top dead-centre, and close at bottom dead-centre; while the exhaust valve should open at bottom dead-centre, at the beginning of the exhaust stroke, and close at top dead-centre. As will be seen from the diagram, however, the actual opening and closing points differ from what might be expected.

Overlapped Timing. It will be observed that at top dead-centre both the inlet and exhaust valve are open simultaneously; this is termed "overlapped" timing, and is a feature of most modern engines. One object is to ensure thorough scavenging of the exhaust gases from the cylinder. By closing the exhaust valve after the piston has reached top dead-centre and is on its way down in the cylinder, full advantage can be taken of the extractive effect of the rapidly moving column of gas in the exhaust manifold, which tends to suck any remaining burnt gas out of the combustion chamber. By opening the inlet valve early, a charge of fresh mixture is drawn in to replace the burnt gas, and the inlet valve is, moreover, fairly well off its seat by the time that the suction exerted by the downward moving piston begins to take effect.

Inertia Filling. Similarly, at the end of the inlet stroke the inlet valve can be left open for as much as 51 degrees of crankshaft rotation although the piston is now moving up on the compression stroke, since the inertia of the gas in the inlet manifold will maintain the flow into the cylinder although suction has ceased.

This inertia filling, as it is termed, provides a valuable additional charge of mixture.

The reason for opening the exhaust valve 51 degrees before the end of the power stroke is explained by the fact that very little extra work can be obtained from the expanding gases when the piston is near the bottom of the cylinder.

The exhaust gas is, therefore, allowed to escape, so that there will be less to scavenge at the top of the exhaust stroke. Early opening of a valve is termed lead, and late closing is called lag.

Correct Timing. With a clear idea of the principles of valve timing, it should be a simple matter to reconnect the timing chain or to mesh the timing gears correctly. When dealing with the removal of timing chains and camshafts earlier in this chapter the importance of noting any timing marks was stressed. Sometimes punch dots or lines on the teeth of the camshaft and crankshaft sprockets must be opposite one another, or the teeth of gears are similarly marked. Another arrangement is to bring a marked tooth on the camshaft wheel opposite a line on the timing case when the crankshaft is turned so that No. 1 cylinder is at top dead-centre.

In most cases the engine flywheel is marked to indicate top dead-centre of No. 1 piston, the mark being visible through an inspection aperture. Sometimes the letters I.O. or E.O. also appear, indicating the opening point for inlet and exhaust valves respectively. It is then a simple matter to rotate the camshaft until a feeler gauge $1\frac{1}{2}$ thousandths of an inch thick, or a sheet of thin paper, is just gripped between the tappet or rocker and the valve stem, and to connect up the timing chain or mesh the gears.

Sometimes the design of the cam provides such a gradual opening that the exact point at which the valve begins to lift is difficult to judge. Timing is then carried out when one valve, generally the exhaust, is at the highest point of its lift, the flywheel being marked with the letters E.P., denoting exhaust peak. A further point is that for timing purposes the valve clearance must sometimes be set to a figure about 20–25 per cent greater than normal. If the timing chain will not engage with the sprocket or the gears will

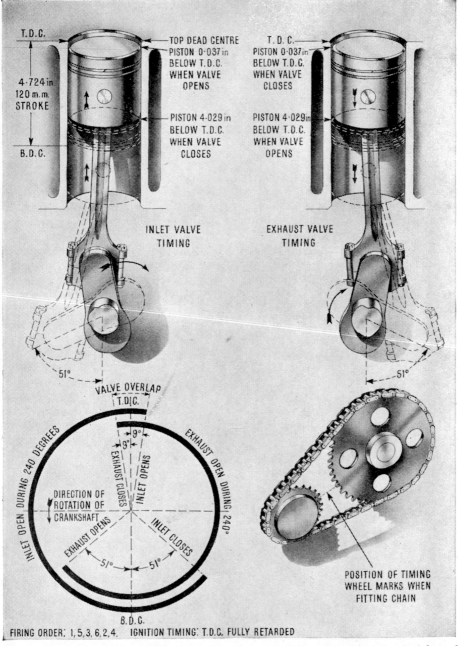

T.D.C.

4·724 in
120 m.m.
STROKE

B.D.C.

TOP DEAD CENTRE
PISTON 0·037 in
BELOW T.D.C.
WHEN VALVE
OPENS

PISTON 4·029 in
BELOW T.D.C.
WHEN VALVE
CLOSES

INLET VALVE
TIMING

T.D.C.
PISTON 0·037 in
BELOW T.D.C.
WHEN VALVE
CLOSES

PISTON 4·029 in
BELOW T.D.C.
WHEN VALVE
OPENS

EXHAUST VALVE
TIMING

51°

51°

VALVE OVERLAP

T.D.C.

INLET OPEN DURING 240 DEGREES

EXHAUST OPEN DURING 240°

9°
9°

EXHAUST CLOSES
INLET OPENS

DIRECTION OF
ROTATION OF
CRANKSHAFT

EXHAUST OPENS
INLET CLOSES

51°
51°

B.D.C.

POSITION OF TIMING
WHEEL MARKS WHEN
FITTING CHAIN

FIRING ORDER: 1, 5, 3, 6, 2, 4.   IGNITION TIMING: T.D.C. FULLY RETARDED

FIG. 36. TIMING THE VALVES. *The upper views show typical dimensions for timing the inlet and exhaust valves; the specific dimensions are usually given by the manufacturer. The lower right-hand view illustrates the alinement of the timing marks on the camshaft and crankshaft wheels.*

191

not mesh when the flywheel marks are alined correctly, a fresh attempt should be made with the tappets set to the wider clearance.

Simple Method of Timing. When the correct timing is not known, it is still possible to time the engine by rule of thumb methods. Bring a pair of pistons to top dead-centre, and rotate the camshaft until the valves of one cylinder are off their seatings by the same amount. From the explanation of valve overlap, it will be appreciated that the piston in this cylinder, which we can take for example to be No. 4, will now be at the end of the exhaust stroke, and the beginning of the inlet stroke. It follows that the other piston of the pair, which will be No. 1 on a four cylinder engine, will be at top dead-centre at the beginning of the power stroke, both valves being closed.

The timing chain should now slip over the sprockets, or the gears should mesh without difficulty. If a slight movement of the camshaft is necessary, this simply means that the amount of overlap in the inlet and exhaust valves is not equal. The difference, however, is rarely so great as to call for rotation of the camshaft or gear to the extent of a whole tooth.

On some engines the camshaft wheel is driven by two dowels for which two alternative pairs of holes are provided, thus allowing the timing of the wheel to be varied to the extent of half a tooth.

Timing the Ignition. The next step is to arrange the ignition timing to suit. When the distributor shaft is driven by a skew gear from the camshaft, it should be engaged so that the rotor will be pointing towards the electrode in the cap connected to the sparking plug lead serving the cylinder which is at the beginning of the power stroke. Remember that the rotor will rotate slightly as the gears slide into mesh, and allow for this movement. If the distributor is driven from the dynamo, engage the chain with the dynamo driving sprocket when the rotor is in the correct position.

The distributor points should now be just about to break, and the timing will thus be at top dead-centre, which is an average setting for many engines when a centrifugal advance

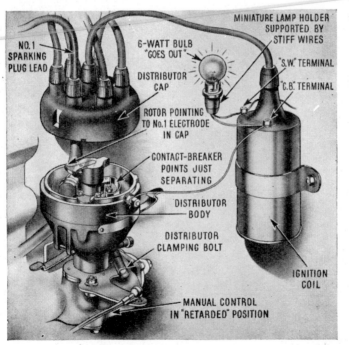

NO.1 SPARKING PLUG LEAD

6-WATT BULB "GOES OUT"

DISTRIBUTOR CAP

ROTOR POINTING TO No.1 ELECTRODE IN CAP

CONTACT-BREAKER POINTS JUST SEPARATING

DISTRIBUTOR BODY

DISTRIBUTOR CLAMPING BOLT

MANUAL CONTROL IN "RETARDED" POSITION

MINIATURE LAMP HOLDER SUPPORTED BY STIFF WIRES

"S.W." TERMINAL

"C.B." TERMINAL

IGNITION COIL

FIG. 37. *A method of checking the point at which the contacts open when adjusting the ignition timing, i.e. after retiming the valves.*

mechanism is embodied in the distributor. If the points are not breaking, or are fully open, slacken the clamping bolt in the clip which secures the distributor, and rotate the body in one direction or the other until the correct position is obtained. A simple method of checking the exact point at which the contacts open is shown in Fig. 37.

With this basic setting to start from, the best ignition timing can be found as a result of road tests. In the interests of economy and performance, the maximum degree of advance should be used which does not cause pinking when the engine is pulling hard at low speeds. Rotating the distributor body in the opposite direction to that in which the rotor turns will advance the ignition, while the timing will be retarded if the distributor is turned in the same direction as the rotor.

COOLING SYSTEM

Provided that the water level in the radiator header tank is maintained at the correct height, and that the system is occasionally drained to remove any accumulation of sediment, the cooling system should seldom give trouble. Faults which do occur can be classified under three main headings; leakage, freezing, and overheating. Freezing troubles are fully covered under "Winter Precautions" in Chapter 5.

Leaks can sometimes prove difficult to cure. When leakage occurs around the junctions of rubber hoses, tightening of the hose clip may be all that is required. Sometimes this aggravates the trouble, however, due to the clip not being truly concentric. The remedy is to fit a clip of the "Jubilee" type, and to tighten it just sufficiently to prevent leakage.

In time the hoses become perished, and it is a wise precaution to renew them whenever the engine is decarbonized, even if the rubber is not damaged during removal. Do not use jointing compound when fitting the hose. A thin coating of soft soap will enable it to be eased into place. When the cooling system is pressurised the hoses must be in good condition. A further point to be watched with this type of system is that the radiator filler cap must be unscrewed carefully to relieve the pressure before removal.

Curing Radiator Leaks. Minor leaks from the radiator itself are difficult to repair, since modern types of radiator block do not lend themselves to simple repair by soldering, as did the earlier true honeycomb type. Leakage can, however, be cured in most cases by the use of one of the many proprietary sealing compounds which are available. This is poured into the radiator when the water is hot, and the engine is allowed to tick over for a few minutes to circulate the mixture. The leak will gradually diminish, as the compound comes into contact with the air, and will finally cease, providing a more or less permanent repair.

In this connexion it is worth remembering that even a serious leakage caused by a cracked cylinder block can be cured by the use of a special compound which is poured into the upper water connexion on the cylinder head when the hose has been disconnected. Experience has shown that the compound will provide a lasting repair, saving the expense of dismantling the block and welding the crack.

Causes of Overheating. When overheating is experienced, look for any faults which may restrict the circulation of the cooling water. Likely causes are a perished water hose, from the interior lining of which small sections have become partly detached, so that they obstruct the water flow; a weak hose between the radiator and the water pump intake, which collapses under the influence of the suction of the pump at high engine speeds, although it may appear serviceable on casual inspection; a slip-

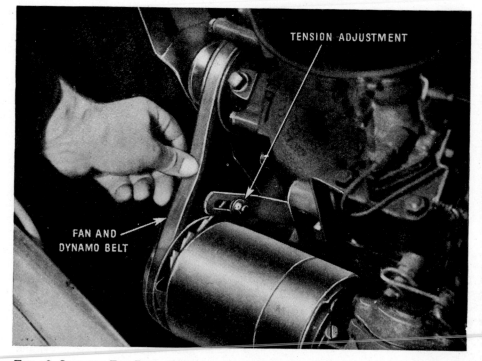

TENSION ADJUSTMENT

FAN AND
DYNAMO BELT

FIG. 38. SLIPPING FAN BELT. *This view shows the tension of the fan and dynamo belt being tested. Should it be slack the belt will slip, and may be responsible for overheating the engine: in some designs the belt not only drives the fan but also the water pump.*

ping fan belt, particularly if this also drives a water pump; and general restriction of the water passages due to an accumulation of sediment and fur which is deposited when hard water is used for topping up the radiator.

Preventing Corrosion. On many modern engines high-velocity jets of cool water are sprayed around the exhaust valve seats and the sparking plug bosses inside the cylinder head by a perforated tube which passes down the centre of the water space, or by suitably placed nozzles. As any restriction of these relatively small orifices will affect the efficiency of the engine, the manufacturers often recommend that a corrosion inhibitor, in the form of a soluble oil which forms an emulsion with the water, should be added to the cooling system.

Thermostats. Among other causes of overheating are a defective thermostat, which fails to open when the temperature of the water in the cylinder block rises, and an inefficient water pump. Thermostats can seldom be repaired; the usual course is to replace them. It is often possible to detach the water pump from the engine, however, and to dismantle it without any great difficulty, as it is a comparatively simple affair. Reconditioning is usually limited to the replacement of worn or corroded parts, such as the impellor, spindle, bearing and gland. Sometimes the pump case itself is so badly corroded that renewal is necessary.

Overheating is not invariably due to cooling system faults; a number of the engine faults dealt with in Chapter 5 will cause or contribute to the trouble.

CHAPTER 7

ELECTRICAL EQUIPMENT

THE electrical equipment—battery, generator, starter motor, accessories and ignition system—will operate for long periods without trouble if routine maintenance is systematically carried out. The fact that, in practice, electrical and ignition faults account for a high percentage of roadside breakdowns and cases of difficult starting can usually be attributed to neglect or incorrect servicing.

THE BATTERY

A new battery is an expensive item in the motoring budget, yet all too often the life of this vital component is unnecessarily shortened by under- or overcharging, or failure to top-up the cells at regular intervals. Since the modern battery will usually have a life of two or three years even under conditions that are far from ideal, it is not surprising that many owners tend to take it for granted. Yet here is a case in which careful maintenance pays very real dividends.

The lead-acid storage battery is an electro-chemical device for converting chemical energy into electrical energy. Active materials within the battery react chemically to produce a flow of direct current whenever an electrical device is connected to the battery terminal posts. The amount of electrical power the battery can produce is limited; the active materials are, in effect, "used up" as the battery becomes discharged. The battery must then be recharged by connecting it to a flow of direct current from an external source. This reverses the discharge reaction and restores the materials to an active condition.

The battery provides a source of current to the electric motor for starting the engine, acts as a stabilizer to the voltage in the electrical system, and can for a limited time furnish current when the electrical demands of the vehicle exceed the output of the generator.

Battery Construction. In a 6-volt car battery (Fig. 1) there are three compartments or cells, whereas a 12-volt battery has six cells. Each cell supplies approximately 2 volts. The cells are connected in series to provide a total of 6 or 12 volts (depending on the number of cells) at the battery terminal posts.

Each cell contains an "element" composed of negative plates, positive plates, separators (one on each side of each positive plate) and two plate straps. One strap connects together all negative plates and the other the positive plates.

The plates are made by applying special lead-oxide pastes to rectangular grids which are cast from an alloy of lead and antimony. The grid has the important additional function of distributing current uniformly over the plate during charging and discharging. The pastes, after processing, are converted to active materials in the completed battery.

When the battery is in a fully-charged condition, the positive plates contain essentially pure chocolate-brown lead peroxide and the negative plates consist of grey spongy lead. The electrolyte is a solution of sulphuric acid in water.

During discharge, the active materials in the positive and negative plates react

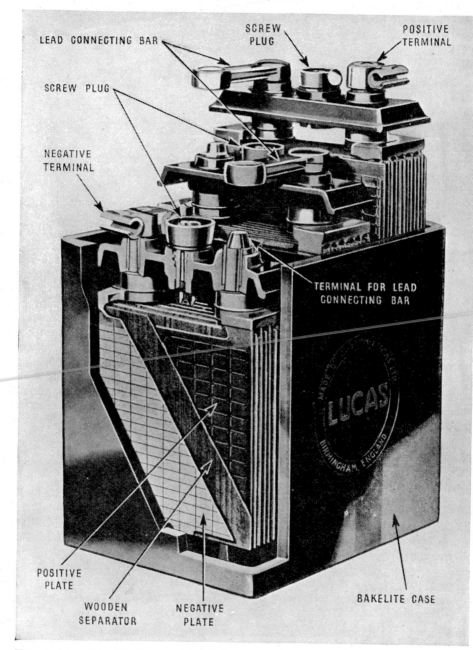

FIG. 1. LEAD-ACID BATTERY. *A 6-volt battery partly dismantled and with the case cut away to show the internal construction. The groups of positive and negative plates are connected by lead bars that may be sunk beneath the surface of the cell-top insulators instead of being visible as illustrated.*

chemically with the sulphuric acid. Some sulphate from the acid enters the positive plate and replaces the oxygen, while other sulphate also combines with the spongy lead in the negative plate. The displaced oxygen leaves the positive plate and combines with the hydrogen from the acid to form water. Thus, in both plates, lead sulphate is formed while the acid in the electrolyte is replaced with water.

During the charging process the chemical actions are reversed. The sulphate leaves both the negative and positive plates to recombine with the hydrogen in the water. The oxygen displaced by this process re-enters the positive plate where it combines with the lead to form, once again, lead peroxide. The material in the negative plate again becomes spongy metallic lead.

Hydrometer Tests. A battery hydrometer should be used to test the specific gravity of the electrolyte in each of the battery cells, as shown in Fig. 2. The hydrometer should be held vertically and too much electrolyte should not be drawn up. The float must be freely suspended in the electrolyte and the reading should be taken at eye level. The stem of the float will protrude from the electrolyte by varying amounts according to the specific gravity of the electrolyte. From the above description of the charging and discharging processes, it will be appreciated that the specific gravity has a direct bearing on the state of charge of the battery.

Specific gravity readings at 60 deg. F. of 1·280 to 1·300 (fully charged) and 1·215 (discharged) can be considered satisfactory, assuming that the battery has not lost electrolyte. A specific gravity below 1·215 must be considered unsatisfactory for continued use and the battery should be restored to a fully-charged condition as soon as possible.

Effect of Temperature. The specific gravity of the electrolyte varies not only with the percentage of the acid in the liquid but also with temperature. As the temperature rises, the electrolyte expands or becomes thinner, so that its specific gravity is reduced. As the temperature falls, the electrolyte contracts or becomes thicker and its specific gravity increases. Unless these variations are taken into account, the hydrometer readings may not give a true indication of the state of charge of the battery.

Correction can be made for temperature by adding two gravity points to the reading for every 5 deg. that the electrolyte is above 60 deg. F. For every 5 deg. that the electrolyte is below 60 deg. F., two gravity points must be subtracted from the gravity reading.

Example 1 : A specific gravity reading of 1·272 is obtained at 80 deg. F. Add 8 gravity points (4 × 2) to get a corrected reading of 1·280. *Example* 2: A specific gravity reading of 1·227 at

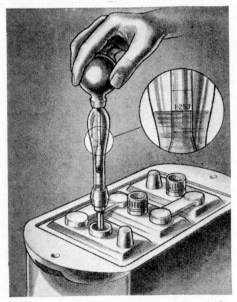

FIG. 2. *Testing the specific gravity of the electrolyte with a hydrometer. The reading is taken on the graduated stem of the float.*

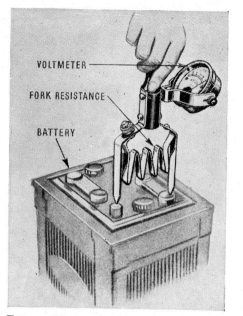

VOLTMETER

FORK RESISTANCE

BATTERY

FIG. 3. *Testing the battery with a high-rate-discharge meter which imposes a heavy load on each individual cell.*

freezing temperatures are not encountered, there will be no danger from these lower gravities.

Avoiding Risk of Freezing. The freezing point of the electrolyte depends on its specific gravity. The following table gives the freezing temperature of the battery solution at various specific gravities:

Specific Gravity	Freezing Temp. (Deg. F.)
1·100	18
1·120	13
1·140	8
1·160	1
1·180	− 6
1·200	− 17
1·220	− 31
1·240	− 50

32 deg. F. is corrected by subtracting 12 gravity points (6 approx. × 2) to get a corrected reading of 1·125. In the latter case the battery is discharged. If the temperature is not too far from the 60 deg. F. standard, however, or if only an approximate idea of the specific gravity reading is required, it will not be necessary to make the temperature correction.

In tropical climates, or regions where high temperatures are prevalent, the specific gravity is often adjusted so that it will not increase beyond 1·225 with the battery fully charged. This corresponds to 31 per cent sulphuric acid by weight. Adjustment is made by removing part of the electrolyte and adding water until the desired gravity reading is obtained. The reduced acid concentration prolongs the life of the negative plates and separators and also reduces the rate of self-discharge of the battery. Where

Since freezing may damage the battery beyond repair, it should be protected against freezing during cold weather by being kept in a charged condition.

High-rate Discharge Test. This is a common method of testing the condition of the battery; it should be applied, however, only when the battery is well charged. A high-rate discharge tester (Fig. 3) consists of a voltmeter attached to two sharp-pointed legs bridged by a resistance strip which imposes a heavy load on the cell under test. A cell that is in good condition and fully charged will show a reading of just over 1·75 volts. The reading should be steady. If the needle drops back, the cell is faulty. The test should not be applied, however, for more than 15 to 20 seconds.

It must be remembered that when the battery is at a low temperature, the voltage drops to lower values under high discharge. For example, a warm battery in good condition might show a reading as high as 1·8 volts per cell under a high-rate discharge test, but might record only 1·4 volts per cell at 0 deg. F. on the same test. For this reason, it is recommended that the load test be made with the battery at approximately 60 deg. F.

If the high-rate discharge test shows that there is a variation between cells of more than 0·2 volt, then there is some unbalance between cells which may have resulted from a short-circuited cell, from loss of electrolyte, or from the fact that the battery is wearing out.

Battery Service. Probably the most important battery service of all is the addition of distilled water periodically to prevent the electrolyte level from falling below the tops of the battery plates. If this should happen, the plates and separators will be exposed to air so that they will dry out and be ruined. Periodic addition of water will replace in the cells the water lost by evaporation.

After the battery has been checked with a hydrometer, water should be added if necessary to bring the electrolyte level up to the proper height above the tops of the battery plates. If the battery is not fitted with an acid-level indicator, a battery filler will be found useful for topping-up. This ensures that the correct level is automatically obtained and also prevents distilled water from being spilled on top of the battery. Its use is particularly recommended- on cars where visual examination of the electrolyte level is difficult.

Never use a naked light when examining the condition of the cells because of the risk of a hydrogen explosion.

A "correct acid-level" device is fitted to each cell of recent Lucas batteries. Distilled water should be poured into the flange (not down the central tube) until the electrolyte level reaches the bottom of the central tube, preventing further escape of air displaced by the topping-up water. By lifting the tube

INTERPRETING RESULTS OF TESTS

HYDROMETER TEST

	Condition	Procedure
1. 1·280—1·215	Satisfactory for high-rate discharge test	Make high-rate discharge test
2. Below 1·215	Unsatisfactory for high-rate discharge test	Recharge—make high-rate discharge test
3. More than 25 gravity points (0·025 sp. gr.) variation between cells	a. Shorted cell b. Acid loss c. Worn-out battery	Recharge or adjust gravity. Make high-rate discharge test

HIGH-RATE DISCHARGE TEST
(load = 2 × ampere-hour rating)

4. Voltage below 1·5 volts per cell	a. Discharged b. Worn-out battery	Recharge and test
5. Voltage varies 0·2 volt between cells	Same as 3. Also high internal resistance	Same as 3. Rebuild or replace

slightly, the small amount of water in the flange will drain into the cell and the electrolyte level will be correct.

Overfilling, causing the electrolyte to overflow, is always to be avoided, as it not only means a loss of battery capacity but also results in corrosion of any metal or fabric on to which the electrolyte finds its way. Any such overflow should be sponged with clean water, while a little household ammonia will neutralize the acid and help to prevent corrosion.

Only distilled or demineralized water should be used for topping-up. Use of water with high mineral content tends to shorten battery life, since these minerals remain in the cells as the water evaporates and eventually seriously impair the efficiency of the battery.

The top of the battery should be kept clean and dry. Any dirt on it may be cleaned off with a brush dipped in ammonia or soda solution. The vent plugs should be tightened first to prevent any of the solution from getting into the battery cells, and after foaming ceases the battery should be flushed with clean water.

It is especially important to keep a 12-volt battery clean and dry as the higher voltage increases current leakage and corrosion.

The holding-down clamps should be sufficiently tight to prevent the battery from vibrating in its holder but should not be tightened excessively, as this may warp or break the battery case.

The battery cable clamps should be tight on the battery terminals to maintain a good contact area between the clamps and the terminal posts. The cables should be in good condition, without broken strands or defective insulation. If the terminal posts and cable clamps are corroded they should be disconnected and scraped bright and clean. The cables can then be reconnected and clamps tightened. A coating of petroleum jelly on the cable clamps will help to retard corrosion.

GENERATOR AND CONTROL BOX

Compensated Voltage Control. The dynamo or generator fitted to most modern cars is of the compensated-voltage-control type and operates in conjunction with a regulator housed, together with the cut-out, in the control box.

The regulator controls the generator output according to the load on the battery and its state of charge. When the battery is discharged, the generator gives a high output so that the battery receives a quick recharge which brings it back to its normal state in the minimum possible time. When the battery is fully charged, the generator is arranged to give only a trickle charge which is sufficient to keep it in good condition without the possibility of causing damage by overcharging.

The regulator also causes the generator to give a controlled boosting charge at the beginning of a run. This quickly restores to the battery the energy taken from it when starting. After about 30 minutes' running, the output of the generator will have fallen to a steady rate, best suited to the particular state of charge of the battery.

Normally the regulator gives no trouble and should not be tampered with, as a moving-coil voltmeter is required to set it correctly. Such adjustments should be left to an authorized electrical service station.

The control box shown in Fig. 4 contains two units, a voltage regulator and a cut-out. Although combined structurally, the regulator and cut-out are electrically separate. Both are accurately adjusted during manufacture, and the cover protecting them should not be removed unnecessarily. Cable connexions are secured by grub-screw terminals.

The regulator is set to maintain the generator terminal voltage between close limits at all speeds above the regulating point, the field strength being controlled by the automatic insertion and withdrawal of a resistance in the generator field circuit.

The cut-out is an electro-magnetically operated switch connected in the charging circuit between the generator and the battery. Its function is automatically to connect the generator with the battery when the voltage of the generator is sufficient to charge the battery, and to disconnect it when the generator is not running, or when the voltage falls below that of the battery, and so prevent the battery from discharging through and possibly damaging the generator.

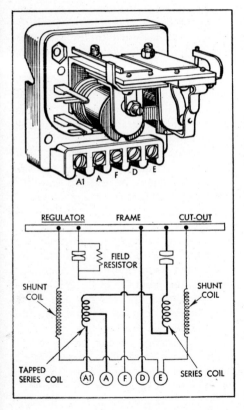

FIG. 4. *The Lucas compensated-voltage-control regulator, combined with a cut-out.*

Current-voltage Control. With the development of higher-output generators to meet increasing electrical loads, the number of series turns wound over the voltage winding to restrict the maximum output of the generator is reduced, and control of maximum output by the regulator becomes less effective. Eventually a stage is reached when the compensated voltage regulator is no longer capable of exerting adequate influence over the generator output, and some other means of control then becomes necessary.

In American 6-volt circuits with their heavier currents, this stage has long been passed, as it has in both 12- and 24-volt circuits for passenger service vehicles in Great Britain.

The solution adopted in such cases (including an increasing proportion of British cars) is to provide two regulators with their contacts in series in the dynamo field circuit, one regulator being shunt-wound and responsive only to voltage and the other being series-wound and responsive only to current. Such a system is known as current-voltage control (see Fig. 5). The voltage regulator is compensated for temperature changes.

Ammeter Readings. When noting ammeter readings, it should be remembered that during daytime running, when the battery is in good condition, the generator gives only a trickle charge so that the charge reading will seldom be more than a few amperes.

A discharge reading may be given immediately after switching on the headlamps. This usually happens after a long run, when the voltage of the battery is high. After a short time, the battery voltage will fall, and the regulator will respond, causing the generator output to balance the load.

When starting from cold, the charging current will rise until it reaches a steady maximum at a speed of about 20 m.p.h.,

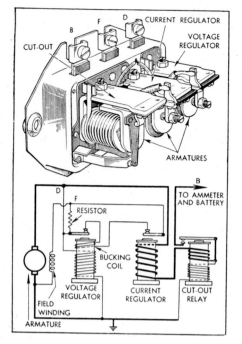

FIG. 5. *Lucas current-voltage control in which two regulators are combined with the cut-out to form one unit.*

rent-voltage control, generator output was regulated by the constant-current or third-brush control system. In addition to the two main brushes, a third and smaller brush is situated between the main brushes. The position of this brush can be altered and the effect of moving it in the direction of rotation of the armature is to increase the output from the generator; conversely, moving the brush in the opposite direction reduces the output. The maximum output should be such that the total load, including the headlamps, is balanced, with one or two amperes indicated on the charging side of the ammeter. The charge reading shown with all lamps and auxiliaries switched off should not exceed 10-15 amp.

Sometimes an additional control resistance was included in the generator field circuit to allow the generator output to be regulated by a switch for "summer" (reduced charge) and "winter" (full charge) settings. When the headlamps are switched on, this resistance is cut out to allow the generator to give its full output irrespective of setting.

Generator Maintenance. A few drops of high-quality medium-viscosity engine oil should be injected into the hole marked OIL at the commutator end of modern generators. This attention is required at about 10,000-mile intervals. With earlier dynamos, unscrew the lubricator cap, lift out the felt pad and spring, and about half-fill the cap with high-melting-point (H.M.P.) grease. Replace the spring and felt pad and screw the lubricator cap in position on the commutator-end bracket.

On generators having metal cover bands fitted over the brushgear, remove the cover band to inspect the brushes and commutator. Check that the brushes move freely in their holders by holding back the brush springs and pulling gently on the flexible connectors. If a brush is

at which value it will remain for about 10 minutes and then fall to a steady charge which is most suitable for the particular state of the battery.

It will be noticed from the ammeter readings that the generator does not charge at very low engine speeds. This is because it is not rotating fast enough to generate sufficient energy to charge the battery. The cut-out, which (as already described) is an automatic switch connected between the dynamo and battery, allows the flow of current from the dynamo to the battery only. It closes when the dynamo is running fast enough to charge the battery, and opens when the speed is low or the engine is stationary, thus preventing current flowing from the battery through the dynamo windings.

Third-brush Regulation. Before the introduction of constant-voltage or cur-

inclined to stick, remove it from its holder and clean its sides with a petrol-moistened cloth. Be careful to replace brushes in their original positions in order to retain their "bedding".

In service, wear of the brushes takes place and the brushes become shorter. If the brushes are permitted to wear down until the embedded ends of the flexible connectors are exposed at the running surfaces, serious damage can occur to the commutator. It is therefore important to renew the brushes from time to time.

Some generators are not fitted with cover bands. The commutator and brush-gear in these units should be checked about every 2 years by a competent automobile electrician.

Occasionally inspect the generator driving belt and adjust, if necessary, to take up any undue slackness by turning the dynamo on its mounting. Care should be taken to avoid over-tightening the belt, which should have sufficient tension only to drive without slipping. See that the machine is properly aligned, otherwise undue strain will be thrown on the generator bearings.

When the car is undergoing a general overhaul, say after about 50,000 miles, it is advisable to have the generator checked by an electrical service station.

Servicing the Generator. At regular intervals, the generator should be inspected to determine its condition. The work is best left to the expert, but a practically-minded owner should be able to tackle it successfully. The frequency with which this should be done will be determined by the type and design of generator as well as the conditions of service under which it is used. High-speed operation, excessive dust or dirt, high temperature, and operation at or near full output most of the time, are all factors which increase bearing, commutator and brush wear. Generally speaking, the smaller units should be inspected at approximately 25,000-mile intervals, although the 50,000-mile period mentioned above will suffice in many cases.

First, inspect the terminals, external connexions and wiring, mounting, pulley and belt. Then remove the cover band (when fitted) so that the commutator, brushes and internal connexions can be inspected. If the commutator is dirty it may be cleaned with a strip of No. oo sandpaper. *Never use emery-cloth to clean the commutator.* Extruded frame generators (Fig. 6) may be inspected through the ample openings in the commutator-end frame.

The sandpaper may be used by holding it against the commutator with a wood

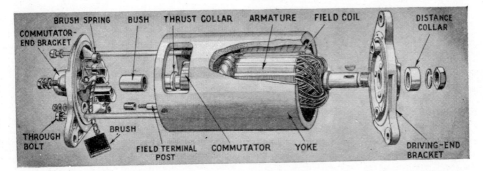

FIG. 6. *Typical modern two-brush generator. This unit requires attention only at comparatively long intervals, as described in the text.*

stick while the generator is in operation, moving it back and forth across the commutator. Glaze and dirt will be removed in a few seconds. All dust should be blown from the generator after the commutator has been cleaned.

If the commutator is rough, out-of-round, or has high mica, the generator must be removed and stripped down so that the armature can be turned down in a lathe and the mica undercut.

If the brushes are worn down to less than half their original length, they should be replaced. Compare the old brush with a new one to determine how much it is worn. New brushes should be seated to make sure that they are in good contact with the commutator. A convenient tool for seating brushes is a brush seating or bedding stone. This is a soft, abrasive material which, when held against a revolving commutator, disintegrates so

that particles are carried under the brushes and wear their contacting faces to the contour of the commutator in a few seconds. Alternatively, a strip of sandpaper can be used as shown in Fig. 7.

The brushes supplied for modern Lucas generators are pre-formed to the correct curvature and do not require bedding.

After replacing brushes on a third-brush generator, the generator output should be checked, since this sometimes causes a change in generator output.

The brush-spring tension must be correct, since excessive tension will cause rapid brush and commutator wear; low tension causes arcing and burning of the brushes and commutator. Consequently, care must be taken not to over-stretch or bend the springs.

If a spring shows evidence of overheating (if it is blued or burnt) do not attempt to readjust it but install a new spring. Overheating will cause a spring to lose its temper.

STARTER MOTOR

There is a great similarity in construction between the starter motor of the average vehicle and the type of generator already described. Each machine has a cylindrical magnet frame, field coils, rotating armature, commutator and brushgear, but the windings of both field assembly and armature are much heavier in the starter motor, illustrated in Figs. 8 and 9. The maintenance required is similar to that for the generator.

The starter motor is mounted in a position adjacent to the flywheel and is generally secured by bolting its flanged end-covers to the engine flywheel housing. It is a common practice to control the starter by means of a flexible steel wire connected to a swivel lever controlling a direct-acting switch fitted on the starter-motor end-cover. The other

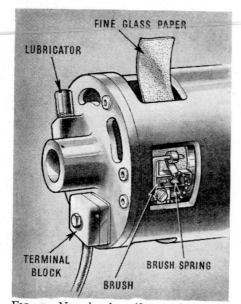

FIG. 7. *New brushes, if not of the pre-formed type, must be bedded to the curvature of the commutator by sliding a strip of fine glass-paper backwards and forwards beneath them.*

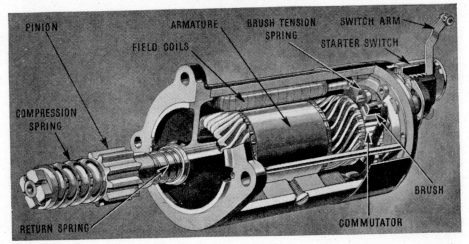

FIG. 8. *Older type of starter motor, cut away to show the armature, field coils, commutator and brushes. The pinion drive is similar to those in* FIG. 9 *but of simpler construction.*

end of the wire is secured to a knob projecting through the dash panel, adjacent to the other controls. An alternative to the direct-acting switch is the electrically controlled solenoid switch also mounted on the starter motor. This is controlled by a small push-in type of switch situated on the instrument panel.

Starter Drives. Most starter-motor drives are of the inertia-engaged type illustrated in Fig. 9. The extended armature spindle is splined, and on these splines slides a sleeve having a very coarse thread corresponding to a similar thread cut on the inner surface of the pinion gear which is loosely fitted on the sleeve. One end of the sleeve abuts against a heavy coil spring or a rubber shock-absorber, while the other end fits closely up to a collar fitted on the end of the spindle and secured by a locknut. Over the collar is a light spring to return the pinion to a position clear of the flywheel when the engine is running.

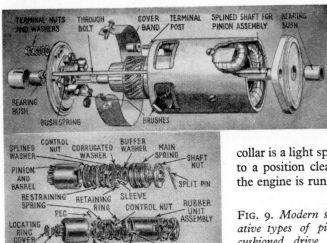

FIG. 9. *Modern starter motor with alternative types of pinion drive. The spring-cushioned drive* (upper), *operates on a similar principle to the rubber-cushioned drive* (lower).

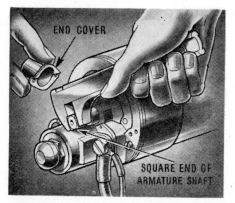

FIG. 10. *A jammed starter-motor pinion can often be freed by rotating the squared end of the shaft as shown.*

As the starter switch is pressed the armature rotates at high speed. The pinion tries to remain stationary, but as the sleeve is rotating, the pinion is screwed into engagement with the flywheel ring until it comes up against the collar, and can move no further. Since the flywheel resists the turning effort the pinion is screwed further along the sleeve which in turn is forced against the heavy spring or the rubber unit, thereby compressing it. The resistance of the spring causes the whole assembly to rotate and turn the flywheel, but because the spring is compressed, the turning effort applied to the flywheel is gradual. The pinion is still in mesh as the engine fires and begins to run on its own power, but the flywheel drives the pinion faster than the armature shaft and the pinion is screwed back out of engagement, where it is held by the light return spring.

Starter Maintenance. The brushes of the starter motor are harder than those used for generators and are not interchangeable. The wear between brushes and commutator is considerable, and periodical inspection of these is recommended. Whenever brushes show signs of wear they should be renewed and bedded in the same way as that adopted

for generators, and the deposits of accumulated dust from the brushes removed.

Failure to engage can often be traced to high resistance set up by dirty or burned switch contacts, loose terminal connexions, corroded battery terminals or a run-down battery.

The screwed sleeve on the starter drive should be kept clean and free from grease to prevent grit fouling the pinion, and the splines may be washed with petrol to ensure freedom of movement of the pinion. The starter drive should be in proper alignment with the flywheel ring. Securing bolts and set-screws must be kept tight. If the pinion and flywheel teeth are badly burred there is danger of the pinion sticking in engagement, and damage to the armature is likely to occur. On rare occasions the starter-motor pinion may become jammed in mesh with the flywheel. The pinion can sometimes be released by putting the gear lever in top-gear position and pushing the car forwards.

Some starters have an extended shaft with a square end over which a spanner can be placed to rotate the shaft, in a clockwise direction in most cases, and so release the pinion from the flywheel (Fig. 10). Access to the square is obtained by pulling off a metal cap at the centre of the commutator-end cover. Broken compression springs are caused by backfiring or engaging the starter drive with the engine running, and in many cases are responsible for noisy starter action.

FUSES

Most cars are fitted with at least two fuses which protect the circuits of the auxiliary accessories (that is, the horn, windscreen wiper, etc.) although on some cars no fuses are fitted.

Where, on many older cars, the fuses are housed under the control-box cover (which can be withdrawn when the spring clip is moved aside) take care to avoid closing the cut-out contacts when removing or replacing the cover, as this may cause damage to the equipment. Should they become accidentally closed when the engine is stationary, promptly and carefully pull them apart.

The fuse marked A1-A2 or AUX protects the accessories which are connected so that they operate irrespective of whether the ignition is on or off.

The fuse marked A3-A4 or AUX IGN protects the accessories which are connected so that they operate only when the ignition is switched on.

Testing Circuits. A test lamp, comprising two lengths of wire, a lampholder and a bulb of similar voltage to that of the system, is used to test circuits for continuity. Connect one end of the test wire to earth and the other end to terminals or cable ends which are live, that is, indirectly connected to the battery. Continuity is shown when a light is obtained.

A blown fuse indicates a short-circuit in the electrical system, and as a fuse often protects more than one circuit, the cause of failure must be located before a new fuse is fitted. To isolate the faulty circuit, disconnect all the cables from the fuse terminal and, with all relative circuits switched on, connect the test lamp between the live side of the fuse and each cable in turn. The circuit giving a bright light is the defective one. Switch off, reconnect the satisfactory circuits, but do not replace the blown fuse or switch on again until the faulty circuit has been dealt with.

Line Fuses. A line fuse, comprising a 35-amp cartridge-type fuse contained in a bayonet holder, is incorporated in the main wiring harness of 1955 and later Vauxhall models. The fuse holder is retained on a clip located under the instrument panel, below the combined instrument assembly. Protection for the following components and their circuits is provided: ignition and oil warning lamps, direction flasher indicator, direction flasher unit and circuits, stop and flasher lamps, fuel gauge, and in addition, on the Cresta model, the heater and cigarette lighter.

To renew this fuse, withdraw the fuse holder from the clip under the instrument panel, grip one end of the holder and rotate the other end anti-clockwise. The two sections of the holder can then be separated and the fuse renewed.

Thermostatic-interrupter. Incorporated in the lighting switch on recent Vauxhall models is a thermostatic-interrupter which protects the entire lighting system and the components which are not covered by the line fuse, with the exception of the ignition system.

It comprises a pair of contacts, one of which is mounted on a bracket attached to the switch body and the other on one end of a bi-metal blade. The other end of the blade is secured to the switch body.

The contacts of the thermostatic-interrupter are connected in series with the lighting and component circuits. In the event of a short-circuit, therefore, an abnormal flow of current will pass through the contacts and heat up the bi-metal blade, causing it to deflect and separate the contacts. After the contacts open, the current flow is broken and the bi-metal blade cools, allowing the contacts to close. The cycle is repeated and as long as the short-circuit exists the contacts will vibrate, thus reducing the current flow. In this manner the wiring and components are protected from overheating and damage.

HEADLAMPS AND FOGLAMPS

The different models of headlamps and foglamps can be grouped into two classes: those lamps which incorporate a "light-unit" consisting of a combined reflector

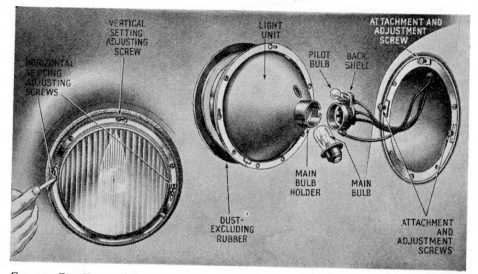

FIG. 11. PRE-FOCUS HEADLAMP UNIT. *On the left is shown the method of aligning the headlamp beam by screwing the adjustment screws inwards or outwards. On the right, the headlamp bulb has been removed from the bulb carrier of the pre-focus unit. In many cases the sidelamp bulb is carried in a separate lamp, and not incorporated in the headlamp unit.*

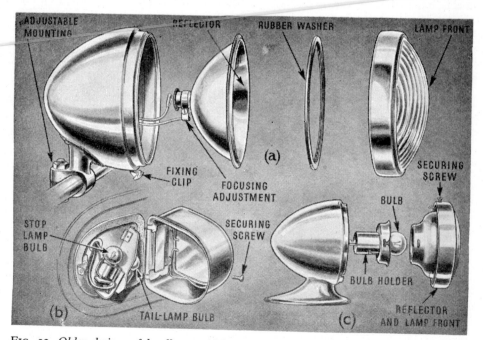

FIG. 12. *Older designs of headlamp, sidelamps and stop and tail-lamp. The bulb carrier on the headlamp can be moved, after slackening the clamp, to allow the lamp to be focused.*

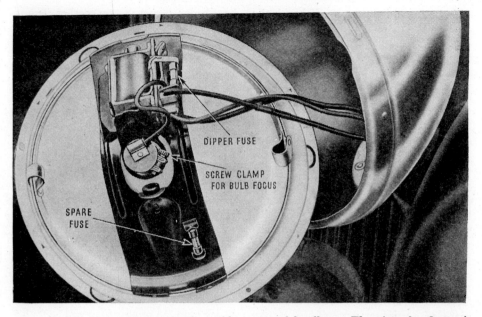

DIPPER FUSE

SCREW CLAMP
FOR BULB FOCUS

SPARE
FUSE

FIG. 13. *Dipping mechanism fitted to older types of headlamp. The pivoted reflector is tilted by the action of the solenoid when energized by the dip switch.*

and front lens assembly and using a special "pre-focus" bulb (Fig. 11); and those in which the bulb is carried in an adjustable bayonet holder (Fig. 12). Lamps of the former pattern may be either flush-fitting or stem-mounted types, while those of the latter type are invariably stem-mounted.

One anti-dazzle arrangement in use in Great Britain is that in which operation of the dip switch extinguishes the off-side headlamp and, at the same time, deflects the near-side headlamp downwards and to the left. This is achieved by the use of a double-filament bulb in the near-side lamp, if of the light-unit type, or by an electrically operated dipping mechanism which moves the reflector (Fig. 13).

Since the introduction of the "block-pattern" lens depicted in Fig. 11, a double-dipping system by which both headlamp beams are deflected downwards and to the left has been adopted

on new vehicles for use in the United Kingdom.

Aligning the Lamps. The Lighting Regulations state that a lighting system must be arranged so that it can give a light which is "incapable of dazzling any person standing on the same horizontal plane as the vehicle at a greater distance than twenty-five feet from the lamp, whose eye-level is not less than three feet six inches above that plane."

The foglamp must be set so that the beam does not rise above the horizontal when the car is standing on level ground. To ensure this, dip the lamp very slightly to compensate for road inequalities or an extra heavy load in the rear of the car, and also tilt the lamp to the right to allow for road camber. In addition, the lamp can be swung slightly to the left in order to give additional illumination on the near-side of the road.

The headlamps must be set so that when the car is normally loaded, the main beams of light are parallel with the road and with each other, as shown in Fig. 14. Check the setting by placing the car in front of a blank wall at the greatest possible distance, taking care that the surface on which the car is standing is not sloping relative to the wall. On external or stem-mounted lamps, slacken the single fixing nut at the base of the lamp and move the lamp on its adjustable mounting to the required position. Then firmly tighten the locknut.

On flush-fitting lamps, remove the front rim by pressing down the catch at the bottom of the lamp or removing the securing screw. Remove the rubber dust excluder (when fitted). Adjust the vertical setting by turning the vertical trim adjustment screw in a clockwise direction to raise the beam, or in an anti-clockwise direction to lower it. Horizontal adjustment of setting is normally a factory operation, and further adjustment should be unnecessary. If, however, the setting

has been disturbed, on earlier lamps slacken the two nuts and move the light unit to the required position, afterwards tightening the nuts. On later lamps the two horizontal adjustment screws should be used.

Focusing. If a lamp is to give the best results, the bulb must be as near as possible to the focal point of the reflector. If the bulb is out of focus, the lamps will have a poor range and will cause dazzle to approaching traffic.

As mentioned above, lamps incorporating a light unit or sealed-beam reflector employ a bulb of special construction which ensures that when the bulb is fitted, the filament is correctly positioned in relation to the reflector, and no focusing is necessary.

When focusing other types of headlamp or foglamp on which the position of the bulb can be altered, it will be found an advantage to cover one lamp while testing the other. If the lamp does not

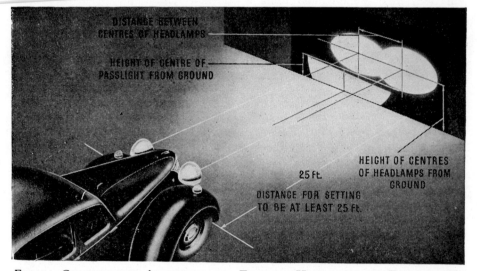

FIG. 14. CHECKING THE ALIGNMENT AND FOCUS OF HEADLAMPS AND FOGLAMP. *The car must be about 25 feet away from a garage door or wall and on a level surface. The centres of the headlamp beams should be at the same height as the lamp centres and spaced the same distance apart. The fog-lamp beam should be deflected slightly downward and to the near side.*

give a uniform long-range beam without any dark centre, the bulb needs adjusting. The position of the bulb must be adjusted until any top light is removed and until the beam of light is of the greatest concentration; that is, the area of the beam must be as small as possible.

DIRECTION INDICATORS

The Lucas Trafficator semaphore indicator, and similar units made by other firms, are to be found on many thousands of cars, although flashing lamps or "winkers" are now adopted on the majority of new models. The following notes refer specifically to the Lucas type, but are applicable to most semaphore indicators.

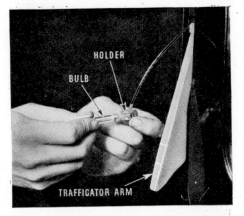

FIG. 16. *Fitting a new bulb in a trafficator. The caps must make good contact with the bulb holder and the underside of the cover.*

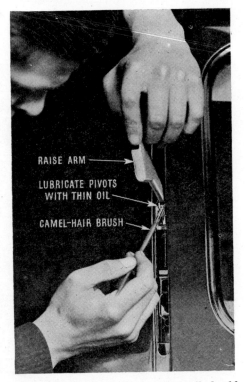

FIG. 15. *A drop of thin machine oil should be applied to the pivot-pin of the trafficator arm by means of a small brush.*

Trafficator Maintenance. Switch on the trafficator, support it in the raised position and switch off. A drop of thin oil, such as sewing-machine oil, should now be applied to the catch pin or the pivot between the arm and the operating mechanism (Fig. 15). Use only the slightest trace, as any excess may cause sluggish operation. Next, withdraw the screw on the underside of the arm and slide off the arm cover. Place the connecting wire to the bulb on one side. If a lubricating pad is seen at the top of the arm, apply a drop of thin machine oil to the pad. To replace the arm cover, slide it in an upwards direction so that the side plates or the locating tongue engage with the slots on the underside of the spindle bearing, and secure the arm cover with the screw.

A new bulb may be fitted by removing the cover as just described (see Fig. 16). Make sure that there is a good contact between the ends of the bulb and the cover and bulb holder.

Flashing Direction Indicators. The Lucas flasher unit is contained in a small cylindrical metal container, one end of which is rolled over on to an insulated plate carrying the mechanism and three terminals. In Fig. 17 the mechanism is shown without its protective cover.

The unit depends for its operation on the linear expansion of a length of wire which becomes heated by an electric current flowing through it. This actuating wire controls the movement of an over-centre spring blade carrying a moving contact. The Magna-Lite unit operates on a similar principle.

When the direction-indicator switch is turned to either left or right, current flows through the actuating wire and current-limiting resistance winding. The control wire grows in length under the heating influence of the current until the spring blade is allowed to snap into its alternative position, thereby closing a pair of contacts on the supply circuit to the light signals and at the same time short-circuiting the actuating wire.

The current passing to the light signals flows through a small coil on the unit base, and the resulting electro-magnetic effect causes movement of an iron core, which closes the circuit to the switch warning lamp, so that now the light signals and the warning lamp are illuminated. Since, however, there is no longer a heating current flowing in the actuating wire, the latter cools down and consequently contracts in length. The spring blade will thus again be deflected, opening the contacts and so extinguishing the light signals and warning lamp, allowing current again to flow through the actuating wire. The direction indicating lamps are thus caused to flash on and off about 80 times per minute.

The control warning lamp serves not only as an indication that the flasher unit is functioning correctly, but also gives warning of bulb failure in any of the direction-indicator lamps—an important feature, as the latter cannot, of course, be seen from the driving seat.

Checking Faulty Operation. If trouble occurs with a flasher system, check the bulbs for broken filaments, and then refer to the wiring diagram (Fig. 17) to check all flasher circuit connexions.

If no fault can be found, switch on the ignition and check with a voltmeter that the flasher unit terminal B is at 12 volts potential with respect to earth. Next, connect together flasher-unit terminals B and L and operate the direction-indicator control. If the flasher lamps now light, the flasher unit is defective and must be replaced.

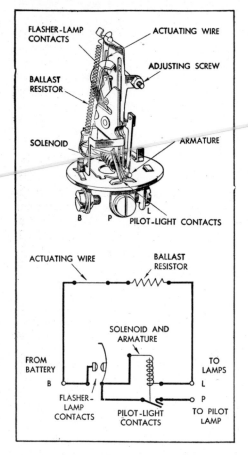

FIG. 17. LUCAS FLASHER UNIT *with outer case removed. The unit is delicate and no attempt should be made to adjust it.*

Flasher units must be handled with care. They are precision devices and the factory-made settings, though entirely satisfactory for normal conditions of service, may be thrown off balance by rough handling or if the unit is dropped.

The flasher unit will operate correctly only if used in conjunction with the lamp load specified on the case of the unit. Use only replacement bulbs of the same wattage as those originally fitted.

The flasher unit is mounted vertically, with its terminals at the bottom, in a position where it will be unaffected by engine vibration or exposure to the weather. This position must not be changed.

WINDSCREEN WIPERS

Electrically operated windscreen wipers require very little attention, as all moving parts are packed with grease on assembly and no adjustments are neces-sary. When a wiper motor unit does fail, in fact, the most economical procedure is to exchange it for a works-recondi-tioned unit.

Similarly, when the wiper is of the type that drives the arms through a flexible cable-rack mechanism, the cable-rack and wheel boxes (shown in Fig. 18) are usually inaccessibly mounted behind the facia panel and their removal may call for expert advice and assistance. If the wipers fail as the result of wear on the cable-rack and driving pinions, the only practicable remedy is to renew the parts.

Fault-tracing, therefore, is confined to ascertaining (1) whether current is reach-ing the motor; (2) whether the motor is running (in which case the fault must be in the drive); and (3), whether the drive is seized or jammed, thus preventing the motor from operating.

In the latter respect it should be borne in mind that some remote-drive wipers

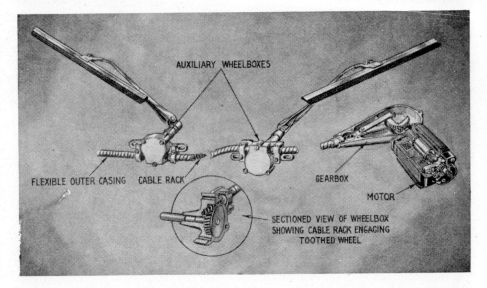

FIG. 18. REMOTE-DRIVE WINDSCREEN WIPER ASSEMBLY. *The motor drives the cable-rack mechanism through reduction gears and a crank that imparts a push-pull motion to the flexible rack. The rack in turn drives pinions in the wheel boxes that are mounted beneath the windscreen. This type of motor may incorporate a thermostatic overload switch to protect the windings if the movement of the wiper blades is obstructed.*

213

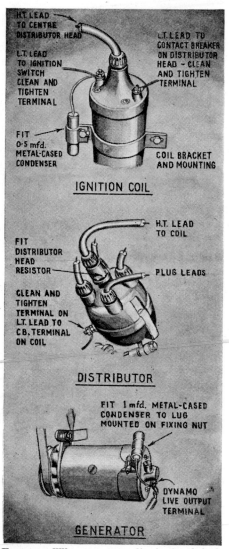

H.T. LEAD TO CENTRE DISTRIBUTOR HEAD

L.T. LEAD TO IGNITION SWITCH CLEAN AND TIGHTEN TERMINAL

L.T. LEAD TO CONTACT BREAKER ON DISTRIBUTOR HEAD – CLEAN AND TIGHTEN TERMINAL

FIT 0·5 mfd. METAL-CASED CONDENSER

COIL BRACKET AND MOUNTING

IGNITION COIL

H.T. LEAD TO COIL

FIT DISTRIBUTOR HEAD RESISTOR

PLUG LEADS

CLEAN AND TIGHTEN TERMINAL ON L.T. LEAD TO C.B. TERMINAL ON COIL

DISTRIBUTOR

FIT 1 mfd. METAL-CASED CONDENSER TO LUG MOUNTED ON FIXING NUT

DYNAMO LIVE OUTPUT TERMINAL

GENERATOR

FIG. 19. *When a car radio is fitted it is necessary to suppress interference at the three points illustrated.*

incorporate a thermostat which cuts off the supply of current to the motor if there is any risk of the windings overheating— as may occur, for example, if the wiper blades are obstructed by packed ice or snow on the windscreen. The motor will operate normally when it has cooled

down, but this may take about 10 minutes. It should not be assumed, therefore, that the motor is necessarily damaged if the wipers do not operate immediately the obstruction to the blades has been removed.

CAR RADIO

Modern car radios are available as compact kits, usually split up into two or three units: the tuning circuits, housed in a case that is designed to fit the dashboard or facia opening provided by the car manufacturer; the power pack, including the vibrator that changes the direct current from the car's electrical supply into alternating current that is supplied to the high-tension transformer; and sometimes a separate loudspeaker unit.

If it is necessary for an owner without previous experience to fit a car radio, the first step should invariably be to get into touch with the manufacturer of the set or his local agent; with the benefit of expert advice, the job should not be too difficult.

It will be necessary, of course, to suppress interference from the ignition equipment and the generator. Most radios incorporate filter circuits that prevent interference from other sources.

Fitting Suppressors. Car manufacturers now fit suppressors to the ignition system of their cars but do not suppress the interference from the coil or generator. With most radio sets two capacitors are provided for this purpose, and Fig. 19 shows how to install them. On the generator the wire should be connected to the brush terminal, never to the field coil. Make certain that the surface to which the capacitor is mounted is free of all paint or grease to ensure good electrical contact. Ensure also that the connecting wire is as short as possible.

If the distributor of the car is not suppressed (many modern distributors incorporate a resistor in the high-tension distributor brush) a suitable screw-in distributor head resistor may be fitted as shown in Fig. 19. On some types of car a screw-in resistor cannot be used and it is necessary to fit a cut-lead type suppressor in the H.T. lead close to the distributor head.

ELECTRIC HORNS

If a horn fails or its note becomes uncertain, first ascertain that the trouble is not due to a discharged battery, or a loose connexion, or short-circuit in the wiring to the horn. A short-circuit in the horn wiring will cause the fuse, if one is fitted, to blow. Check that the horn and any adjacent fixtures are rigidly secured to their mountings, but remember that this mounting should be flexibly attached to the car in order to prevent vibration upsetting the note of the horn.

When two horns are fitted and both fail or become uncertain in action, the trouble is probably due to a blown fuse or a discharged battery. If the fuse has blown, examine the wiring for faults before replacing the fuse.

If, after carrying out these checks, the trouble is not rectified, the horn may need adjustment but this should not be necessary until it has been in service for a long period. Adjustment does not alter the pitch of the note, but merely takes up wear of moving parts. Moreover, for satisfactory results it is preferable to connect an accurate ammeter in the horn circuit and adjust each horn to give the current consumption specified for that particular model by the manufacturer. If the horns do not sound after adjustment, release the push instantly.

When making adjustments to a horn, short-circuit the fuse and always disconnect the supply lead of the other horn, taking care to ensure that it does not come into contact with any part of the chassis or engine.

On Lucas Windtone horns, remove the horn cover, after withdrawing the fixing screw, and detach the cover securing bracket by springing it from its fixing. The two contacts will then be accessible.

Slacken the locknut on the fixed contact and rotate the adjusting nut until the contacts are just separated (indicated by the horn failing to sound). Turn the adjusting nut half a turn in the opposite direction and secure it in this position by tightening the locknut. If the note is still unsatisfactory do not dismantle the horn but return it to a Lucas service depot or service agent for examination.

On Lucas high-frequency horns, adjustment is made by turning the adjusting screw in an anti-clockwise direction until, with the horn push depressed, the horn just fails to sound. Then turn the screw for one-quarter turn (six notches) in a clockwise direction. The screw is usually towards the edge of the rear cover, at about the "seven o'clock" position.

No attempt should be made to alter the adjustment of the diaphragm screw on older types of high-frequency horn. The domed nut that secures the separate tone disk must be kept tight or the note will be altered.

IGNITION SYSTEM

The Ignition Circuit. Referring to Fig. 20, it will be seen that the ignition circuit is divided into two sections: the low-voltage circuit that comprises the ignition switch, the primary winding of the ignition coil, and the contact-breaker; and the high-voltage circuit that includes the secondary windings of the coil, from which the high-voltage current passes to the distributor and the sparking plugs.

The primary winding of the coil, consisting of a few hundred turns, is wound over several thousand turns of fine wire that form the secondary winding; both windings surround a laminated iron core, so that the coil forms a small transformer

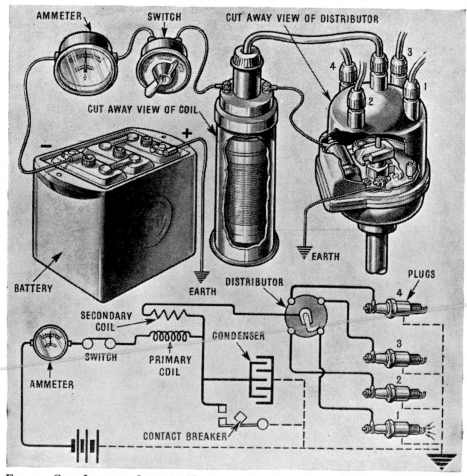

FIG. 20. COIL IGNITION SYSTEM. *The upper view shows in pictorial form the manner in which the components of a coil-ignition system are arranged. The wiring diagram will enable the flow of primary and secondary current to be traced and shows how the four sparking plugs are connected to give the correct firing sequence.*

that steps up the 6-volt or 12-volt battery supply to 20,000 volts, or even 30,000 volts if the coil is of the "sports" or oil-filled type.

The surge of high-voltage current is produced by the building-up and collapse of a magnetic field around the windings of the coil. When the contact-breaker points close, the field builds up rapidly; when they open and the flow of current in the primary winding is interrupted, the field collapses; as the lines of force pass through the windings, a voltage of 250 volts may be induced in the primary winding and, as just described, up to 30,000 volts in the secondary. The latter value is sufficient to cause a spark to bridge the points on a sparking plug. A condenser, connected in parallel with the points, prevents excessive sparking and helps to bring about the collapse of the magnetic field.

The current is carried to the sparking plugs by a rotating arm mounted on the spindle that carries the contact-breaker cam. The rotor is timed to be opposite one of the electrodes connected to the sparking plugs whenever the contact-breaker points separate. The electrodes are connected to the sparking plug leads in the correct sequence to suit the firing order of the engine.

Automatic Ignition Timing. Normally, the contact-breaker is timed so that the points open at the instant that a piston reaches top dead centre on the compression stroke, or a few degrees before top dead centre. A fixed timing, however, would be efficient only at a given engine speed and throttle opening. During test-bed running, in fact, it is usual to establish a series of such timing points and from these to construct a graph that shows the most effective ignition timing over a range of speeds.

To enable this curve to be approximated to, or followed, as closely as possible in practice, an automatic timing mechanism is built into the distributor. The upper part of the distributor spindle that carries the cam is not rigidly attached to the lower part, however, but is connected to it through two levers actuated by spring-restrained centrifugal weights. As the engine speed varies, therefore, the cam is slightly

advanced or retarded in relation to the driven spindle.

To give maximum fuel economy and liveliness, it is desirable to provide a certain amount of over-advance when the engine is running at moderately high speeds at part-throttle openings. This additional degree of advance is provided by a suction-operated diaphragm which is connected by a vacuum pipe to a point just on the atmospheric side of the carburettor throttle valve (Fig. 21).

When the engine speed is relatively high, and the throttle is partly closed, the vacuum-operated diaphragm rotates the contact-breaker base-plate or the distributor body to advance the ignition. At full-throttle openings, however, when over-advance would cause pinking and loss of power, the diaphragm spring retards the ignition. When the engine is

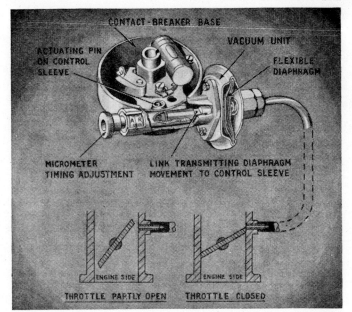

FIG. 21. *Diagrammatic illustration of vacuum-operated ignition-timing unit. The partial vacuum present in the induction manifold draws the diaphragm to the right and advances the ignition by rotating the contact-breaker baseplate.*

idling and the depression in the induction manifold is normally at its highest figure, the intake to the vacuum connexion is masked by the throttle valve, so that the ignition remains fully retarded.

IGNITION MAINTENANCE

To obtain maximum service with minimum trouble, a regular inspection and maintenance procedure should be followed. Periodic lubrication where required, and inspection of the distributor contact points, centrifugal and vacuum advance mechanisms, are essential. In addition, it is advisable to arrange with a service station to check the distributor in a special motor-driven tester at regular intervals so that the action of the contact-breaker and advance mechanism can be checked. The ignition coil and condenser should also be checked on testers designed for the purpose.

Distributor Lubrication. The driving shaft, advance mechanism, breaker cam, breaker plate assembly (rotating types), and breaker lever pivot require periodical lubrication. The shaft is lubricated by a variety of methods: hinge-cap oilers should be filled with S.A.E. 20 oil at each vehicle lubrication period, while grease cups should be turned down one turn every 5,000 miles and refilled with grease as required.

High-pressure grease fittings, on distributors so equipped, should be supplied with grease every 5,000 miles; force lubricant into the fittings until it comes out of the relief hole in a steady stream. Use Delco-Remy Cam and Ball Bearing Lubricant on distributors equipped with ball bearings and No. $2\frac{1}{2}$ grease on others. Repack sealed tachometer or governor drive-gear chambers with graphited grease every 25,000 miles. Gear chambers equipped with grease cups require the addition of one full cup of grease every 5,000 miles.

A trace of petroleum jelly should be placed on the contact-breaker cam every 5,000 miles, except on distributors having felt cam lubricators. With these, grease the cam every 10,000 miles. Fit a new cam lubricator if the felt appears worn.

Pull the rotor off the top of the spindle, or carefully prise it off with a screw-driver if it is tight, and add a few drops of thin machine oil to lubricate the bearing. Do not remove the screw which is exposed to view as there is a clearance through which the oil passes between the screw and the inner face of the spindle. On some distributors the screw is drilled to allow passage of the oil to the main shaft bearing. Replace the rotor correctly and push it on to the spindle as far as it will go; otherwise there is a risk of the moulded cap becoming burned or tracked.

The automatic timing control should be lubricated by carefully injecting a few drops of thin machine oil through the aperture at the micrometer adjustment side of the contact-breaker base plate. With earlier models the oil can be introduced by way of the hole through which the cam passes.

Place a small amount of petroleum jelly or clean engine oil on the pivot on which the contact-breaker lever works.

On ball-supported breaker plates fitted to Delco-Remy distributors place a small amount of Delco-Remy Cam and Ball Bearing Lubricant on each ball every 5,000 miles; on centre-bearing breaker plates, add 3 to 4 drops of light engine oil (10 W) to the felt wick between the plates every 5,000 miles. Apply oil slowly at the oil hole or at the edge of the plate, allowing time for absorption. Wipe off any overflow of oil from the plate.

Avoid excessive lubrication. If too much oil is used, the excess is apt to get on the contact points and cause them to burn.

Check and Inspection. At regular intervals the components of the ignition system should be inspected and serviced as explained in the following paragraphs.

As a first step in the inspection procedure, check the condition of the battery and battery cable. Then examine the vacuum-advance mechanism to make sure it operates freely. On the type which rotates the complete distributor, turn the distributor in its mounting by hand and then release it. The vacuum advance spring should return it to its original position without sticking. On the type which rotates the breaker plate only, turn the plate by hand. It should return to its original position when released.

The centrifugal advance mechanism can also be checked for freedom by turning the contact-breaker cam in the direction of rotation and then releasing it. The springs should return the cam to its original position without sticking.

These checks provide information on the condition of the advance mechanisms, but do not, of course, supply data on the manner in which they actually operate. To obtain that data, the distributor must be removed from the engine and checked on a distributor tester of the type installed in many large service stations. If the mechanisms do not function normally, the distributor will require servicing.

Wipe the inside and outside of the moulded distributor cap with a soft dry cloth, paying particular attention to the spaces between the terminals. See that the small carbon brush on the inside of the moulding works freely in its holder.

Next examine the contact breaker. The contacts must be free from grease or oil. If they are burned or blackened, clean them with a fine Carborundum stone or very fine emery-cloth, afterwards wiping away any trace of dirt or metal dust with a petrol-moistened cloth. Cleaning of the contacts is made easier if the contact-breaker lever carrying the moving contact is removed. (Figs. 22 and 23 show typical assemblies.) The method

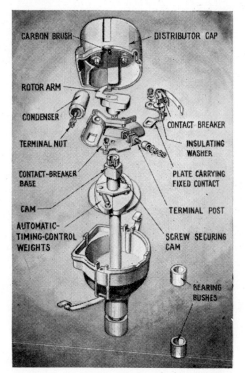

FIG. 22. *A modern distributor incorporating centrifugal advance mechanism. The timing control consists of two weights which move outwards, as engine speed increases, and rotate the cam in relation to the main driving shaft.*

of detaching the arm will be evident on examination. When removing it, make a careful note of the position of insulating washers and bushes.

Adjusting Contact-breaker Gap. After cleaning, check the contact-breaker gap. It is useless to check the gap before the points have been dressed, since a small "pip" forms on one point and a "crater" in the other as the result of normal burning in service. Consequently, if the blade of a feeler gauge is passed between points in this condition, the pip will alter this measurement by several thousandths of an inch.

To set the contact-breaker gap in the

majority of distributors, keep the engine in the position giving maximum opening of the contacts and slacken the two screws which secure the plate carrying the fixed contact. Now move the plate until the gap is set to the thickness of the gauge and tighten the locking screws. It is advisable to re-check the gap to ensure that no movement has taken place while tightening the screws.

With some later distributors the method of gap setting has been altered. For ease of adjustment, a third screw is fitted in the fixed contact plate. The head of this screw is offset with respect to its threaded portion so that, at a turn of this

screw, the contact-breaker gap can be opened or closed as required.

The fixed contact plate of yet another type of distributor is provided with screwdriver adjusting slots and is secured with a single screw. To set the gap, slacken the screw and move the fixed contact plate by inserting a screwdriver in the slot provided and twisting it clockwise or anti-clockwise as required.

The width of contact-breaker gap required for British cars will, due to differences in cam design, depend on the year in which the distributor was manufactured. After 500 miles' running, the gap of distributors made prior to 1952 must be reset and maintained at between 0·010 and 0·012 in., whilst the gap of distributors made during and since 1952 should be between 0·014 and 0·016 in.

If, with a pre-1952 distributor, it is found that there is a tendency for excessive "pitting and piling" of the contacts to occur, even though the recommended routine maintenance operations are regularly carried out, the specified gap setting of 0·010 to 0·012 in. for earlier distributors may be increased to 0·015 in. This increase will improve the service life of the contacts under such conditions, although the performance of

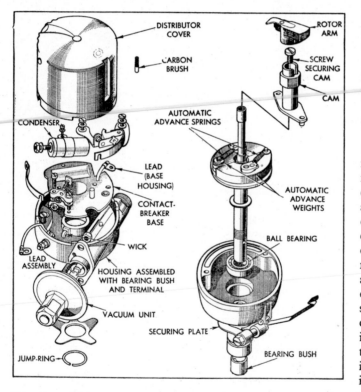

DISTRIBUTOR COVER

CARBON BRUSH

ROTOR ARM

SCREW SECURING CAM

CAM

AUTOMATIC ADVANCE SPRINGS

CONDENSER

LEAD (BASE HOUSING)

CONTACT-BREAKER BASE

AUTOMATIC ADVANCE WEIGHTS

BALL BEARING

WICK

LEAD ASSEMBLY

HOUSING ASSEMBLED WITH BEARING BUSH AND TERMINAL

VACUUM UNIT

SECURING PLATE

JUMP-RING

BEARING BUSH

FIG. 23. *Distributor incorporating centrifugal and vacuum-operated advance and retard mechanism. Dismantling is straight-forward, provided that a note is made of the position of the various parts, including insulating washers, the omission of which will prevent the distributor functioning.*

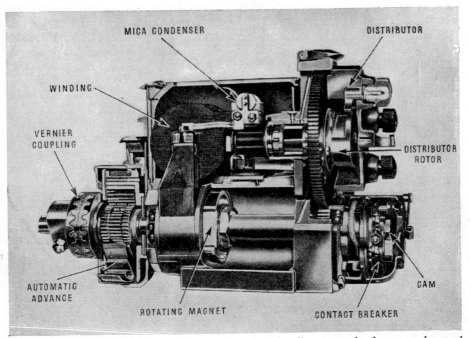

MICA CONDENSER   DISTRIBUTOR

WINDING

VERNIER
COUPLING

DISTRIBUTOR
ROTOR

AUTOMATIC
ADVANCE   CAM

ROTATING MAGNET   CONTACT BREAKER

FIG. 24. *High-tension magneto, incorporating centrifugally operated advance and retard mechanism. The contact breaker and inductor magnet rotate; the windings are stationary.*

the engine at very high speeds may be slightly impaired. Under no circumstances must the gap be allowed to fall below 0·010 in.

Synchronizing Contact-breaker Points. On six-cylinder or eight-cylinder engines, the distributors of which have only one set of points, the period of time during which the points are closed may be so short that primary current cannot build up to an efficient value. The remedy adopted is to fit two sets of contact points which form parallel circuits for the low-tension current, since the circuit is not broken until both sets of points are opened.

Manufacturers of this equipment supply a special tool with which the correct interval (in cam degrees) at which the points open can be readily checked by following the instructions supplied with the tool.

Renewing High-tension Cables. The high-tension cables connecting the coil to the distributor and the distributor to the sparking plugs should be renewed when they shows signs of perishing or cracking. Only 77 mm. P.V.C.-covered (or neoprene-covered) rubber ignition cable should be used.

With some distributors, the cables are secured by means of pointed fixing screws. To fit new cables, unscrew the pointed fixing screws on the inside of the moulding and push the cables—which should not be bared, but cut off flush to the required length—well home into their respective terminals. The screw securing the centre cable is accessible when the carbon brush is removed. Then tighten up the screws which pierce the insulation and make contact with the cable core.

With other types of distributors, having horizontal cable outlets, the cables are held in position by a moulded cover which is secured by means of screws. The cables, which are cut off flush to the required length, are located in recesses in the distributor moulding and are pressed on to pointed terminal studs which pierce the insulation to contact the cable core.

Ignition Switch and Warning Light. The ignition switch, besides forming a means of stopping the engine, is provided for the purpose of preventing the battery being discharged by the current flowing through the coil windings when the engine comes to rest with the distributor contacts in the closed position. A warning lamp is usually provided in the instrument panel which gives a red light when the ignition is switched on and the car is running very slowly or is stationary.

MAGNETO MAINTENANCE

In earlier magnetos the coils were rotated between the poles of a magnet, whereas in later types the inductor units or magnets rotate and the coils and condenser are stationary (Fig. 25).

As with a coil-ignition system, the magneto has primary and secondary windings and a contact breaker that opens and closes the primary circuit at the correct instant. In a magneto, however, the rotation of the magnet, or armature, induces the alternating magnetic field and electric current in the windings; it is thus independent of the battery for its supply of primary current.

The high-tension (H.T.) current induced in the secondary winding is collected and passed to the distributor which distributes the current to electrodes connected to the appropriate sparking plugs. On earlier, or rotating-armature magnetos, the induced current is picked up from a metal slip-ring by means of a spring-loaded carbon brush to pass to another brush or across an air gap to the distributor segments.

To prevent a high stress on the windings if, for example, a sparking-plug lead should become detached, a safety spark-gap is included in the circuit to provide a path to earth for the H.T. current. In some makes of magneto this takes the form of a screw close to the H.T. slip-ring, while on others it is adjacent to the distributor brush in the upper part of the magnet housing. On most magnetos the gap is set at 8 mm. ($\frac{5}{16}$ in.). On some types of magneto the gear-wheel for the distributor rotor forms the gap in conjunction with the earthed magneto casing.

Ignition Switch. Whereas on coil-ignition systems the ignition switch opens the circuit to interrupt the current supply from the battery, on a magneto system the switch earths the primary current, thus short-circuiting the contact breaker and preventing the building-up of a secondary current. If the engine will not start when the ignition is switched on, it may be found that the switch wire is short-circuited to earth.

Routine Servicing. The contact-breaker points should be cleaned and adjusted to the gap recommended by the car manufacturer, the process being similar to that already described for coil-ignition distributors. On horizontal magnetos, however, the adjustable point is usually carried on a screw that is secured by a locknut, so that a set of magneto spanners will be required.

The H.T. collector brush should be a sliding fit in its socket in the holder and must be clean and dry. The slip-ring should be carefully cleaned before replacing the brush and holder. A petrol-moistened rag, pressed against the slip-ring through the holder aperture while the engine is cranked (with ignition switched off) will clean oil and carbon from the surface. When a jump-spark distributor is fitted, it should be serviced in a similar manner to a coil-ignition distributor.

WIRING DIAGRAM

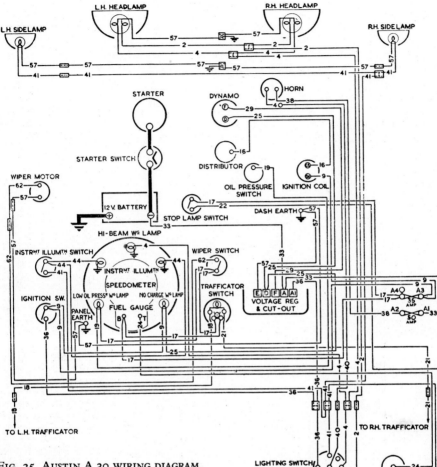

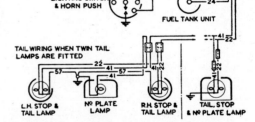

FIG. 25. AUSTIN A.30 WIRING DIAGRAM. *This is a comparatively simple lay-out in which the individual circuits can be traced. The braiding of the wires is colour-coded to facilitate identification, as shown in the key below.*

KEY TO CABLE COLOURS

I BLUE	14 WHITE with PURPLE	27 YELLOW with BLUE	40 BROWN with BLACK	53 PURPLE with WHITE
2 BLUE with RED	15 WHITE with BROWN	28 YELLOW with WHITE	41 RED	54 PURPLE with GREEN
3 BLUE with YELLOW	16 WHITE with BLACK	29 YELLOW with GREEN	42 RED with YELLOW	55 PURPLE with BROWN
4 BLUE with WHITE	17 GREEN	30 YELLOW with PURPLE	43 RED with BLUE	56 PURPLE with BLACK
5 BLUE with GREEN	18 GREEN with RED	31 YELLOW with BROWN	44 RED with WHITE	57 BLACK
6 BLUE with PURPLE	19 GREEN with YELLOW	32 YELLOW with BLACK	45 RED with GREEN	58 BLACK with RED
7 BLUE with BROWN	20 GREEN with BLUE	33 BROWN	46 RED with PURPLE	59 BLACK with YELLOW
8 BLUE with BLACK	21 GREEN with WHITE	34 BROWN with RED	47 RED with BROWN	60 BLACK with BLUE
9 WHITE	22 GREEN with PURPLE	35 BROWN with YELLOW	48 RED with BLACK	61 BLACK with WHITE
10 WHITE with RED	23 GREEN with BROWN	36 BROWN with BLUE	49 PURPLE	62 BLACK with GREEN
11 WHITE with YELLOW	24 GREEN with BLACK	37 BROWN with WHITE	50 PURPLE with RED	63 BLACK with PURPLE
12 WHITE with BLUE	25 YELLOW	38 BROWN with GREEN	51 PURPLE with YELLOW	64 BLACK with BROWN
13 WHITE with GREEN	26 YELLOW with RED	39 BROWN with PURPLE	52 PURPLE with BLUE	

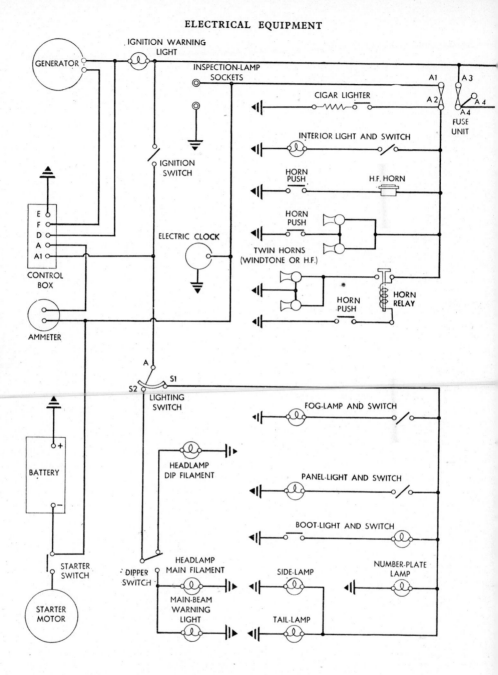

FIG. 26. SIMPLIFIED WIRING DIAGRAM. *The electrical system of a motor vehicle can be considered as a series of simple circuits. This diagram shows the basic circuits on modern cars. It should be compared with the diagrams shown in* FIGS. 25 AND 27.

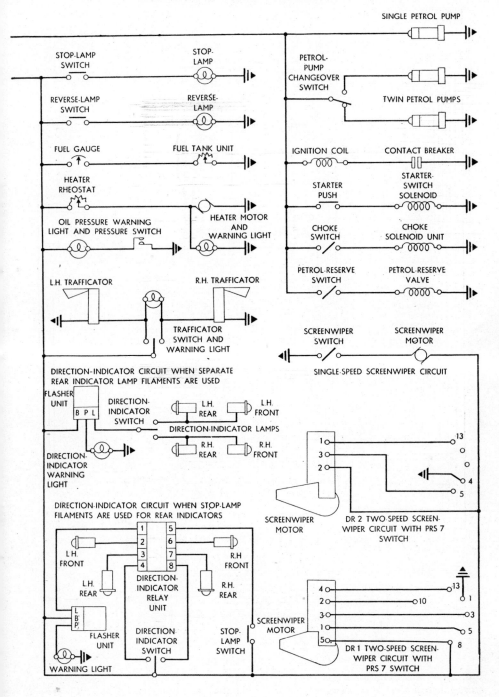

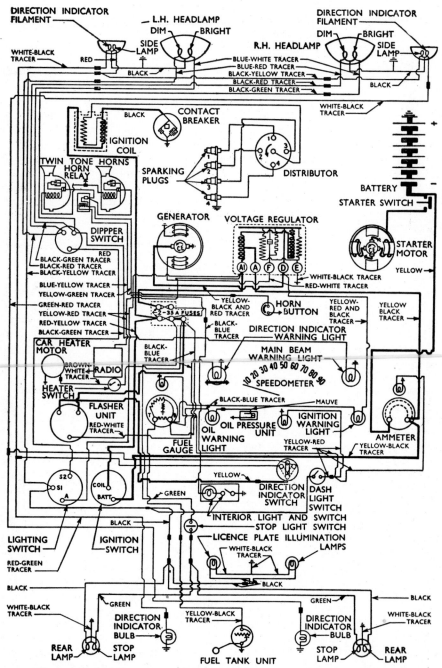

FIG. 27. WIRING DIAGRAM FOR 1953 FORD CONSUL. (*On cars fitted with a water-temperature gauge in place of an ammeter, the battery feed wire is taken direct to the "A" terminal of the regulator. A wire runs from this terminal to the ignition switch.*)

CHAPTER 8

THE TRANSMISSION

THE attention required by the transmission system of the modern car can be summed up as "care and maintenance", rather than "repair and overhaul", that is, so far as the average owner is concerned. As in the case of most other items on the car, lubrication is the most important factor. Repair, when eventually required, is generally the province of the specialist.

In this chapter, then, emphasis is placed on the prevention of trouble, and diagnosis of its causes. It has been necessary, in the space available, to concentrate attention mainly on the more widely used types of component, which are often produced by specialist firms on behalf of the car manufacturer.

It is assumed that the conventional rear-wheel drive is used, although, as explained in Chapter 1, the basic principles will also apply to front-wheel drive transmissions. Little can be said regarding the latest types of automatic transmission, as these are complicated in lay-out, and often embody radical or detailed changes in design on different models of the same car from year to year. Until some measure of standardization is achieved, therefore, advice must be obtained from the individual manufacturers or agents, who are best qualified to carry out any servicing or repair which may be required.

THE CLUTCH

The modern clutch is one of the few items in the transmission system which does not need lubrication. The point which would normally require attention is the thrust bearing on which the with-drawal levers act, and this usually takes the form of a graphite ring which has self-lubricating properties, Fig. 2.

On some clutches, however, chiefly of earlier design, a thrust ball race is used. This is often provided with an extension tube for lubrication purposes, although it may be necessary to remove the floor carpet and an inspection panel in the driver's compartment to obtain access to it. If the lubricator takes the form of an oil cup, a few drops of engine oil at 1,000-mile intervals should be sufficient; if a greaser is fitted, use a high-melting-point grease at the same intervals. Avoid overlubrication, as oil or grease may find its way onto the clutch linings and cause the clutch to slip.

Oil Filled Clutches. The cork-insert type of clutch which runs in oil is not common today, but owners of older cars may find that this type is fitted.

These clutches are apt to give trouble if the wrong grade of oil is used; they are generally supplied from the engine lubrication system, and the manufacturer's recommendation regarding the most suitable grade of oil should be respected. When the engine sump is drained, the clutch must also be emptied by means of the drain plug fitted to its housing. A tendency of the clutch to slip or to fail to disengage fully can often be cured by draining the oil, flushing out the clutch with a flushing oil, and refilling with the correct grade of oil. The clutch must usually be filled separately from the engine sump, but the level is subsequently maintained automatically.

Adjusting the Clutch. It will be clear from Fig. 2 that as the friction linings in

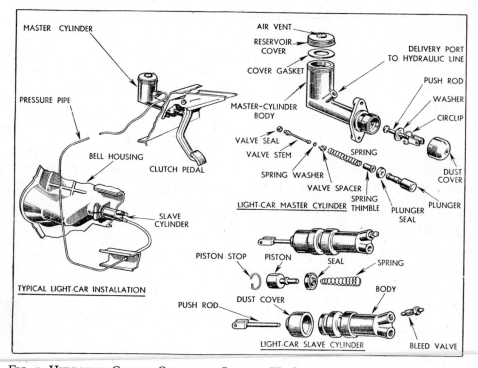

FIG. I. HYDRAULIC CLUTCH OPERATING SYSTEM. *The lay-out and components shown are typical of modern practice. Pressure on the clutch pedal transmits fluid pressure through a pipe line to the piston in the slave cylinder, which operates the clutch withdrawal lever. Mechanical connexion between the chassis and the clutch is thus avoided.*

the driven plate become worn in use, the pressure plate will move nearer towards the flywheel. This will result in the release ring touching the thrust bearing, and prevent the clutch from engaging fully. To prevent clutch slip, then, a clearance of about $\frac{1}{16}$ in. must be maintained between the release levers and the thrust bearing. When multiplied by the leverage afforded by the clutch operating arm and pedal, this amounts to about $\frac{1}{2}$ in. to 1 in. of free movement at the pedal itself.

On earlier types of clutch the adjustment was often carried out at the outer ends of the release levers, which were provided with adjustable set screws and locknuts. Each lever was adjusted in turn

to give a clearance of $\frac{1}{16}$ in. between its inner end and the thrust bearing; equal adjustment was essential to prevent the clutch chattering and wearing rapidly.

On modern clutches, however, the adjustment is carried out by altering the effective length of the linkage between the pedal and the clutch lever, whether this takes the form of a rod or a chain. The adjustment of the release levers in the clutch is accurately set during assembly, and should not be disturbed.

When a hydraulic clutch is fitted, adjustment may be unnecessary. In some cases it is possible to move the slave cylinder in its mounting in order to obtain the correct clearance; the car manufacturer's instructions should always be consulted.

Causes of Clutch Troubles. Clutch slip is the most usual trouble experienced when the car has covered a considerable mileage. It can be due to a number of factors, among which are the need for adjustment as just described, the presence of oil or grease on the clutch linings, or badly worn linings.

The latter fault can be caused quite early in the life of the car if the driver makes a habit of resting his left foot on the clutch pedal; this weakens the clutch springs, and leads to slight slip which burns and glazes the friction linings. A similar effect is caused by slipping the clutch in order to enable the engine to produce a little extra power, instead of changing to a lower gear.

We have already seen that grease or oil on the friction linings can be due to overlubrication of the thrust race when a lubricator is fitted. If the bearing is self-lubricating, the cause must be sought elsewhere, and the most likely culprit is a worn rear main bearing in the engine, or a worn bearing or faulty oil seal at the point at which the clutch shaft enters the gearbox. The first will be revealed by leakage of engine oil from the clutch casing, while the second is betrayed by a similar leakage of gear oil, unless engine oil is specified for the gearbox.

Drainage Obstruction. An oil drainage hole is usually drilled at the lowest point of the clutch casing. This is often found to be partly obstructed by a split pin, or a length of wire, which is inserted with the object of preventing complete blockage of the hole by road grit and mud. If the base of the clutch pit is so caked with mud that the hole is obstructed, however, the drain hole cannot be effective, and the remedy is obvious. Unfortunately, once an appreciable quantity of oil has become carbonized on the linings of a dry-plate clutch, the only real cure for clutch slip is to renew the linings. This is discussed later in this chapter.

It is sometimes recommended that the clutch should be flushed out with petrol, in an attempt to remove as much of the oil as possible. It may be possible to do this by removing an inspection cover from the clutch housing, and injecting petrol through apertures in the clutch casing while the pedal is depressed to separate the pressure plate from the linings. The engine should then be allowed to idle while the clutch pedal is alternately depressed and released a number of times.

It must be emphasized, however, that this treatment may wash away the grease or oil from several internal points which require lubrication, such as the splines, pivots, and spigot bearing, so that the best plan is undoubtedly to dismantle the clutch.

A final point to check is that no part of the clutch release arm, linkage, or pedal is binding, as stiffness will prevent the clutch from engaging fully.

Causes of Fierce Engagement. When the clutch takes up the drive with a snatch although the pedal is released gradually, the cause, in the majority of cases, is again the presence of oil or grease on the linings. In this case the oil has become burnt due to the heat caused by the clutch slipping, and forms a resinous compound of a somewhat sticky nature which causes fierce engagement. Binding of any part of the release linkage, misalinement of the driven plate, or unequal adjustment of the release levers, will also result in fierce engagement. Judder as the drive is taken up is a variation of the trouble just described.

Clutch does not Free Completely. Failure of the clutch to disengage fully when the pedal is depressed may be due simply to incorrect adjustment of the linkage, if this has been disturbed when attempting to adjust the free movement. The same effect is given by overadjustment, resulting in too great a gap between the release levers and the thrust bearing, as the movement of the pressure plate away from the clutch plate will be insufficient. If the adjustment is correct, distortion of the clutch plate is the most likely trouble, and the clutch must be dismantled. This fault may be caused by allowing the weight of the gearbox to deflect the clutch shaft during dismantling, or reassembly, a point that is sometimes overlooked by owners who undertake the removal of the gearbox themselves.

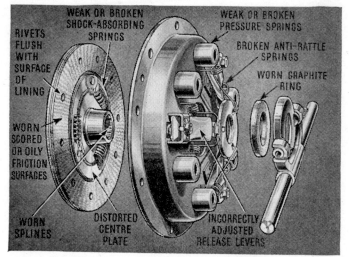

FIG. 2. *Exploded view of a friction clutch showing the parts likely to cause a breakdown. In the case of one or more of these parts requiring replacement, it is advisable to refer to the manufacturer's service handbook to see whether it recommends replacement of individual parts or complete assemblies.*

Noises in the Clutch. A variety of noises can be caused by the various faults just outlined. Lack of lubrication of a ball-bearing thrust race, for instance, will cause a chatter, squeak, or a tinkling noise. A badly-worn carbon thrust ring will also cause a chatter or squeak. Rattles can be traced to wear of the various components in the release mechanism, or to weak or broken anti-rattle springs on the release arms. Distortion of the centre plate, and worn splines in the centre plate hub or on the clutch shaft, will cause knocking or clicking noises. It is a sound precaution, therefore, to dismantle the clutch at the first opportunity when any noise becomes evident, in order that the trouble may be rectified before it becomes more serious.

Overhauling the Clutch. As already stressed, a clutch overhaul is not to be lightly undertaken by the amateur. Apart from a certain amount of experience being necessary, a number of special items of equipment are needed when dismantling and reassembling most types of modern clutch. An arbor press is required, for instance, when dealing with Borg and Beck clutches, while a special adjustment gauge, which is in effect a dummy centre plate, must be used when setting the release arms. Since the method of dismantling, reassembly and adjustment varies with different clutches, an owner who proposes to undertake the work should first obtain an instruction leaflet from the manufacturer of the car or of the clutch.

Preliminary Dismantling. If the clutch is to be dismantled while the engine is still in the chassis, the gearbox, if attached to the clutch housing, as is usual nowadays, must first be removed. This will entail disconnecting the propeller shaft. Both these operations are referred to later in this chapter, so that they need not be detailed at this stage.

When the clutch is exposed, it will be seen that its outer casing is attached to the flywheel by a ring of bolts. One bolt may be stamped with a letter or other mark, while a similar mark will appear on the clutch rim and the flywheel next to it. This indicates that the bolt is of a special weight and is used to balance the assembly. It must, therefore, be replaced in the same hole when the clutch is reassembled. It is advisable in any case to make a light centre-punch mark on the clutch rim and the flywheel to ensure correct reassembly.

Dismantling the Clutch. On most modern designs of clutch the complete unit is removed from the flywheel and dismantled on the bench. As already mentioned, an instruction leaflet is necessary at this stage; the actual operation presents little difficulty, but the correct sequence of dismantling must be followed. Strong springs are of necessity fitted and are apt to fly with a risk of injury to the person carrying out the dismantling unless precautions are taken to prevent this happening.

Relining the Clutch. The term relining is a misnomer nowadays, since the practice of fitting new friction linings to the driven plate is seldom permissible. The modern clutch is a piece of precision

workmanship, and the linings are very accurately fitted during manufacture. The driven plate, moreover, almost invariably incorporates shock absorbing devices, and the heat generated due to excessive clutch slip will probably have distorted the plate and reduced the efficiency of the torsional damping springs. The correct procedure, therefore, is to fit a new driven plate, complete with linings.

Excessive wear of the linings will, of course, be obvious. If the rivets are flush with the surface, instead of recessed, the faces of the flywheel and pressure plate may be scored. This will mean that they must be skimmed up in a lathe, a fairly ambitious job in the case of the flywheel, which must, of course, be removed from the engine. This emphasizes the wisdom of dealing with clutch troubles before the wear reaches an advanced stage.

If the clutch linings are not unduly worn they should not necessarily be condemned because they have a polished appearance. To achieve perfect contact with the flywheel and pressure plate a polished surface, which develops on new linings after a short period of use, is

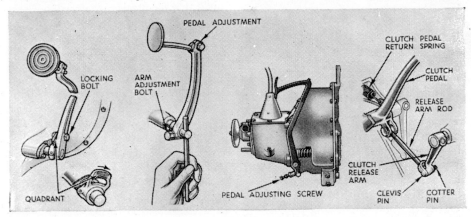

FIG. 3. PEDAL ADJUSTMENTS. *Four views showing the adjustments that can be made to the clutch pedal on various designs of car. When making any of these adjustments it is essential to preserve the free pedal movement laid down by the manufacturer, otherwise the release mechanism will be overstressed.*

essential. If the grain of the friction material can be seen, therefore, the linings are serviceable. If it is hidden by a dark brown glazed surface, on the other hand, the linings have been subjected to oil or grease and should be discarded.

On earlier clutches fitted with driven plates in which cork inserts form the friction surface, the corks should not be renewed, but the plate should be replaced by a new one.

Reassembling the Clutch. Before reassembling the clutch, examine the

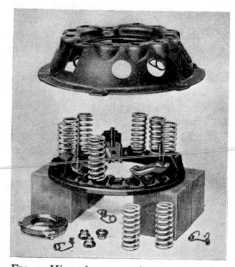

FIG. 4. *View of pressure plate, thrust springs and release levers which are accessible after the clutch cover has been removed. All parts should be marked to ensure correct assembly after the repair has been carried out.*

various parts of the release mechanism for wear, and the springs for weakening: if in any doubt about a part, renew it. It will probably be found, for instance, that the adjusting nuts will assume a different position when the clutch is reassembled, so that the split pins which lock them cannot be inserted in the original holes. As difficulty will be experienced in drilling a second hole, the bolts should be renewed.

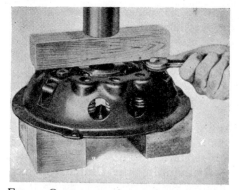

FIG. 5. *Compressing the cover under a press to relieve the pressure of the thrust springs before dismantling the clutch. The press should be eased off gently after the securing nuts have been removed.*

The manufacturer's leaflet must be consulted during reassembly. Among the special tools which may be required are the gauge plate or dummy centre plate already referred to, which is used to set the release levers to the correct clearance. A dummy clutch shaft may also be required to ensure that the driven plate is correctly centralized while the clutch is being assembled. Otherwise, when the time comes to refit the gearbox, it may be found that the primary shaft will not pass

FIG. 6. *Fitting a release lever. After the three levers have been fitted they must be adjusted to the release lever gauge plate or dummy centre plate on the adjusting nuts*

through the centre plate into the spigot bearing in the flywheel.

After the gearbox has been refitted and the withdrawal linkage reconnected, adjustment for free pedal travel must be carried out as already described.

FLUID FLYWHEEL

Fluid Flywheel. Although the fluid flywheel, or hydraulic clutch, is not very widely used, it has nevertheless figured in the specification of several makes of cars for many years; with the increasing development of automatic transmissions, it is likely to be more widely adopted, although it may differ in some respects from its present form.

Due to the fact that it operates on hydraulic principles, the fluid flywheel itself does not wear, and the only attention normally required is topping-up at intervals with the grade of oil recommended by the manufacturer; this is generally the same as that used in the engine. When topping-up, check the condition of the copper washers beneath the filler plugs, and renew both if necessary. Do not change the relative positions of the plugs, as the balance of the flywheel may be upset.

The point at which wear is likely to occur is the gland which prevents oil leakage past the gearbox shaft. As the fluid flywheel should preferably be dismantled in order to renew this gland, the work should be left to a service station. The condition of the bearing can then be checked at the same time.

GEARBOX

Because the gearbox seldom needs topping-up, it is apt to be forgotten. A point should be made of checking the level at 2,000-mile intervals, and draining the oil after every 10,000 miles. The correct grade of oil can be ascertained from the manufacturer or a garage; usually it is the same as that used in the

engine on modern cars, although earlier models require a heavier grade, which gave rise to the term gear oil.

Correct Oil Level. The filler may be accessible from inside the driving compartment, although it is generally necessary to remove the carpet, or the moulded rubber cover enclosing the gearbox. Sometimes the floorboards themselves must be removed. The correct level may be indicated in several different ways. The filler orifice may be arranged at such a height that the oil should be just level with it when the gearbox is correctly topped-up. Sometimes a separate level plug is fitted; this must be removed and oil added until it begins to overflow from the orifice. On many modern cars, however, a dipstick is fitted, so that the oil level can be quickly checked, see Fig. 7.

A point which is sometimes overlooked is that the gearbox oil takes an appreciable time to warm up in cold weather. When it is cold and relatively viscous

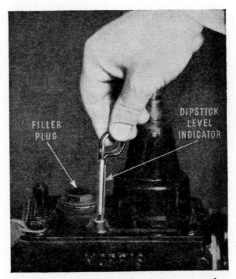

FIG. 7. *Checking the oil level in a gearbox with a dipstick. This should be done about every 2,000 miles. Usually the filler plug and dipstick are accessible from inside the driving compartment.*

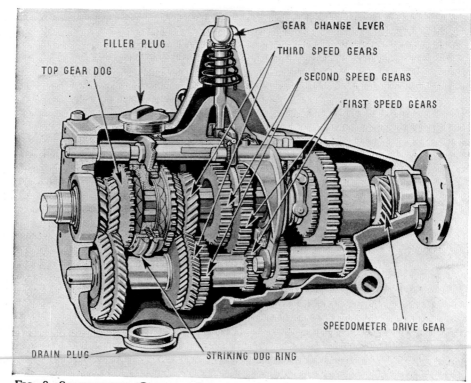

FILLER PLUG

GEAR CHANGE LEVER

THIRD SPEED GEARS

TOP GEAR DOG

SECOND SPEED GEARS

FIRST SPEED GEARS

SPEEDOMETER DRIVE GEAR

DRAIN PLUG

STRIKING DOG RING

FIG. 8. SYNCHROMESH GEARBOX. *Cut-away view of a four-speed gearbox showing the arrangement of the gear trains. The location of the drain and filler plugs is shown, and they should be screwed home tightly after draining and topping up.*

the gears may not pick up and carry round sufficient to ensure effective lubrication; in particular the various bearings in the box may be starved. It pays, therefore, to drive lightly for the first three or four miles on a frosty morning, even though the engine may have been thoroughly warmed up before starting.

The use of colloidal graphite in the gearbox will give beneficial effects, as in the case of the engine. Mixed in the form of a running-in compound, it should be added in the proportion recommended by the makers of the preparation.

Oil Leakage. If the gearbox is over-filled, oil may leak past the oil retainers at the front or the rear of the gearbox. In the first case, the lubricant may find its

way on to the friction surfaces of the clutch, with results already described. Leakage from the rear of the gearbox is less serious, unless the propeller shaft is enclosed in a torque tube. The excess lubricant will find its way down to the rear axle, in which the level will be raised, with the result that oil may eventually reach the rear brake linings. This, however, is a matter which will be discussed later.

If leakage occurs from the gearbox when the oil level is correct, the trouble can usually be attributed to worn oil retainers. This will entail a certain amount of dismantling, depending on the design of the gearbox, and is normally beyond the scope of the average owner for reasons which will be evident later.

Persistent leakage can also be due to a choked breather orifice, since the air in the gearbox must be free to expand as the box warms up in use; otherwise, the pressure generated will be sufficient to force the oil past even the most efficient oil seals.

Overheated Oil. Oil sometimes leaks from the ball joint at the base of the gear lever. This, however, is more likely to be due to too little oil in the gearbox than to too high a level. A small quantity of oil will become overheated, and consequently very much more fluid than normal; it is thus able to pass the oil seal at the base of the gear lever. This symptom, therefore, is a danger signal which should not be ignored, as the oil will possess inadequate lubricating properties under these conditions.

Sometimes leakage is experienced even though the correct grade of oil is in use, and an adequate level maintained. A useful tip which will prevent the driver's clothes from being soiled is to fit one half of a hollow rubber ball of suitable size over the ball joint; the ball must be a close fit on the gear lever, and it will be necessary to remove the gear lever knob before it can be slid down into place.

Gearbox Faults. Considerable space has been devoted to the question of lubrication, since prevention of trouble is a much simpler matter than its rectification. There are few gearbox faults which can be dealt with without dismantling the gearbox, and as this will entail removing it from the engine, and the use of special dismantling and assembly tools, it is one of those operations which should not be undertaken lightly. When symptoms of trouble do develop, however, their rectification should be put in hand without delay to prevent additional damage.

The usual faults can be classified as oil leakage, which we have already dealt with, noisy operation, sticking of a gear in mesh or alternatively jumping out of engagement, and inability to engage one or more gears.

Noisy Operation. If the gearbox is noisy when the car is stationary, the trouble is probably due to worn constant-mesh gears, or to wear on the clutch shaft and layshaft bearings. Noisy operation when the car is in motion can be due to worn gears, possibly being confined to one ratio which is most used, such as second-gear on a three-speed box or third gear on a four-speed one. Noise on all the gears can be due to worn teeth or worn bearings. Accurate diagnosis, however, generally depends on stripping the gearbox and examining the various parts.

Sticking Gears. This is a fault which has come into prominence since the introduction of synchromesh operation, since the cone clutches are apt to jam on occasion. If the trouble is experienced on a new car, it can usually be depended on to cure itself by the time that the running-in period is completed. To free a badly jammed gear, drive at the highest speed possible in that ratio, and suddenly release the accelerator pedal, simultaneously declutching and attempting to force the gear lever towards the neutral position. In obstinate cases it may be necessary to remove the lid of the gearbox and to tap the synchromesh unit in the appropriate direction. This is an operation best left to an expert. To prevent any recurrence of the trouble, an oil activating agent may be added to the oil in the gearbox; from six to ten ounces of this special oil should be poured in, depending on the oil capacity of the gearbox.

Gears Jump out of Engagement. When a gear jumps out of engagement, the trouble is generally due basically to wear of the gear teeth or the teeth of the locking dogs. The spring-loaded selector, however, is usually able to keep the gear engaged until the spring itself weakens, or the notch or groove in the selector bar becomes worn. A reasonably permanent cure can often be effected by filing or milling a deeper notch on the bar, so that the locking ball or plunger is more positively engaged. The amount of dismantling required before the selector rod can be removed again depends on the design of the gearbox, but the work can often be done without removing the gearbox from the chassis.

Sometimes the springs used to locate first and reverse gears are stronger than those used on the other gears. Fitting one of these springs to the offending selector may cure the trouble.

Failure to Engage Gears. When a steering column gear lever is fitted the linkage connecting the lever to the selector mechanism may require adjustment as the result of wear on the various ball joints or stretch in the cables. The manufacturer's instruction book should be consulted. This fault may also indicate a more serious trouble in the selector mechanism. If none of the gears can be engaged, for instance, it is likely that the projection at the lower end of the gear lever has broken off. If two gears cannot

be engaged, the selector arm which moves that synchromesh unit may be fractured. Again, the only method of determining the real trouble is to remove the lid of the gearbox and examine the parts. Failure to engage a gear when the car is at a standstill and the engine is running is not necessarily due to a gearbox defect. If the gears grate, and can only be forced into engagement with difficulty, the trouble lies in failure of the clutch to disengage fully, due to faults outlined earlier.

Removing the Gearbox. As has already been mentioned, the dismantling and reassembly of a modern gearbox is beyond the scope of the amateur. However, the owner may prefer to remove the gearbox from the chassis himself, and send it for reconditioning.

The amount of preliminary dismantling naturally varies on different cars, but will include removal of the front floor carpets, rubber cover, and the floorboards. Any controls attached to the gearbox and clutch housing, when this is integral with the gearbox casting, must of course be disconnected. The weight of the engine should be supported by a jack, and the front end of the propeller shaft must be disconnected at the universal joint.

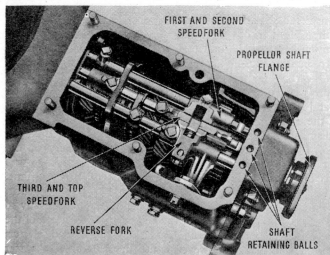

FIRST AND SECOND SPEEDFORK

PROPELLOR SHAFT FLANGE

THIRD AND TOP SPEEDFORK

REVERSE FORK

SHAFT RETAINING BALLS

FIG. 9. *A four-speed synchromesh gearbox with its cover removed showing the gear selector mechanism. When removing the cover every care must be taken to ensure that the selector ball springs are not lost. These are located in the holes that house the retaining balls.*

Open propeller shafts can usually be telescoped on the splines at the forward end sufficiently to clear the flange on the gearbox, while torque tubes can generally be moved back by swinging the rear axle backwards on the spring shackles; the chassis, of course, must be jacked up in this case.

The gearbox itself must be supported while the retaining bolts are unscrewed, so that its weight does not rest on the clutch shaft and distort the driven plate. It may be necessary to remove the gear lever or the lid of the gearbox to enable it to be withdrawn, while it is often necessary to jack up the rear of the engine if a cross-member prevents the gearbox from being drawn back sufficiently. The clutch-operating shaft must be rotated as the gearbox is withdrawn if the bell-housing which carries it is integral with the gearbox; otherwise the withdrawal lever will not clear the clutch thrust race.

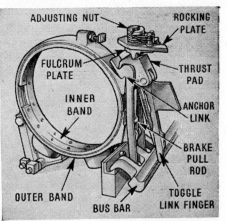

FIG. 10. *Diagram showing one unit of the brake harness in a preselector gearbox. The normal wear of the brakebands are automatically adjusted, but further adjustment can be made on the adjusting nut situated on the rocking plate. As this is a very delicate operation it is recommended that the adjustment be left to the manufacturer or an experienced mechanic.*

PRESELECTOR GEARBOXES

So far we have dealt with the conventional types of gearbox. The Wilson or Daimler preselector differs, of course, both in principle and operation from these types. Lubrication is just as important; with this type of box, in fact, the oil level should be checked at 3,000-mile intervals, and the gearbox should be drained and refilled every 6,000 miles. On some boxes the drain plug acts as a stop for the bus bar, therefore, ensure that it is replaced, otherwise the movement of the bus bar may be restricted just sufficiently to stop the toggle fingers from dropping into or out of engagement.

Adjustment of the Gearbox. The brake bands (Fig. 10) which bring the epicyclic gear trains into action are provided with automatic adjusters which are operated by the movement of the gear-changing pedal, and which compensate for normal wear of the friction linings. As the linings bed down more quickly than usual when the car is new, however, the adjustment may be insufficient under these conditions, and slip may be experienced. This can be overcome by selecting the gear or gears on which slipping is present, with the engine stationary, and depressing and releasing the pedal ten or fifteen times.

If a gear slips in normal service, the cause is usually due to some external fault, such as incorrectly adjusted pedal linkage, or binding of the pedal on its shaft. A clearance of between $\frac{1}{4}$-in. and $\frac{1}{2}$-in. must exist between the pedal and the floorboards or the back stop when it is fully released with a gear engaged; adjustment is carried out at the tie-rod coupling the pedal to the gearbox lever.

If this does not cure the trouble, an adjustment can be carried out on the automatic adjuster inside the gearbox, after the lid has been removed, but this is rarely required, and should preferably be left to an expert. The owner who wishes to service the gearbox himself should apply to the manufacturers of the car or of the gearbox for an illustrated instruction book which describes both the principles of operation and the method of servicing very fully.

PROPELLER SHAFT AND UNIVERSAL JOINTS

Many modern cars are fitted with an open propeller shaft, which has a universal joint at each end. In some cases the shaft is enclosed in a tubular housing termed a torque tube, which resists the turning effort exerted on the rear axle during acceleration and braking. The rear end of the torque tube is bolted to axle casing, while the front end swivels in a large ball joint; the propeller shaft itself, therefore, requires only one universal joint, at its forward end.

On open propeller shafts the Hardy-Spicer universal joint is generally used; all such joints nowadays have needle-roller bearings instead of the phosphor-bronze bushes used on earlier types. On torque tube assemblies, however, universal joints having bronze bushes are common.

Lubrication. It is usual for torque tube universal joints to be lubricated automatically from the gearbox. This does not apply in every case, however: on Ford cars, for example, the joints require attention with a grease gun at 1,000-mile intervals. A non-separating grease prepared for use in universal joints must be used. This also applies to the earlier type of Hardy-Spicer joint on open propeller shafts in which the joint itself is enclosed by a grease-retaining housing provided with a lubrication nipple.

When open Hardy-Spicer joints require lubrication a nipple is fitted on the trunnion. On other models the needle-roller bearings are packed with sufficient oil on assembly to last for a very large mileage: re-packing is not normally required until an overhaul. There is, however, a greasing point which must not be overlooked: this serves the splines of the telescopic portion at the front of the shaft, which allows the length of the shaft to alter slightly in response to rear axle movements. The greasing nipple can be reached from beneath the car or through an inspection opening in the propeller shaft tunnel; in either case it will be necessary to push the car slightly backwards or forwards to rotate the propeller shaft until the nipple is conveniently placed.

Layrub universal joints have rubber bushes in them which absorb the relative movements of the two parts of the joint in a radial and lengthwise direction. Such joints require no lubrication whatever; oil or grease must, in fact, be prevented from reaching the rubber bushes, which will quickly deteriorate under its action.

On one or two small cars the reinforced fabric disk type of joint is used. Here again oil and grease must be kept off the fabric, but the sliding splined portion behind the front joint will require attention.

Oil Leakage Troubles. As will be appreciated, the universal joints on open propeller shafts are not likely to leak, as the lubricant is effectively sealed in the bearings. Overlubrication of the splined portion will cause grease to be flung out, of course, but this is not a serious matter. When a torque tube is fitted, however, two forms of leakage can sometimes be troublesome.

The first is external leakage of oil or grease from the ball joint surrounding the universal joint. An oil seal is usually fitted inside the rear rim of the outer casing of the ball, and this may require renewal. A second seal is fitted between the sleeve which surrounds the torque tube and the tube itself, to allow the two parts to slide on one another. This seal can often be tightened by means of an adjusting sleeve.

The second trouble is internal leakage, resulting in oil or grease finding its way past a seal which surrounds the propeller shaft, and so working down the torque tube into the rear axle. To renew this seal the ball joint assembly must be dismantled as described later.

Vibration and Noise. Owing to the fact that the parts of the joints are in constant movement, and are subjected to considerable stresses, wear is bound to occur in time. When the bearings in the yokes become slack and the splines in the sliding section become worn, appreciable vibration can be set up at high speeds. Wear seldom causes noise, although a knock may be apparent whenever the load on the shaft is reversed, as when suddenly accelerating and decelerating. Worn splines will cause a ridge which may set up an audible knock when travelling over rough road surfaces.

Even if the universal joints are in good condition, vibration can be caused if the propeller shaft is bent, as may sometimes occur with an open prepeller shaft that

has been accidentally damaged. If this trouble is suspected the shaft should be removed and checked by a garage, using V-blocks and a dial gauge. Lack of truth amounting to as little as three-thousandths of an inch is sufficient to cause vibration at speed.

A cause of vibration which may be overlooked on open shafts is incorrect assembly of the front universal joint on the splines. The yokes at each end of the shaft must be in the same plane, or a rhythmic variation in speed will take place at the driven yoke attached to the rear axle pinion shaft. This variation in speed takes place whenever one shaft is driven at an angle to another through the medium of a universal joint. When two joints are used, the variations in them cancel each other out, provided that the yokes are in the same plane. To ensure correct reassembly, arrows are usually stamped on the splined portion and the shaft. Some variation in speed is bound to occur when only one joint is used, as is the case with a torque tube drive; the shaft is generally designed to be as long as possible, in order to reduce

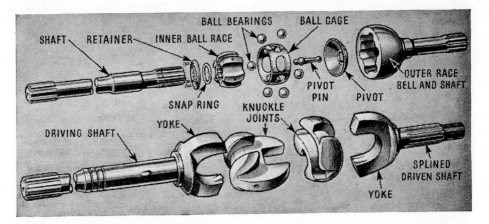

FIG. 11. SPECIAL FORMS OF UNIVERSAL JOINT. *Exploded views of the Bendix-Weiss (above) and Tracta (below) universally-jointed driving shaft. These are generally fitted to cars with front wheel drive, i.e., where the driving shafts are too short to enable two universal joints of the usual type to be fitted.*

239

to a minimum the angularity of the joint.

Special Types of Joint. On front-wheel drive transmissions, and rear-wheel drive systems using certain types of independent suspension for the rear wheels, short, universally-jointed driving shafts convey the drive to the wheels. Since the shaft is too short to enable two universal joints to be fitted, and works through wide angles which would result in pronounced variations of speed, special types of universal joint have been developed. These, although they appear to be a single joint, in reality, consist of two joints built into one compact unit. Two examples which are being increasingly used are the Bendix-Weiss and the Tracta joints, shown in Fig. 11.

It will be seen that the joints are of fairly simple construction, although they embody somewhat complicated geometrical principles. As recommended at the beginning of this chapter, the servicing of specialized transmission systems is best left to the manufacturer or his agent; in any event, experienced advice should be obtained before tackling the work.

Removing the Propeller Shaft. Removal of the conventional open type of propeller shaft is not a very difficult matter. The flanges of the propeller shaft yokes and the gearbox and back axle couplings should be marked before the bolts are removed. The shaft can then be telescoped slightly and withdrawn. If the earlier type of Hardy-Spicer joint is fitted, do not allow the shaft to swing down at either end, or the mouth of the inner member of the oil-retaining casing which surrounds each joint may be damaged. When fabric disk joints are used, removal is, of course, quite straightforward.

Torque tube assemblies present a more difficult problem. It may be necessary, for instance, to remove the rear axle from the springs before the torque tube and

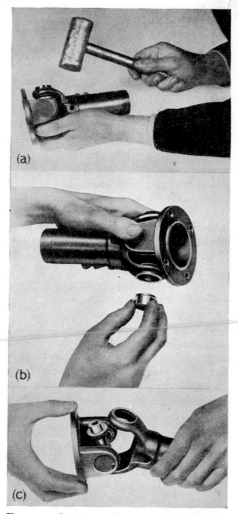

(a)

(b)

(c)

FIG. 12. *Sequence of operations to be observed when dismantling a universal joint. (a) shows the yoke being tapped with a lead hammer to ease the needle roller bearing out of its seating; the circlips having been previously removed. In view (b) the assembly is shown held so that the bearing can be pulled out without disturbing the rollers. This practice should always be adopted when removing a bearing, for should any rollers fall out and be lost, a set of new rollers must be fitted. (c) shows the shaft yoke being removed from the trunnion end of the cross pin.*

universal joint can be dismantled; in other cases it may be possible to swing the axle back on the spring shackles, with the chassis jacked up sufficiently to expose the universal joint. Other points to check are the presence of a speedometer driving gear just in front of the universal joint, the use of a steady bearing for the propeller shaft mid-way down the torque tube, and the types of oil seal fitted to the ball joint, sliding joint, and around the propeller shaft. Obviously, contact should be made with the manufacturer's service station to ascertain any difficulties before carrying out the work.

Servicing Hardy-Spicer Joints. In the needle-roller type of bearing the roller races are retained in the yokes by spring circlips, which must be sprung out of their grooves. Then, holding one half of the bearing in the left hand, gently tap the outside of the other yoke with a lead or copper hammer; this will force out the roller bearing, until it can be extracted with the fingers. Invert the joint before the roller is finally drawn clear of its housing, so that the needle rollers do not fall out. The sequence of operations for dismantling this design of universal joint is illustrated in Fig. 12.

The races and the complete set of rollers should be renewed if any slackness was apparent before dismantling. The races should be a push fit in the yokes. If a good fit cannot be obtained with new races, renewal of the yokes will be required. The splines should be examined; if they appear to be worn or ridged, renewal is indicated. When reassembling the joint, the races and the grease reservoirs in the trunnion should be packed with non-separating lubricant, such as Mobiloil C, rather than grease, which may clog the oil passages. Fit new circlips, and a new cork washer to the dust cover.

Dismantling Earlier Types. The earlier type of bearing is dismantled by unscrewing the dust cap which secures the oil retainer, and sliding off the inner and outer casings, baffle cup and spring; make a note of the correct order for reassembly. The bushes can then be tapped out of the yokes with a flattened drift, used from the inside of the yoke; begin with those in the flange yoke and then remove the trunnion, so that the securing rings in the propeller shaft yokes can be sprung out, and these bushes tapped out in a similar manner.

Before reassembling, renew any part that shows signs of wear, as the slightest slackness between the bushes and the trunnion pins will cause vibration at high speeds. Grease the bearings with non-separating grease, and make sure that the trunnion is fitted the right way round: the flattened sides of its shoulders must be flush with the ends of the yoke. When the grease-retaining casing has been refitted, fill it with non-separating grease.

The type of universal joint used with torque tube assemblies often comprises a split outer ring between which the bushes in which the trunnions work are gripped. In this case the trunnion is separated into two halves, one member being attached to the front yoke and the other to the rear yoke. Dismantling is a simple matter once the bolts securing the two halves of the ring have been removed. In some cases, the ring itself forms the bearing, separate bushes not being fitted.

The other point concerns the fit of the spherical bearing at the forward end of the torque tube. Sometimes a screwed adjustment is provided at this point, or shims are fitted between the flanges of the retainer and the gearbox ball housing. If neither method of adjustment is provided, it will be necessary to machine or grind sufficient metal from the face of the retaining flange to enable it to fit more closely around the ball. While the parts must be perfectly free to swivel in their seatings, no slackness must exist.

Fabric Joints. This type of joint is dangerous if allowed to deteriorate. It should be inspected at regular intervals for once the fabric weakens, deterioration is rapid. Renewal is a very simple matter, but remember that only high-tensile steel bolts should be used to secure the disks; ordinary steel bolts may fracture and allow the shaft to drop, with serious consequences should it be the front end which comes adrift. For the same reason, the nuts must be securely locked by split pins after being fully tightened. A centring plate, which fits over a ball-shaped projection on the propeller shaft, is often fitted. Make sure that this plate is bolted to the yoke attached to the gearbox or back axle; if it should be fitted to the propeller shaft yoke, no centring action will be obtained.

Rubber-bushed Joints. This type of joint is dismantled by removing the bolts which pass through the bushes and the arms of the yokes. While it is possible to fit new rubbers to the steel housing, a press and suitable pilot tools should be used, so that the simplest proposition is to exchange the coupling for a reconditioned one, the cost of which covers the price of new bushes and a small service charge for fitting them.

When refitting the joints, tighten up the retaining nuts as hard as possible with a spanner of normal length. Then increase the leverage, if necessary, to bring a castellation on the nut into line with the split-pin hole. The bolts are of special steel, and are designed to stand this treatment. Do not overlook the chamfered washer which must be fitted under the head of each bolt, with the chamfer towards the rubber bush.

REAR AXLE

Few owners realize the very severe stresses which are imposed on the rear axle. When a car is accelerating in bottom gear or climbing a steep hill, for instance, the load imposed on the teeth of the crown wheel and bevel pinion may be greater then the weight of the vehicle and its passengers. An average figure may be $1\frac{1}{2}$ tons. This load, moreover, is concentrated along a narrow line of contact between two gear teeth. Even on spiral-bevel and hypoid gears the line of contact never exceeds the length of one gear tooth.

The intensity of this concentrated pressure, then, should not need emphasis. The only thing which prevents metal-to-metal contact is a thin film of oil; a film which must be tenacious to a degree if it is to withstand rupturing. When hypoid or worm gears are used, the problem is intensified by the appreciable rubbing action which takes place between the gear teeth, resulting in a rise in temperature and a greater risk of breakdown of the oil film.

Extreme Pressure Lubricants. On normal spiral-bevel rear axles which are not too heavily stressed a first-class gear oil may be sufficiently robust to stand up to the loads. It is general, however, for manufacturers to specify the use of an extreme pressure oil for the rear axle. This is essential, in fact, for worm drives and hypoid gears. A compound is added to this type of oil which enables it to resist extreme pressures. The only drawback is that, due to the presence of the compound, such oils are not as stable as straight mineral oils, so that the rear axle must be drained, flushed out, and refilled at 5,000-mile intervals. Alternatively, even though only a small monthly mileage may be covered, draining and refilling must still take place at intervals of not more than six months, as the lubricant deteriorates whether or not the car is in use.

Different brands of extreme pressure oil will not mix without the risk of forming deposits, so that if topping-up is required between the draining and refilling periods, only the brand of oil in use in the axle at the time should be added.

Excessive Oil Loss. Generally speaking, topping-up should rarely be required between the 5,000-mile refills, although this does not absolve the owner from the responsibility for checking the oil level at 1,000-mile intervals as a safety precaution. If frequent topping-up is required, the indication is that leakage is occurring at some point, and the trouble should be traced and rectified.

Apart from such obvious causes as defective washers under the oil filler, drain or level plugs, leakage often occurs around the joint between the pinion housing or inspection cover and the main axle casing. Tightening up the ring of bolts around the flange equally in rotation may cure the trouble, but if the flange has been distorted or cracked by unequal tightening or the use of too thick a washer, a new part will be required.

Sometimes careful dressing of the flange by tapping it with a hammer on a flat surface will restore its truth, but inexpert use of a hammer can make the trouble worse. If leakage occurs around the forward end of the bevel pinion shaft due to a worn oil retainer, dismantling of the parts may affect the adjustment of the mesh between the bevel pinion and crown wheel, so that this is also a job for the expert.

Check the Breather. The most usual point of leakage, however, is past the oil seals on the axle shafts, so that the oil finds its way into the brake drums, seriously reducing braking efficiency. Before definitely attributing the trouble to the oil retainers, however, it is worth while making sure that the breather on the rear axle is not stopped up by mud. The breather may be a small hole drilled in the filler plug, or may take the form of a pigtail of coiled tube. If it is choked, the pressure caused by the expansion of the air in the axle as it warms up will force oil past even an efficient oil seal. Also make sure that the apparent leakage is not due to lubricant being forced past the oil seal as a result of overenthusiastic lubrication of the hubs.

Oil Seals. The position of the oil seal depends on the construction of the axle and of the hubs, which, as explained in Chapter 1, can be of the fully-floating, three-quarter-floating or semi-floating type. The fully-floating axle is not very widely used, although it has the advantage that it is simple to dismantle, since the axle shaft does not bear any of the weight of the car,

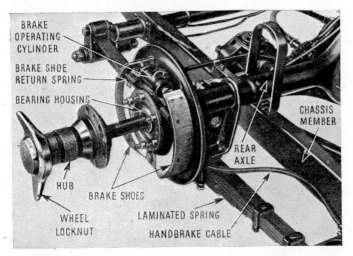

BRAKE OPERATING CYLINDER

BRAKE SHOE RETURN SPRING

BEARING HOUSING

CHASSIS MEMBER

REAR AXLE

HUB

BRAKE SHOES

WHEEL LOCKNUT

LAMINATED SPRING

HANDBRAKE CABLE

FIG. 13. *Rear hub and brake assembly on an M.G. Midget. In this design the wheel fits on a splined hub and is retained by a screwed wheel locknut; when the wheel is rotating the locknut tends to lock itself.*

and is, therefore, simply a splined fit in the hub. Whatever the type of axle, an installation drawing should be obtained, if possible, in order to prevent accidental damage during dismantling. As the following necessarily brief notes on the various types of axle likely to be encountered will show, a working knowledge of the construction of the axle is advisable, if not essential.

Removing the Hubs. On conventional semi-floating and three-quarter-floating axles the hub is often secured to the end of the axle shaft by a taper and key, and is held in place by a nut on the end of the axle. The first step in dismantling will be to remove the wheel and brake drum, revealing the nuts or screws which secure the hub flange. When these have been removed and the hub nut unscrewed, the hub is ready to be drawn off the end of the shaft.

This will call for the use of an extractor in many cases, and a suitable tool can often be borrowed or hired from the maker's service station. An alternative scheme which can often be adopted is to drill a stout steel bar to fit over two diametrically-opposed wheel studs. A suit-

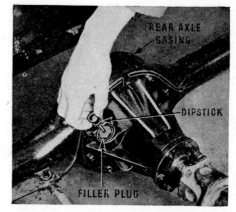

FIG. 14. *Checking the oil level in the rear axle casing with a dipstick fitted in the filler plug.*

able packing piece, such as a large nut, is placed between the centre of the bar and the end of the axle shaft, and the two wheel nuts are replaced and tightened a little in rotation to draw off the hub. To protect the thread on the shaft, the hub retaining nut should preferably be screwed on by several turns. A sharp blow with a hammer on the end of the extractor screw or the centre of the bar will free the hub if it is tight on the taper.

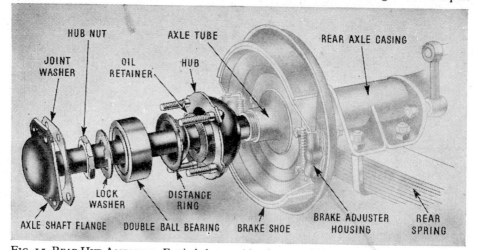

FIG. 15. REAR HUB ASSEMBLY. *Exploded view of an Austin rear hub assembly. In this design the wheel fits on and is secured to the four studs in the hub and not on splines as illustrated in* FIG. 13.

On some cars the hub can be drawn off, after removing the nuts from a bearing retaining plate, by replacing the brake drum and road wheel, and progressively tightening the wheel nuts in rotation. Alternatively, tapped holes may be provided in the flange of the hub. The securing screws, after removal from their normal holes, are screwed into these holes to force off the hub. With both these methods the hub is not detached from the axle shaft; the two parts must subsequently be separated, if necessary, on the bench.

One-piece Hubs and Shafts. In some modern axles, however, the hubs are forged integrally with the outer ends of the shafts. This means that the shaft must be drawn out of the axle as just described. There may be a bearing retaining plate behind the flange of the hub, or it may be necessary to remove the nuts which secure the brake backing plate to the axle casing, so that the backing plate, bearing housing, bearing and hub can all be drawn out with the axle shaft, to be separated on the bench. Yet another arrangement is to secure the inner end of the axle shaft to the pinion in the differential gear by means of a circlip which fits into a groove in the shaft on the inner side of the pinion.

To remove this circlip the spacing block which is fitted between the inner end of each axle shaft must first be removed. This will, of course, entail removal of the inspection cover from the rear axle casing, so that the planet pinion shaft, on which the block fits, can be withdrawn after removing its locking screw. The end of the axle shaft can then be pushed inwards sufficiently to render the circlip accessible.

The most troublesome cases are those in which the axle shafts have the pinions forged integrally with their inner ends. If for any reason it is necessary to remove the shafts, it will be necessary to disconnect the axle from the springs, split the differential casing and withdraw the differential gear, crown wheel, and the two shafts as a unit: obviously no iob for an amateur.

Renewing the Oil Seals. Depending on the design of the axle, withdrawal of the hubs, with or without the shafts, may expose the oil seal; it may be necessary, however, subsequently to remove the bearing either from the axle casing or the hub to gain access to the seal. A properly designed extractor should be used to prevent damage to the bearing.

The seal may be a simple felt ring, pressed into a housing behind the bearing, or may take the form of a leather cup washer, compressed around the axle shaft by a coil spring. As this is difficult to remove without damage even with a special extractor, the best plan is to split it with a small, sharp cold chisel, taking care not to damage its seating, and to fit a fresh seal. The outside of the replacement seal must be coated with gasket cement before it is tapped into place with a drift of suitable diameter. Sometimes the leather must be soaked in hot engine oil for two hours before fitting in order to render it pliable. See that the concave face of the seal faces the inside of the axle, and take great care not to damage or distort its inner edge when refitting the axle shaft.

Defective Bearings and Shafts. The dismantling just described will be necessary if worn hub bearings require renewal, or a broken axle shaft is to be replaced. Worn bearings, incidentally, can be a cause of persistent oil leakage which quickly recurs after a new oil seal has been fitted. The bearings should, therefore, be carefully examined, and if any doubt exists as to their condition they should be replaced.

Similarly, the axle shafts should be checked for signs of twisting, or the formation of cracks, particularly at radii

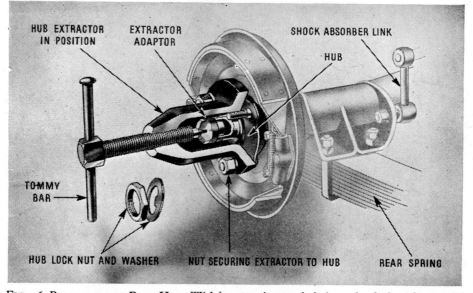

HUB EXTRACTOR IN POSITION · EXTRACTOR ADAPTOR · SHOCK ABSORBER LINK · HUB · TOMMY BAR · HUB LOCK NUT AND WASHER · NUT SECURING EXTRACTOR TO HUB · REAR SPRING

FIG. 16. REMOVING THE REAR HUB. *Withdrawing the rear hub from the shaft with a special hub extractor tool. The tool is temporarily held with nuts to the hub studs and screwed against the adaptor in the mouth of the shaft. When the hub is replaced a new washer should be fitted.*

or at the beginning of splines; the splines themselves, if worn, will necessitate renewal of the shaft. Also, check the condition of the taper on the shaft and in the hub, and the fit of the key in both keyways, i.e., when this method of attachment is used.

Rear Axle Noises. The work just described is within the scope of a practically-minded owner, but attention to the bevel gears and differential pinions should be left to a specialist. When an axle becomes noisy, either on the drive or when over-running, the trouble cannot be cured, as some owners believe, by adjustment of the mesh of the crown wheel and pinion. Noise is due either to wear of gear teeth and the pinion or crown wheel bearings, or both. When the axle has seen a considerable mileage, the surfaces of the teeth will have become run-in or lapped together, and any adjustment at this stage will merely increase the noise.

Adjustment is, of course, required when the gears are first assembled. Correct mesh is determined by applying "marking blue" to the teeth of one gear, so that the extent to which they mesh with those of the other gear will be revealed by the point at which the marking is transferred.

Adjustment of the back axle gears calls for some degree of skill, while the pinion bearings must often be pre-loaded during assembly, so that they operate under the correct conditions when under load. If, after adjustment of the pinion into or out of mesh, the trouble should still be present, it is strongly recommended that the whole differential assembly be removed from the axle casing and correctly adjusted. It will be evident, therefore, that when rear axle noises develop, the diagnosis and rectification of the trouble should be left to a service station which has the necessary special tools and equipment to carry out such repairs.

CHAPTER 9

CHASSIS AND SUSPENSION

THE instruction book originally issued with a car includes a diagram which shows the location of every point which requires periodical lubrication. Unfortunately, the instruction book tends to go astray when a car changes hands, but the owner of a second-hand car can usually obtain a copy of the lubrication chart from the manufacturers of the car, or from one of the large oil companies. Fig. I shows the lubrication points on a modern chassis.

It is always advisable to adhere to the manufacturer's recommendations. In some cases, for instance, grease is specified for the chassis lubrication points, while other manufacturers have designed the oilways for gear oil or engine oil. A high-melting-point grease is required for the fan and water pump bearings, while non-separating grease must be used to resist the effect of centrifugal force in such components as the universal joints.

Since the practical aspects of lubricating the various chassis components are covered in some detail when dealing with the various parts elsewhere in this book, it should be sufficient to confine this section to hints of a general nature.

Using a Grease Gun. Should the chassis be plastered with mud, clean the lubrication nipples before greasing is carried out; the new grease will then force any water and grit out of the bearings. Similarly, the chassis points should always be greased as soon as possible after driving on flooded roads.

Each greasing nipple contains a tiny spring-loaded ball non-return valve, which will be held off its seating if any grit is forced in with the lubricant, quite apart from the adverse effect of grit on the bearing surfaces. An old paint brush, a tin of petrol or paraffin, a flat tin to catch the drips and a cloth are, therefore, essential adjuncts to the grease gun.

Sometimes grease refuses to enter the nipple, which may be damaged or choked. The best plan is to unscrew the nipple and fit a replacement; two or three spares should always be available. A temporary cure is to try injecting gear oil with a layer of cheesecloth placed beneath the gun and the nipple. This will often prevent leakage even when the surface of the nipple is damaged.

GROUPED LUBRICATION POINTS

At one time a number of car manufacturers adopted the grouped chassis lubrication system, in which oil is conveyed by copper pipes from accessibly placed nipples to inaccessible components. The system is, however, less popular nowadays. Probably the improved high-pressure greasing equipment installed by garages, which enables a complete chassis lubrication service to be offered at a very low cost, had something to do with the decline in popularity of the system.

At its best, grouped lubrication can prove a boon to the owner who carries out his own servicing. It must be admitted, however, that the system may have drawbacks. If grease is used, for instance, instead of engine oil or gear oil as specified by the manufacturer, the long lengths of small-bore tubing may become clogged, resulting in the expense of removing and clearing them.

FIG. I. LUBRICATING POINTS. *Plan view of a modern chassis showing some of the main points that require regular lubrication. The lubricating points shown in the insets are fitted with nipples*

CK ROD

WATER PUMP

STEERING CENTRE PIVOT

FRONT SUSPENSION LINK

STEERING DRAG LINK

to allow a grease gun to be used. The owner of a particular make and design of car should refer to the instruction handbook which contains a chart and recommends what grease to use.

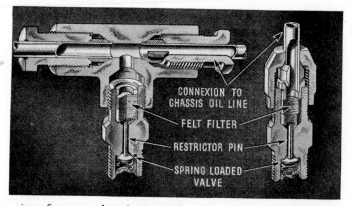

CONNEXION TO CHASSIS OIL LINE

FELT FILTER

RESTRICTOR PIN

SPRING LOADED VALVE

On early systems one pipe often served two or more adjacent bearings; the bearing which developed the most wear thus allowed most of the oil to escape without reaching the other bearings. A broken pipe, too, will allow oil to be pumped onto the garage floor without reaching the bearings.

It must not be inferred, however, that the system is necessarily unreliable. Properly used, it can save a lot of trouble. Remember that it cannot always cover every point needing attention: examples are those on some of the steering connexions, and the propeller shaft splines.

AUTOMATIC CHASSIS LUBRICATION

As an improvement on the grouped nipple arrangement, various forms of automatic chassis lubrication have been developed during recent years. Of these, the Luvax-Bijur system is the most widely used. Actually there are three of these systems in common use, but they all employ the principle of a pump which delivers a metered quantity of oil to a number of distribution pipes supplying the various chassis bearings. At each oiling point is a connexion in which a standard-sized hole is drilled. In this hole is a restrictor pin which governs the amount of oil which reaches the bearing; a large pin, which has only a limited clearance in the hole, will supply a correspondingly limited amount of oil to such points as the brake cross-shaft or clutch pedal bearings; a small pin will allow a greater flow of oil to lubricate the front-wheel pivots, steering connexions, and so on. The difference between the systems lies in the type of pump used to distribute the oil.

VACUUM-OPERATED SYSTEM

One method is to operate a small plunger pump by connecting it to a diaphragm which is raised and lowered by the variations in the depression in the inlet manifold of the engine which occur during normal driving. Fig. 3 shows the mechanism clearly. The action of the pump is regulated by the restrictor pin fitted in a small hole drilled in the union to which the suction pipe is connected; this damps out the variations in suction which reach the diaphragm, the resistance of the regulator being chosen to give a suitable total output from the pump for any particular car.

The only attention normally required by this system is to keep the reservoir topped up with the special chassis oil, or an alternative recommended by the maker of the car. The correct functioning of the system depends on using oil of the right viscosity; if clean oil is added, moreover, it will not be necessary to clean

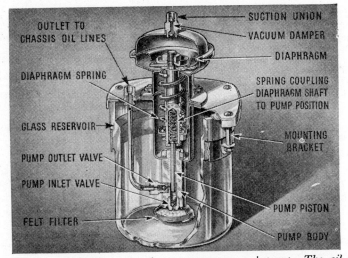

OUTLET TO
CHASSIS OIL LINES

DIAPHRAGM SPRING

GLASS RESERVOIR

PUMP OUTLET VALVE

PUMP INLET VALVE

FELT FILTER

SUCTION UNION

VACUUM DAMPER

DIAPHRAGM

SPRING COUPLING
DIAPHRAGM SHAFT
TO PUMP POSITION

MOUNTING
BRACKET

PUMP PISTON

PUMP BODY

FIG. 3. *Cut-away view of a vacuum-operated pump. The oil pressure is generated by the up and down movement of the piston that is connected to the diaphragm. The latter is actuated by variations in the depression in the inlet manifold.*

the filter, although this is accessible by disconnecting the oil line between the pump and the outlet on the body of the unit, after removing the reservoir and withdrawing the cover plate and pump assembly. The filter can then be removed and cleaned in petrol.

Testing the Pump. If it is suspected that the pump is not functioning correctly, two tests can be made. Disconnect the delivery pipe from the union on the cover plate, and the vacuum pipe from the regulator. With the engine idling, press the vacuum pipe union firmly against the regulator. This should cause the piston to rise. When the pipe is withdrawn from the regulator, the piston should return within 5 seconds or less, and a few drops of clear oil, free from air bubbles, should be discharged from the outlet union.

If this does not happen, the regulator may be choked by dirt and dust drawn in from the engine manifold. Regulators should in any case be replaced at intervals of 10,000 miles. The "rate" of the regu-

lator is stamped on it; see that the replacement bears the same number. A little jointing compound on the threads of the regulator will ensure an air-tight joint when it is screwed into place.

If the pump does not function when a new regulator has been fitted, unscrew the two bolts which secure the pump and diaphragm assembly to the cover plate and raise and lower the diaphragm housing about ¾ in. by hand. One or two drops of oil should be expelled from the outlet union on each downstroke. If this is not the case, and the filter is clean, the complete pump and diaphragm must be returned to a Lucas-C.A.V.-Rotax service station for repair or replacement, as special tools and fixtures are needed to dismantle it.

THERMAL SYSTEM

A simpler system than that just described is the arrangement in which the pumping action is obtained by the expansion of oil in a cylinder which is mounted close to the exhaust manifold. When the engine is started, the oil in the cylinder expands and passes through a non-return valve at the top of the cylinder to the pipe lines serving the chassis points. As the engine cools down, the oil in the cylinder contracts and a fresh supply is drawn in through a second non-return valve at the base of cylinder. A small amount of oil will also be delivered when the temperature of the exhaust manifold varies during normal running. The only likely faults in this simple system are those caused by air leakage into the suction pipe connecting the thermal cylinder to the reservoir, or leaking valves. These can be unscrewed and flushed with paraffin to clean them. A touch of jointing compound should be put on the threads of the joint to ensure an oil-tight connexion.

PEDAL-OPERATED SYSTEM

The pedal-operated system consists of a pump which is fitted beneath an oil reservoir, and connected to a foot pedal operated by the driver. Depression of the pedal raises the pump plunger and draws oil into the cylinder through a non-return valve in the centre of the piston. The piston is then returned by a spring, forcing a small quantity of oil to the chassis bearings. For normal lubrication the pedal should be depressed once during every hundred miles of driving.

If the pedal returns in less than a minute, the inference is that the oil reservoir is empty or that there is a fault in the system, such as a broken delivery pipe, or a faulty pump plunger or ball valve. Servicing the pump is a job for a Lucas-C.A.V.-Rotax depot.

If the pedal fails to return, the filter, which prevents any grit or other matter entering the pipe line, may need cleaning, although this is only likely if an incorrect grade of oil has been used. To remove the filter, disconnect the chassis oil line from the outlet unions, tie or wedge the pedal in a partly depressed position, and unscrew the cap at the base of the pump unit, catching the oil which flows out in a clean tin or jar.

Make a note of the position of the filter retaining plate and gaskets before removing them from the cap. The filter may be washed in petrol. The gauze disk beneath it need not be disturbed; its ridges should be next to the cap. When reassembling, the hollow side of the retainer must face the filter disk. Screw the cap home firmly.

Chassis Pipe Lines. With any of the pumps just described, a similar chassis pipe-line layout is used, each oiling point being served by a union embodying a restrictor of the type mentioned earlier. Fault tracing is, therefore, a fairly simple matter, since starvation of one or more unions served by a common pipe will

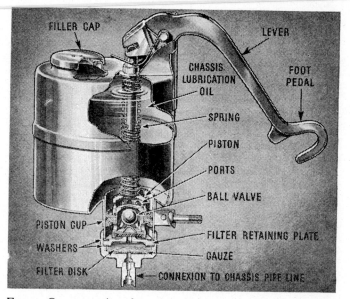

FIG. 4. *Cut-away view of a pedal-operated pump. In this design the oil pressure is generated by the up and down movement of the piston connected to the foot pedal lever. During normal running the pedal should be depressed about once during every hundred miles of driving.*

indicate that the pipe must be blocked, dented or broken. Most of the points already covered when dealing with grouped nipple lubrication systems will also apply to the automatic systems.

ROAD SPRINGS

While most owners fully appreciate the effect that the road springs have on the comfort of the car, the fact that they also exercise a very pronounced influence on steering and general controllability is sometimes overlooked. Modern suspension systems are the result of careful design, but their efficiency cannot be maintained if servicing is neglected. In this section we will consider the conventional type of semi-elliptic leaf spring suspension; independent suspension systems will be dealt with in the next section.

Lubricating the Springs. In the majority of cases manufacturers specify that the road springs should be lubricated. In one or two instances, however, the designer has taken advantage of the inherent damping effect provided by the friction between the spring leaves; if the springs are lubricated the suspension will then become unduly "lively."

When it is recommended that the springs should be lubricated at 1,000-mile intervals, the car should be jacked up with the jack placed beneath the chassis, so that the weight is removed from the springs. Some authorities recommend grease as a lubricant, preferably graphited, and this is excellent provided that it can be forced right in between the leaves, which should be separated by a screwdriver or similar tool while the grease is inserted with a knife blade. Pay particular attention to the ends of each leaf, where these rub upon the underside of the leaf above.

In some cases the car manufacturer has had the foresight to arrange for lubrication of the spring leaves by means of a grease-gun nipple fitted to the centre bolt, but this, unfortunately, is the exception rather than the rule.

For general use, penetrating oil, of the graphited variety for preference, is probably a safer lubricant than grease; if applied fairly liberally with a spray or brush to the edges of the leaves, it will work in between them and coat the interior surfaces. The springs must, of course, be freed from mud and grit first; a brisk scrub with a wire brush and paraffin before the weight of the car is removed from the springs, so that the grit which is dislodged is not forced between the leaves, is the best plan.

Lubricating the Shackles. The shackle pins and bushes must be lubricated with gear oil or grease, as recommended by the manufacturer, at the same time; this is best done while the weight of the car is carried by the jack, so that the lubricant is forced between the upper surfaces of the pins and bushes, which normally carry the weight of the car. If Silentbloc rubber bushes are fitted to the shackles, lubrication is, of course, unnecessary. Oil and grease must, in fact, be kept away from the rubber bushes, otherwise they will deteriorate.

Alinement of the Leaves. When the springs are lubricated it is a good plan to check the tightness of the U-bolts which hold the springs to the front or rear axle; during the running-in period in particular, the nuts may be found to be appreciably loose. At the same time, check the alinement of the spring leaves. The longer leaves are generally held securely by clips, but the shorter ones may become twisted slightly out of line with the remainder, particularly if the U-bolts have slackened. To correct this, loosen the U-bolts slightly and tap the leaves back into place with a hammer; tighten the U-bolts firmly and lock them.

Worn Spring Leaves. After a considerable mileage it may be found that the suspension is no longer as flexible as when new. This is due to wear of the tips of the spring leaves, each of which tends to dig into the underside of the leaf above it: when new, the ends of the leaves are ground to a radius to prevent this. The only remedy is to remove the springs and dismantle them so that the tips of the leaves can be ground or filed to restore the radius, and the depression formed in each leaf smoothed out as far as possible. On a number of recent models the use of hardened steel rollers, zinc disks, or interleaving strips between the leaves prevents this trouble. Such parts can easily be removed when they become worn.

Weakened and Broken Springs. Eventually the springs lose their resilience and become flattened. The fact that the spring appears to be flat, however, is not necessarily an indication that it has weakened. On a number of modern cars the spring is intended to be flat when loaded, especially in the case of the front

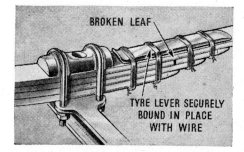

FIG. 5. *A temporary way of repairing a broken spring to meet an emergency.*

springs. Sometimes a negative camber, or upward bend at the centre, is specified for rear springs. In most cases, however, the position of the swinging shackle at one end of the spring gives a clue to the true state of affairs. If the spring has weakened, the shackle will no longer be approximately vertical, but will be appreciably inclined one way or the other, due to the altered length of the spring.

When one spring of a pair appears to be much weaker than its fellow, look for

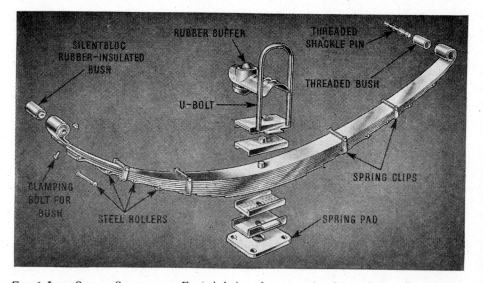

FIG. 6. LEAF SPRING SUSPENSION. *Exploded view of a conventional type of semi-elliptic laminated spring. The hardened steel rollers fitted in the ends of the upper leaves prevent wear due to friction. In principle the spring is a beam loaded at two ends and supported at the middle.*

one or more broken leaves; an accumulation of sand or grit often hides the fracture, but the slight gap between the broken ends can usually be seen when the edges of the leaves have been cleaned. Do not be led astray, however, by the intentional gap left in one leaf on some modern suspension systems: for example such a gap is apparent on the type fitted on recent Wolseley models.

Strain Caused by Fracture. The car should not be driven when a spring leaf is fractured. The additional strain thrown on the remaining leaves will cause others to break before very long. If it is essential to complete a journey, a get-you-home repair can be adopted on the lines shown in Fig. 5. When it is the main leaf which has fractured, it will be necessary to arrange a wedge or block between the end of the swinging shackle and the chassis to prevent the shackle from swinging too far forward.

If a spring has weakened, it can be "set up", or recambered by a smith, and will generally be equal to new if a specialist who knows the correct heat treatment carries out the work. Any fractured leaves can, of course, be renewed at the same time. This will entail removing the spring from the axle, a somewhat awkward job best left to a garage which has the necessary equipment to deal with any obstinate shackle pins or other unexpected snags. Brief details of the work are, however, given for the benefit of the owner intending to carry out the work himself.

Shackle Pins and Bushes. When the conventional type of shackle pin and bronze bush become worn, steering trouble is often caused or aggravated. On recent models the pins and bushes are sometimes threaded, to provide a positive sideways location for the spring, while the Silentbloc rubber bushes already referred to are also widely used. The fitting of new parts does not in itself present much difficulty: the chief complication is the removal of the springs from the axle and chassis.

Removing the Springs. Before the shackle pins can be removed, it will be necessary to jack up the chassis and support it on substantial and rigid blocks, so that there will be no risk of it falling when leverage is applied to any part. The brake cables, rods or tubes and the shock absorber arms must be disconnected as necessary.

Place a jack under the axle, and raise the axle until the springs are in a neutral position, neither compressed nor carrying the weight of the axle. If radius arms or torque rods are fitted, these must now be unbolted from the axle; the services of an assistant may be needed to rotate the axle slightly on the springs by means of a bar clamped to it, so that the pin securing the torsion rod to the axle bracket is relieved of strain and can be pushed out.

After removing the nuts from the ends of the shackle pins, these, if of the normal type in plain bushes, can be tapped out. A fairly sharp blow is often needed to start them, especially if they have seized in the bushes due to lack of lubrication. Threaded shackle pins cannot be removed in this manner, but must be screwed out of the bushes. Since the design of the shackles differs on various cars, it will be necessary to obtain the advice of the local agent or the manufacturer. When Silentbloc bushes are used, the spring is disconnected by removing the bolt which passes through the centre of the bush.

When both ends of the spring have been freed, the axle can be lowered with the springs still attached. If only the shackle pins and bushes need renewal, it may be preferred to leave the springs attached to the axle, but in most cases the slight extra work of undoing the U-bolts is compensated by the greater ease of working with the springs on the bench.

Pressing Out Bushes. Bronze bushes or Silentbloc bushes can be drawn out of the eye by means of a bolt, washer and distance piece to give the necessary clearance. By reversing the arrangement, the new bushes can be fitted. With ordinary bushes, it may be found that the new shackle pin is a very tight fit when the bush is in place, due to the slight compression of the bush in the spring-eye. To obtain a snug push-fit the bush must be reamered out, preferably using an expanding reamer.

The side-play between the spring-eye and the shackle is important, and the correct figure must be ascertained. This may be controlled by spring-steel washers, fibre washers, or by a tubular steel distance piece. When screwed shackle pins are fitted, each end must protrude from the bush by the same amount, the pin being screwed inwards or outwards until this is obtained. A point to note

when Silentbloc bushes are refitted is that the bolts should not be fully tightened until reassembly has been completed and the car lowered from the jacks. With the springs normally deflected, the bolts may be tightened up.

Dismantling the Springs. If the springs are to be dismantled, a press, strong screw clamp, or a vice will be required, so that the leaves can be kept compressed while the nut on the centre bolt is unscrewed. Before separating the leaves, mark each with a centre punch to ensure correct reassembly. When clips are used to hold the longer leaves together, remove the bolt or file off the head of the rivet which passes through the ends of the clip. If the clip is riveted at the centre to the lowest leaf, it may be possible to bend back the arms sufficiently to allow the upper leaves to be slid out.

The leaves should be thoroughly cleaned and examined for any of the defects mentioned earlier. When re-

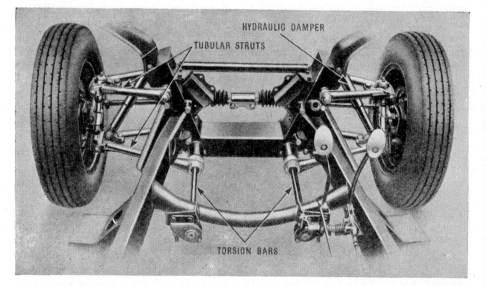

FIG. 7. TORSION BAR SUSPENSION. *Rear view of the torsion bars in the front wheel suspension of a Riley 1½ litre model. The torsion bars are provided with a cam adjustment at the rear end. The tubular struts are mounted in special bushings which do not require any lubrication.*

assembling the spring, coat the leaves with graphite grease. A long bolt will assist in centring them while they are compressed in the vice or clamp, and this can be replaced by the centre bolt when the leaves are fully compressed and properly alined. Always fit a new centre bolt if any doubt exists regarding the condition of the original; this is sound advice, too, where the U-bolts and nuts securing the spring are concerned.

INDEPENDENT SUSPENSION SYSTEMS

Independent front and rear wheel suspension systems are not such a straightforward proposition from the owner's point of view. A number of different arrangements are in use. Some employ leaf springs arranged transversely across the chassis, as on Standard and Humber cars; some use torsion bars, as on Vauxhall models, and others make use of large coil springs, examples being the Daimler and Lanchester systems. The examples quoted refer, of course, only to some typical British cars; most of these types of suspension are to be found on American and Continental models as well.

It is difficult to advise the owner regarding dismantling any given system, as the detail arrangement varies widely on different models. As is so often the case, the only safe procedure is to consult the manufacturer or his agent, since special tools may be required, and important measurements affecting the steering geometry are likely to be upset. Fortunately lubrication in accordance with the manufacturer's recommendation, and a periodical check of the steering adjustments, should be all that is required.

Diagnosing Faults. The majority of the troubles likely to be experienced fall more properly under the heading of steering faults, and can be rectified by maintaining the correct steering

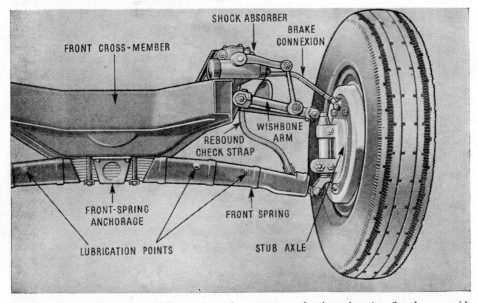

FIG. 8. FRONT SUSPENSION. *Front view of a transverse laminated spring fitted to provide independent suspension for the front wheels. Nipples are provided in the spring cover for lubricating the spring leaves. A shock absorber is fitted between the chassis and wishbone.*

257

geometry, adjusting the tyre pressures, or by renewing any worn parts, such as the swivel pins and bushes in the wishbone linkage.

A fault sometimes experienced, however, is sagging of the car to one side. With coil spring systems this can be due to one spring weakening slightly. Sometimes this can be corrected by placing shims or washers beneath the weak spring, but renewal of the spring is usually the only effective cure.

When the coil spring is enclosed in a tube, however, the end cap against which it butts can usually be screwed downwards to increase its resistance and so raise that side of the car. On torsion bar systems it may be possible to readjust the anchorage of the bar. When the bar fits into splines, for instance, rotating it by a distance equal to one or more splines may correct the trouble.

Adjusting Steering Angles. Some types of independent suspension are apt to cause fairly rapid tyre wear unless a careful check is kept on the castor and camber angles. As these angles are often readily adjustable, in contrast to conventional suspension systems, some general notes on the methods of carrying out the work will be of interest. No reference will be made to adjusting the toe-in or toe-out of the front wheels, as this is done by altering the length of the track rod, or the two halves of the rod when a divided track rod is used, and the operation is similar to that on the conventional systems dealt with in Chapter 10.

A word of warning is necessary at this stage; the correct angles must be ascertained from the manufacturer or his agent, while in order to carry out the work accurately, a set of specialized gauges of the type used by garages should be available, although it is possible to obtain reasonable results by straightforward measurement. The definitions of the

terms used and methods of measurement are explained in Chapter 10, so that there is no point in mentioning them here.

It will be observed that on some systems no adjustment of castor or camber angle, or both, is possible. In these cases incorrect angles can only be corrected by replacing worn pivot pins, bushes, or other components, or by renewing or straightening such parts as wishbones, axle carriers or stub axles which have been bent, as the result of an accident. The initial setting of the angles is carried out by using hydraulic bending or twisting tools, and is obviously beyond the scope of the private owner.

TRANSVERSE SPRING SYSTEMS

The most usual version of this system is a single transverse spring, the outer ends of which are pivoted to the base of the stub-axle carrier; short connecting links, termed wishbones, between the chassis and the top of the axle carrier position the axle as shown in Fig. 8.

The camber is usually adjusted by means of an eccentric bush in the outer end of the wishbone which carries the swivel pin. It should be remembered that the camber angle will be affected by the camber of the front spring. If this flattens, it becomes longer and thus moves the lower end of the axle carrier outwards.

The castor angle is not adjustable, since the wishbone and the spring position of the axle pivot pin is in the vertical plane. To ensure positive endwise location, the wishbone pivots are often fitted with screwed bushes. These require lubrication with an extreme pressure oil instead of the normal gear oil or grease.

COIL SPRING SYSTEMS

A widely-used coil spring system is to arrange a large coil spring between a hinged arm and the chassis. The stub axle carrier is connected between the outer end of the arm and a wishbone above it. Eccentric pivot pins are generally fitted to the upper wishbone so that the camber may be adjusted. In some cases the pivot pin is threaded, and by screwing it in one direction or the other the castor angle can be increased or decreased. It will be necessary to carry out this adjustment in multiples of one complete turn, so that the desired camber may be maintained, since rotation of the pin also affects the camber.

When rubber bushes are fitted to the upper wishbones, they may be provided with thimbles which give different offsets, thus altering the camber. The castor angle may be adjusted by fitting tapered shims between the lower wishbone and the torque rods which steady the axles, the base of the stub axle carrier is thus moved slightly backwards or forwards, the resilience of the rubber bushes in the upper wishbone affording sufficient latitude for this movement.

On recent Ford models the front suspension consists essentially of two coil-spring suspension units incorporating hydraulic double-acting shock absorbers. Two track control arms govern the limits of the front-wheel track and are pivoted on the front suspension cross tube. The stabilizer bar is secured at the forward end to rubber-mounted suspension feet and located at the rear ends in rubber bushes in the track control arms. Normally, the only attention required is periodical lubrication.

Coil springs are also used in sliding-axle systems. In these the upper and lower chassis cross-members are attached to sleeves which enclose the springs, and which surround a vertical pin that carries the stub axle, so that the springs are compressed between the ends of the sleeves and flanges on the pin. In these designs, adjustments are seldom possible.

TORSION BAR SUSPENSION

In some designs the front wheels are carried on arms which swing about pivots moving parallel with the chassis. The pivoted end of the arm is attached

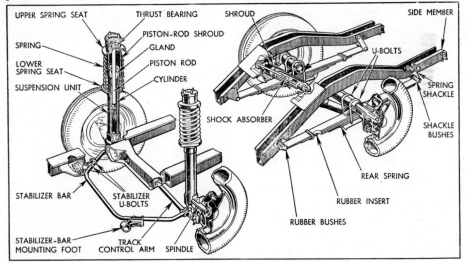

UPPER SPRING SEAT THRUST BEARING SHROUD SIDE MEMBER
SPRING PISTON-ROD SHROUD GLAND U-BOLTS
LOWER SPRING SEAT PISTON ROD SPRING SHACKLE
SUSPENSION UNIT CYLINDER
SHOCK ABSORBER SHACKLE BUSHES
STABILIZER BAR STABILIZER U-BOLTS REAR SPRING
RUBBER INSERT
STABILIZER-BAR MOUNTING FOOT TRACK CONTROL ARM SPINDLE RUBBER BUSHES

FIG. 9. (*Left*). *Coil spring independent front suspension system, used on the Ford New Anglia and New Prefect models; the front suspension units embody telescopic shock absorbers. (Right). The rear springs are conventional units, but the inclined mounting of the rear telescopic shock absorbers should be noted.*

to a torsion bar, which is arranged transversely across the chassis. Due to the construction of the arm, adjustment for camber or castor is rarely possible. It may, however, be necessary to readjust the setting of the torsion bar occasionally as already described, should the chassis sag to one side.

On the Vauxhall system a small but stiff compensating spring assists the movement of the axle through small deflections, thus softening the suspension, but goes out of action during large movements of the wheel carrier arms, so that the full effect of the torsion bar and tube is exerted. If the suspension is unsatisfactory, it may be necessary to readjust the torsion bar and tube so that the spring and toggle arm are in line when the car is at rest with two people occupying the front seats. This is a somewhat critical adjustment best left to a Vauxhall dealer. However, the oil bath in which the operating parts work should be checked every 2,000 miles and topped up if necessary.

An alternative torsion bar layout is for the axle to be carried between two wishbones in a similar manner to the coil spring systems described above, but suspension is provided by a torsion bar which fits into splines in the inner end of the lower wishbone, and runs parallel with the chassis side member, to which it is anchored at its rear end. It is not usual to provide adjustments for castor or camber angles on these systems.

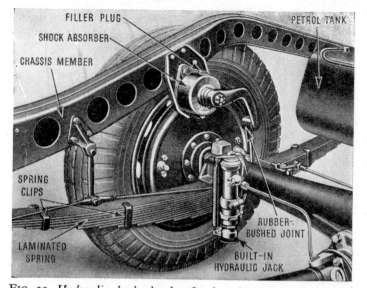

FIG. 10. *Hydraulic shock absorber fitted to the side member of the chassis. Its function is to damp down the recoil of the laminated springs when the car is travelling over uneven road surfaces. The fluid level in the shock absorber should be checked at intervals of 5,000 miles.*

SHOCK ABSORBERS

A car travelling along a level road encounters a bump. The passengers are lifted up by the car, perhaps suddenly, with an uncomfortable sensation, perhaps even with a definite jar. It all depends on the speed of the car, the rate of vertical acceleration, and the efficiency of the springs.

What actually happens is that the bump lifts the wheels, producing energy which is stored up during the compression of the springs against the weight of the body. The energy thus stored up must be given out by the springs, and this results in recoil almost as powerful as the original shock load. This recoil forces the wheels downwards and lifts the body so that the passengers actually feel the thrust of the springs against the body, in a ratio directly proportionate to the original shock.

Deficiencies of Springs. This is the greatest deficiency of springs. They must

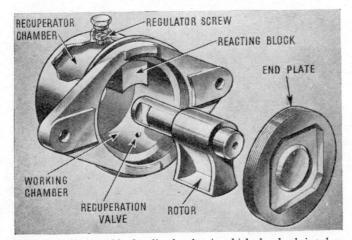

RECUPERATOR CHAMBER — REGULATOR SCREW — REACTING BLOCK — END PLATE — WORKING CHAMBER — RECUPERATION VALVE — ROTOR

FIG. 11. *A design of hydraulic absorber in which the shock is taken by the rotor displacing the oil from the working to the recuperating chamber.*

give out the energy which they store up, therefore, the rate of recoil is far too great. It is true that leaf springs do absorb a certain amount of energy during compression and recoil because of the friction between leaves, but this type of spring appears to be giving way to coil or torsion bar types in which there is no inherent damping. Some method of dissipating or absorbing the energy stored by a spring becomes more necessary as road speeds increase. This is the function of the shock absorber.

On the road, a high-performance car weighing, when loaded, about 22 cwt. will require a set of shock absorbers capable of a maximum rate of absorption of the order of $6\frac{3}{4}$ h.p. This emphasizes the vital necessity for adequate control over the suspension.

HYDRAULIC SHOCK ABSORBERS

Some of the earliest shock absorbers consisted of friction disks which could be manually tightened. These types, however, have been practically superseded by hydraulic shock absorbers, consisting of two main designs; the arm type, in which the arm operates a vane or pistons, and the direct-piston type, consisting of a telescopic tubular shock absorber which is connected between the chassis frame and the axle, or the chassis and the lower wishbone on an independent suspension system. Of the arm-operated types, the most widely used are the Luvax vane-type and Luvax, Luvax-Girling or Newton piston-type shock absorbers; the Armstrong shock absorber also comes into this class. The chief direct-piston types are the Newton and the Girling; the former type is illustrated in Fig. 7.

Topping-up the Shock Absorbers. It is as well to check the level of the fluid in the shock absorbers at 5,000-mile intervals. The filler cap must be unscrewed, and fresh fluid added to bring the level to just below the orifice, leaving a small air space to allow the fluid to expand as it warms up in use. In some piston-type shock absorbers the filler plug also acts as a level indicator, and fluid should be added until it begins to overflow.

Newton shock absorbers have a level plug in the upper part of the casing, or a small hole drilled in the side to allow surplus fluid to overflow. Some Newton models are fitted with an oil-gun nipple so that the fluid can be forced in with a grease gun, which must, of course, be very thoroughly cleaned out before filling it with shock absorber fluid. Better still, a special pressure-filling gun is available with a flexible spout fitted with a nozzle which grips the union.

Unfortunately, it is easy to give instructions regarding topping-up, but the operation is by no means a simple one in practice. The shock absorbers are generally inaccessible, so that a torch and small mirror may be needed to enable the level to be checked. In addition, when the filler plug is unscrewed and a funnel or the nozzle of a special filler gun is inserted, it is almost inevitable that grit will find its way inside the shock absorber, leading to any amount of subsequent trouble.

Clean Topping-up. The moral, therefore, is to clean the top of the shock absorber very thoroughly before the plug is removed; it is as well, too, to hose down the underside of the wings before topping-up the front shock absorbers, and to clean the underside of the floorboards if the rear shock absorbers cannot be reached from above through inspection openings. This will prevent mud and grit being accidentally dislodged while the filler plug is out.

Strictly speaking, the soundest plan is to remove the shock absorbers and deal with them on the bench; the additional trouble will be well repaid. If this is not done, at least disconnect one end of the operating link so that the arm can be moved up and down to expel any air from the pressure chamber while the fluid is being added.

The final point concerns the fluid. It is essential to use the fluid recommended by the makers of the shock absorber, and to make sure that it is the correct grade. Piston-type shock absorbers need a much thinner fluid than that used in vane-type units, for instance.

Possible Troubles. When the operating link is detached from the chassis, the action of the shock absorber can be easily checked. There should be a uniform resistance throughout the movement of the arm. Any free movement usually indicates the presence of air in the pressure chamber, and should disappear when topping-up is correctly carried out.

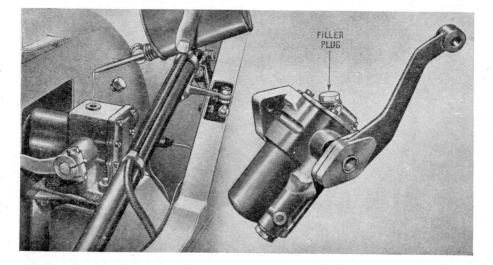

Fig. 12. Topping-Up the Shock Absorbers. *On many modern cars the front shock absorbers can be reached when the bonnet is lifted. The rear shock absorbers (a typical example is shown on the right) should be removed and topped-up on the bench owing to the risk of grit entering the working chamber if they are topped-up while in place on the car.*

FIG. 13. *Hydraulic shock absorber fitted between the chassis and axle shaft. The connecting link is housed in rubber bushes.*

springs fitted or by the diameter of by-pass passages in the body.

When adjustment is possible, however, it may have been altered from its original setting. If the resistance to the movement of the arms on a pair of shock absorbers on the front or rear axle is not substantially the same when tested with the link disconnected, adjustment is necessary. Remember that the front shock absorbers are not necessarily set to give the same resistance as the rear; it is the resistance of a pair which must be equal.

On Luvax vane-type shock absorbers the adjusting screw is beneath the filler plug. It is locked by a small spring, so that it turns with a series of clicks. To equalize the two shock absorbers, screw

If free movement persists, it is possibly due to wear on the splines or the key which secures the operating arm to the shaft. Renewal calls for special tools, and should be left to the manufacturer. If the resistance is erratic or jerky, the trouble probably lies in defective pistons or valves. Leakage past the spindle or end caps on Lucas shock absorbers also calls for special tools to rectify the trouble.

On Armstrong types, however, a gland nut is fitted which can be tightened with a C-spanner. Generally speaking, when a shock absorber develops any trouble, the cheapest and most effective course is to have it reconditioned by the makers.

Adjusting the Shock Absorbers. When the shock absorbers are first fitted to the car they are correctly adjusted and should not need any subsequent readjustment. Many types, in fact, have no provision for adjustment, the correct characteristics being determined during manufacture by the strength of the valve

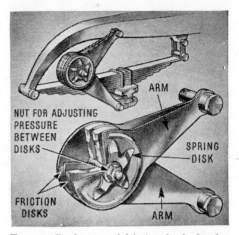

FIG. 14. *Early type of friction shock absorber fitted between the chassis and spring support.*

one screw down as far as possible, counting the number of clicks; then unscrew it to the original position. Screw the adjuster in the other shock absorber fully home, and then unscrew it by the same number of clicks as the first. From this initial setting, which in most cases is from 1½ to 2 full turns from the fully closed position, the resistance of both shock absorbers can be reduced or increased as desired to give satisfactory suspension. The adjustment is very sensitive, and the screws should be moved only two or three clicks at a time between tests on the road.

On some Armstrong shock absorbers an adjusting screw projects from the side of the casing at the narrower end. It can be screwed inwards to increase the resistance, or outwards to decrease it, after slackening off the locking nut.

Reaching the Adjusting Screw. Earlier Newton shock absorbers must be dismantled to give access to the adjusting screw. These models have a packing ring half-way up the body. This must be unscrewed with a C-spanner so that the dust cover may be removed. The gland revealed can now be unscrewed, allowing the piston to be withdrawn. On recent Newton types adjustment is a simpler proposition. It is simply necessary to uncouple one link and compress the shock absorber to its minimum length; this causes a projection in the upper part of the shock absorber to engage with the head of the adjusting screw, so that by rotating one half in relation to the other the screw can be screwed inwards or outwards.

FRICTION-TYPE SHOCK ABSORBERS

Although the early type of friction shock absorber is now almost obsolete, a modern Andre version is sometimes used. This consists of a number of stainless-steel

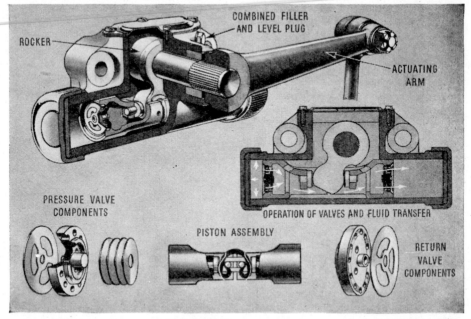

FIG. 15. HYDRAULIC SHOCK ABSORBER. *Views of the Luvax hydraulic shock absorber showing the location and action of the piston assembly. The movement of the axle is transmitted to the rocker by the actuating arm which is coupled to the spring by a link.*

plates sandwiched between friction disks, which in turn are clamped between the arms which are attached to the axle and chassis. Pressure is applied to the friction disks by tightening the nut on the centre bolt so as to compress a spring-steel star-shaped washer. Adjustment is, therefore, a simple matter, although it is best to check the resistance of each shock absorber by clamping one arm in a vice and measuring the force required to move the free arm. A spring balance capable of weighing up to 25 lb. will be suitable. As an initial setting, the following figures will be found about right.

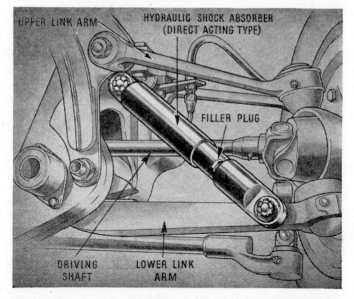

FIG. 16. *Direct-acting hydraulic shock absorber fitted between the upper and lower link arms on a front wheel drive provided with torsion bar suspension.*

Approximate Weight of Car	*Tension to move Arm*	
Up to 12 cwt.	16 lb.	
12–20 ,,	19 ,,	
20–25 ,,	23 ,,	
25–30 ,,	16 ,,	(Multiplex shock absorber).
30–40 ,,	19 ,,	,, ,,
over 40 ,,	23 ,,	,, ,,

LOOSE MOUNTINGS AND CONNEXIONS

No shock absorber, even when in good condition and correctly adjusted, can control the suspension properly if the bolts attaching it to the chassis are loose, or play has developed in the bushes which attach its operating member to the axle. Nowadays rubber bushes are used in the operating linkage and need no lubrication or attention. When they become worn, however, it is generally necessary to enlist the aid of a service depot, since the fitting of replacement rubbers calls for a set of special tools. When normal Silent-bloc bushes are fitted, however, replacement is often within the scope of the owner, as the outer steel liner can be pressed into its housing without much difficulty.

AUTOMATIC CONTROL OF SHOCK ABSORBERS

Both hydraulic and friction-type shock absorbers may be controlled from the dashboard, the amount of damping being varied at will in accordance with road conditions, although such systems are at present fitted only to the higher-priced cars and sports models. The only additional servicing required is to top-up the control system with the fluid specified by the makers. For the Luvax types thin winter grade engine oil is specified for the control system; the shock absorbers themselves still require the correct fluid, of course. On Andre Telecontrol shock absorbers the control system is filled with a mixture of 30 per cent glycerine in distilled water.

SHOCK ABSORBERS ON INDEPENDENT SUSPENSION SYSTEMS

On most of the independent suspension systems one of the types of shock absorbers described in this chapter is used. Sometimes, however, the shock absorber is built into the suspension unit, as on Vauxhall designs, to take one example. The suspension housing must then be filled with shock absorber fluid. Provided that the casing is kept topped-up, the only likely trouble is the presence of grit under the valves in the shock absorber.

Before attempting to dismantle the unit, obtain the advice of an expert.

CHASSIS AND BODY REPAIRS

As far as the owner is concerned, little can be done to repair more than minor damage to the body and chassis. The modern tendency to combine the body and chassis further complicates the matter; among the items of equipment required to tackle even a moderate amount of damage on a body of this type are a power jack with extensions and pads, a trammel, welding outfit, panel-beating equipment, solder-filling gun, sanding machine and spraying equipment.

This is, however, looking rather on the black side of the question: to the credit of the all-steel body can be placed its greater strength and resistance to damage, and the manner in which such damage can be made good by forcing distorted

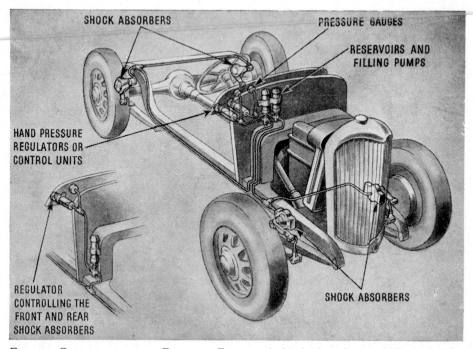

SHOCK ABSORBERS   PRESSURE GAUGES

RESERVOIRS AND FILLING PUMPS

HAND PRESSURE REGULATORS OR CONTROL UNITS

REGULATOR CONTROLLING THE FRONT AND REAR SHOCK ABSORBERS

SHOCK ABSORBERS

Fig. 17. Controlling the Damping Effect. *Andre hydro-telecontrol shock absorber system in which the damping effect can be varied at will by hand pressure regulators.*

members back into shape with the use of jacks, heating the metal if required; the comparative ease with which large sections of the body can be cut out with an oxyacetylene flame, and replaced by new panels and structural members welded into place is also an advantage. Such methods are, of course, impossible with a coachbuilt body; if the two types of body receive the same amount of damage in a crash, in fact, the repairs to the modern type will almost certainly cost considerably less.

Checking Chassis Alinement. When a car is damaged, possibly only to a minor degree, it is always advisable to check the chassis alinement. The job can be carried out quite simply in the garage or on any level concrete surface, and the only equipment required is a plumbline, a tape measure, and a chalk.

The plumbline should be suspended from the centre of each of the spring shackle pins; the fixed pin must be chosen in each case. Beneath the point at which the tip of the plumb-bob reaches the floor make a chalk dot. When each shackle pin has been dealt with in this manner, drive or push the car away.

We now have eight points, projected from the chassis in a convenient position for measurement. The diagonals between the various points should be measured with a trammel or steel tape. If there is a difference of more than about $\frac{1}{4}$ in. on any of the shorter pairs of diagonals, or about $\frac{5}{16}$ in. on the longer ones, it can be assumed that the chassis is distorted. The maker of the car will usually be able to furnish accurate figures.

Checking Body Structure. A somewhat similar method may be used to check the body structure, again relying on any discrepancy between pairs of diagonals to show up distortion. A coachbuilder uses a steel trammel to take the measurements, but the owner can probably obtain quite good results by using a wooden lath, to which a very simple adjustable telescopic section has been fitted. Before measurements can be taken, reference points must be established. This can be done by arranging a straightedge as high as possible on a door pillar, using a spirit-level to make sure that it is not tilted. Mark the points at which it touches the front and rear pillars, and with the plumbline registering with these points, mark the door sill immediately below them. Repeat the operation on the other side of the car, making sure that the straightedge is at exactly the same height as before.

The points marked now form the corners of two rectangles, and the eight together can be visualized as forming a rectangular box. By measuring the diagonals of the sides, ends, and across the "box", such faults as the pushing back of one door frame, sideways distortion of the pillars, and so on, can be quickly detected.

Loose Chassis Fastenings. Sometimes the various rivets which secure the chassis members work loose, with the result that the chassis looses rigidity and will warp or deflect under the influence of road shocks. Chassis are often of welded construction nowadays, but it is worth checking for loose rivets if instability and poor steering cannot be cured by normal adjustments.

When a rivet loosens, the holes in which it fits quickly become worn; the best plan is to drill them out to take the next largest size of B.S.F. bolt, and to bolt the parts up securely, using a spring locking washer to prevent the nut from slackening. For vital parts such as spring brackets, it is preferable to drill the bolts and fit castellated nuts, securing them with split pins or locking wire. Since it is not an easy matter to drill the chassis by hand, an electric drill is practically essential; if one is not available, the local garage will probably undertake the work.

CHAPTER 10

BRAKES, STEERING, WHEELS AND TYRES

THE braking and steering systems, and the wheels and tyres are grouped in this chapter because they are to a large extent interdependent: each exercises a considerable influence on the stability and safety of the car, and one inefficient unit in any of these assemblies can adversely affect the performance of the rest.

BRAKES

As with the other components on the modern car, it is the general rule for manufacturers to fit braking systems designed and produced by specialist firms; Lockheed, Girling, Bendix, or Bendix-Cowdrey systems are to be found on most cars today. These systems, although differing in principle, possess two features in common: great power in response to moderate pedal pressure, and ease of adjustment, which is usually carried out at each wheel. Some types of high-powered cars are fitted with a servo brake operating mechanism which utilizes suction from the engine induction system to assist the manual effort on the pedal.

The Lockheed system, being operated by fluid pressure, is, of course, self-compensating. The Girling, Bendix and Bendix-Cowdrey systems employ mechanical linkage, and have automatic compensation devices included in the

FIG. I. BRAKE ADJUSTMENT. *This view shows the brakes on the off-side front wheel being adjusted on the hexagon headed adjuster. The car is jacked-up to allow the wheels to spin.*

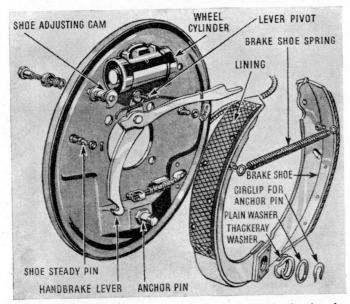

SHOE ADJUSTING CAM   WHEEL CYLINDER   LEVER PIVOT

BRAKE SHOE SPRING

LINING

BRAKE SHOE

CIRCLIP FOR ANCHOR PIN

PLAIN WASHER

THACKERAY WASHER

SHOE STEADY PIN

HANDBRAKE LEVER   ANCHOR PIN

FIG. 2. *Exploded view of a Lockheed brake assembly showing the location of the various components. Note the position of the adjusting cam at the head of the wheel cylinder.*

Again, if the hub bearings are worn and it is necessary to jack up the wheel, the hub and brake drum will drop slightly in relation to the shoes, which are carried on the stationary backplate, thus rendering accurate adjustment impossible.

LOCKHEED BRAKE ADJUSTMENT

The most common method of adjustment on Lockheed brakes takes the form of two large hexagonal nuts on the brake backplate, one on each side of the hydraulic pipe union. Fig. 1 shows their position and the manner in which they must be rotated in order to bring the shoes nearer to the drums. The nuts rotate cams which act as stops to limit the movement of the shoes away from the drum. The wheel must be jacked up and each adjuster should be rotated in turn until the wheel is locked; it is then turned in the reverse direction until the wheel is able to revolve freely.

Some Lockheed brakes have a different form of adjuster; only one nut is used, and this is fitted with a star-shaped handwheel which is rotated until the shoes touch the drum. On releasing the handwheel, the adjuster will spring back and automatically set the shoes to the correct clearance. It is unnecessary to jack up the wheel.

As the adjuster must move slightly on the backplate to centralize itself, all mud should be cleared away from around it, and a small quantity of penetrating

linkage, but these, once adjusted on assembly, should not need readjustment until some part of the linkage is dismantled. In the space at our disposal, therefore, only normal running adjustment and maintenance will be dealt with.

Adjusting the Brakes. In each of the systems to be described the method of adjustment is to bring the shoes into contact with the drum, and then to slacken the adjustment off by a specified amount, or until the shoes just cease to rub. After this adjustment the car should be driven a few miles to ensure that the braking effort of all four brakes is equal, i.e., the car does not tend to wander to the left or the right when the brakes are applied. If this tendency is apparent, the appropriate brake should be readjusted.

It will be evident, therefore, that accurate adjustment cannot be obtained if any part of the operating linkage is binding. Lubrication of all pivots, cross-shafts and cables should be the first step.

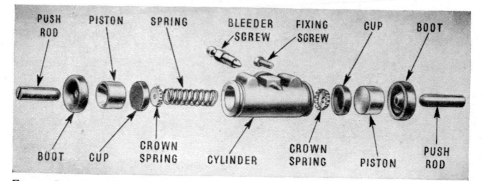

FIG. 3. LOCKHEED NON-ADJUSTABLE WHEEL CYLINDER. *Exploded view of the cylinder which is fitted to the outside of the brake backplate, and transmits the action of the brake pedal, via the master cylinder, to the brake shoes.*

oil should be applied to the base of the adjuster and allowed to soak in before carrying out the adjustment.

Notched Disk Method. A third form of adjustment which is used on one or two models consists of notched disks attached to the end caps of the hydraulic cylinder inside the brake drum. These disks are accessible through holes in the brake drum and wheel. The hub cap should be removed from the wheel, which should be jacked up and rotated until the hole is opposite one of the adjusting disks, which can then be rotated with a screwdriver until the wheel is locked. Slacken it back until the wheel is just free, and repeat the operation on the other adjuster after rotating the wheel to bring the hole into line with it.

Since the hydraulic cylinder must be free to slide on the backplate, the precautions regarding removal of mud, and the application of penetrating oil described earlier must be observed. A somewhat similar method of adjustment is used on modern Lockheed brakes, except that in this case the screwdriver is passed through the holes in the brake drum to engage with the slotted heads of adjusting screws. Each screw should be turned in a clockwise direction until the drum is locked, and then rotated anti-clockwise by one notch only, when the drum should be free to rotate.

Maintenance of System. The only other attention required by Lockheed brakes is periodical inspection of the level of the fluid in the supply tank. The

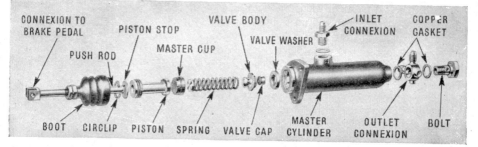

FIG. 4. LOCKHEED MASTER CYLINDER. *This cylinder is directly operated by the brake pedal and communicates with the wheel cylinders fitted to the separate wheels.*

FIG. 5. *Topping-up the fluid supply tank which feeds the master cylinder. If the level gets too low, air will leak into the system.*

reservoir may be integral with the master cylinder, in which case it is generally reached through an inspection trap in the floorboards; alternatively a separate tank may be fitted to the engine side of the scuttle. The fluid level should remain constant for long periods at approximately half-an-inch to one inch below the filler cap. Only genuine Lockheed fluid should be used for topping-up; oil or any other unauthorized liquid may damage the rubber components in the system.

If the level of the fluid is allowed to fall too low, air will enter the system and the brakes will feel spongy. Removal of the air is carried out by an operation known as bleeding. The need for frequent bleeding is an indication of worn rubber cups in the master cylinder and wheel cylinders, and renewal of these parts calls for expert attention.

Extracting the Air. Bleeding, which must be carried out at each brake in turn, is effected by attaching a rubber tube to a bleeder valve on each brake backplate and unscrewing the valve one turn by means of a special spanner, through which the tube passes. Sometimes the tube can be pushed directly onto the bleeder valve; in other cases it is necessary to remove a plug from the backplate and substitute a special nipple.

The free end of the tube is allowed to hang into a clean glass jar, and the brake pedal is then depressed quickly, and allowed to return slowly. At each depression fluid is pumped into the jar, and pumping is continued until the fluid issuing from the tube is free from air bubbles. The level of the fluid in the reservoir must be maintained by adding fresh fluid. If the fluid pumped out is clean, it may be subsequently used for topping-up, i.e., after it has been allowed to stand until the minute bubbles of air in it have disappeared. It should not be used to replenish the container while the bleeding operation is in progress.

ADJUSTING GIRLING BRAKES

On Girling brakes the adjuster takes the form of a conical wedge between two plungers which locate the stationary ends of the brake shoes. It is screwed inwards to expand the shoes by means of a square spindle which projects through the brake backplate. The cone has four flats machined on it, so that a series of clicks can be heard and felt as the adjusting spindle is turned. The adjuster

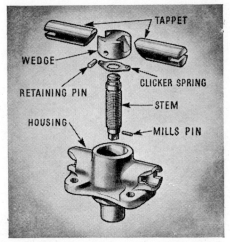

FIG. 6. *Exploded view of a Girling brake adjuster assembly. Its location in the brake assembly is illustrated in* FIG. 8.

271

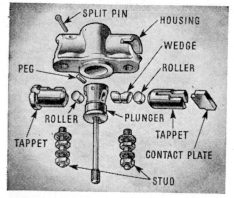

FIG. 7. *Exploded view of a Girling expander mechanism. Its location in the assembly is shown in* FIG. 8.

work in oversize holes, and roll round the inside of the hole instead of turning in it in the usual way. Slackness at these points, therefore, does not indicate the need for renewal. Besides eliminating friction, this type of joint does not require lubrication.

The maintenance of Girling hydraulic brakes is similar to that for the Lockheed system so far as the hydraulic components are concerned. The adjusters for the brake shoes are similar to those used on Girling mechanically operated brakes, it being necessary only to rotate an adjusting spindle on each drum. On certain designs the front brakes are self-adjusting.

SERVICING BENDIX BRAKES

Bendix brakes are cable-operated and are fitted with several different types of adjuster, adjustment being carried out at each individual brake. One type of adjuster consists of a flexible shaft terminating at its upper end in a square spindle which may be rotated with a spanner in a clockwise direction on the off-side, or right-hand brakes, and anti-clockwise on the near-side, until a slight drag is felt when the wheel is rotated. The adjuster is then slackened off until the wheel just rotates freely.

An alternative arrangement is for the adjuster to project horizontally from the

should be turned as far as possible in a clockwise direction, and should then be slackened back to the nearest click. The flats will then prevent it from rotating in service, while the depths of the flats ensure just the right clearance between the shoes and the drum. Accurate adjustment is thus possible without jacking up the wheel.

The brass nuts on the outside of the brake backplate, which secure the expander unit inside the brake, should not be tightened up, as the expander must be free to move and centralize itself. It should also be noticed that the various pins in the joints of the operating linkage

FIG. 8. *Girling two-leading shoe assembly. The shoe consists of two members, a carrier and the shoe. The shoes are free to move circumferentially on the rockers when the brakes are applied. The trigger springs return both rockers and shoes to their repose position when the brakes are off.*

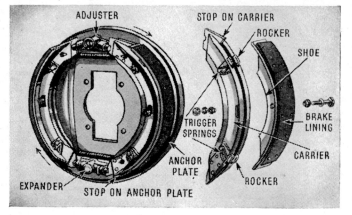

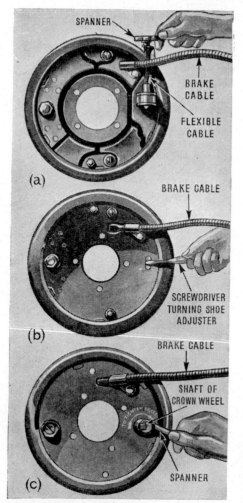

FIG. 9. *Three methods of adjusting the brake shoes on Bendix brakes. (a) is the flexible shaft type of adjustment. To expand the shoes in the drum, apply a spanner to the nut as shown; turn the spanner clockwise on right-hand and anti-clockwise on left-hand side of car. (b) is the screwdriver type in which the notched adjuster is levered with a screwdriver to expand the shoes. (c) is the crown wheel type of adjuster. To adjust the shoes apply a spanner to the square shaft protruding through the backplate. To expand the shoes turn the adjuster in a clockwise direction.*

backplate. This may be square, in which case a spanner is used to turn it, or may have a small tommy-bar passing through it so that it can be turned by hand. Yet another scheme is to rotate a notched wheel inside the brake drum by passing a screwdriver through a slot in the backplate.

The cables are generally provided with greasing nipples, and a graphite grease should be used to lubricate them. If lubricators are not fitted, it is as well to take the car to a service station at 10,000-mile intervals so that the cables may be dismantled and lubricated with a special Bendix grease gun. At the same time the system will be given a general overhaul, the cables being adjusted for length, and the brakes equalized and compensated.

BENDIX-COWDREY BRAKES

The Bendix-Cowdrey shoe assemblies are very similar to the anchor pin Bendix shoe assemblies. The expander is different and enables the mechanism to work at right-angles to the anchor plate. The adjuster is fitted with a ratchet device. It is necessary only to turn it clockwise until

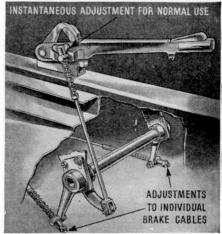

FIG. 10. *View showing the mechanism for adjusting the brake lever travel and individual brake cables.*

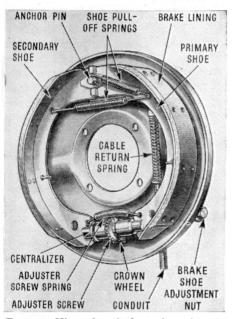

FIG. 11. *View of a single anchor pin type of Bendix brake shoe assembly showing the position of the shoe adjuster and anchor pin.*

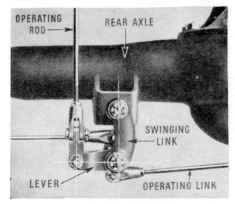

FIG. 12. (*a*) *Arrangement of Bendix-Cowdrey rear compensator. The centre lines have been drawn to show that the lever should be at an angle of 90 deg. to the centres of the swinging link, the latter being parallel with the operating rod.*

FIG. 12. (*b*) *The Bendix-Cowdrey front compensator. The centre lines show the measurements which should be observed when checking and resetting the compensator.*

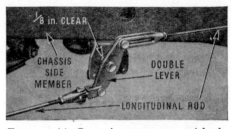

FIG. 12. (*c*) *Central compensator with the clearance at the compensator shaft indicated. Adjustments, when necessary, can be made on the ends of the longitudinal rods.*

the shoes meet the drum, and then to turn it back by five clicks. This will give the correct clearance without the need for jacking up the wheel.

The brakes are operated by rods and cables, and the layout includes an efficient compensator which will ensure equalized braking even though a measure of unequal adjustment may exist at individual brakes. The compensator must work freely, and should, therefore, be sprayed at intervals with penetrating oil. It is well worth while having the complete braking system checked by a service station at 25,000-mile intervals, so parts may be renewed and the operating rods and cables readjusted, see Figs. 12 (a), (b) and (c).

ADJUSTING THE HANDBRAKE

In any of the systems just described the handbrake operates on the rear wheels in most cases, through a separate linkage. The method of adjustment varies on different cars: sometimes a wing nut is accessible from inside the driving compartment, or can be reached from below the car, Fig. 10 illustrates the method of adjusting the handbrake and brake cables. It may be necessary, on the other hand, to alter the lengths of the operating rods or cables by means of adjusting nuts or screwed yoke ends at the handbrake or brake drum.

Causes of Unequal Braking. When any of the foregoing systems has been correctly adjusted, equal braking power should be obtained at each wheel. After adjusting the brakes, a test should be made on a dry, level road having a good surface, to make sure that all is in order. If it is found that one or more wheels lock before the others, it is probable that the less powerful brakes are suffering from oil, grease or water on the linings. While water will dry off, oil or grease in any quantity cannot be satisfactorily removed, and the only remedy will be to fit replacement linings. The trouble is generally due to overenthusiastic lubrication of the hubs, or a faulty oil retainer, both of which are the subject of advice in other chapters of this book.

When only one brake locks violently, however, the trouble may be due to loose backplate mounting bolts, worn brake shoe pivots, or similar mechanical defects which allow the backplate or shoes to rotate with the drum to some extent. If the leading edges of the linings have picked-up, or dust and grit have accumulated at the ends of the linings, progressive action will not be possible.

Brake Judder and Squeal. Any of the defects just mentioned will cause the brakes to judder when applied, and, to a lesser degree, to squeal; this noise being caused by a high-pitched vibration of the shoes and drums, instead of a low-frequency juddering. Some brakes are apt to squeal even when in good condition, although modern designs are not

as subject to this trouble as were earlier types. If careful attention to such points as cleaning the linings, chamfering the leading edges, and making sure that no mechanical faults exist does not cure the trouble, it may be necessary to adopt a more drastic method, such as fitting a silencing band to the outside of the brake drum, or attaching lead strips to the webs of the brake shoes, to damp out the

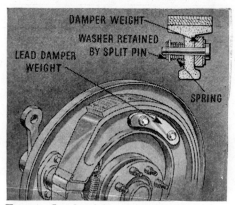

FIG. 13. *Lead weights attached to the web of a brake shoe to damp out vibration and prevent brake judder.*

vibrations. One or two manufacturers have in the past adopted the latter method with success, see Fig. 13.

Relining the Brakes. When the linings become worn, their renewal is not a difficult matter, since replacement brake shoes, fitted with linings which have been accurately ground to size, are available in exchange for the old shoes when the modern types of brake, described earlier, are fitted. There is no object, therefore, in attempting to rivet new linings to the existing shoes.

The first step is to remove the brake drums. First slacken off the adjustment completely. On removing the wheel, it will often be found that the drum is secured by countersunk screws or a ring of studs. In some cases it is necessary to draw off the hub, see Chapter 8.

Inspecting the Drum. It will probably be necessary to lever the drum off carefully with the aid of two large screwdrivers or tyre levers, taking care to keep it square, and not to bend the backplate. A series of light taps will help to free an obstinate drum. The interior surface of the drum should be inspected carefully.

It will probably be found to be scored, or worn so that a ridge is formed at each side of the path of contact with the shoes.

It will be necessary to have the drum lightly ground or skimmed in a lathe to restore a smooth surface. Only a minimum amount of metal must be removed, as the new shoes are accurately ground to

BRAKE FAULT-

Fault	Mechanical	Girling	Bendix
Excessive pedal travel	Linings worn	Linings worn	Linings worn
Brakes unbalanced	Broken connexions Oil on linings Maladjustment of system Loose spring security bolts Wrong and uneven tyre pressures Seized parts Drums distorted	Oil on linings Loose axle anchorages Tyre pressures Compensators fouling Distorted drums	Oil on linings Maladjustment Loose axle anchorage Tyre pressures Seized cable Distorted drums
Brakes grab	Shoes picking up Pins or anchor plate loose Drums distorted	Anchor plate loose Distorted drums	Anchor plate or pins loose Distorted drums
Brakes drag or remain on	Shoes seized on pins Pull-off springs broken Cams over centre	Seized compensators	Seized cables Pull-off springs broken
Pedal springy or needs pumping			
Fail to operate	Connexion severed Pedal fouls boards or stop	Expander at limit of travel	Pedal fouls boards or stop

the standard diameter, unless oversize shoes are available, and will take a considerable time to bed down and give maximum contact in an oversize drum. When the drum is badly worn it is better to replace it, or to have it machined to take a hardened steel liner. The latter method gives better braking power.

Removing Shoes and Springs. The method of removing the brake shoes naturally differs with individual designs of brake, but will be evident on inspection. Take care not to overstretch the pull-off springs, and make a note of the position of each spring when more than one is fitted, they may differ in tension.

TRACING CHART

BENDIX-COWDREY	LOCKHEED	REMEDY
Linings worn	Linings worn Air in system	Adjust for wear Bleed system
Oil on linings	Leaks in system Oil on linings	Locate and fit new parts Fit new linings and rectify oil leak Balance the system
Loose axle anchorages Tyre pressures	Loose axle anchorages Tyre pressures	Locate and secure Inflate when necessary
Compensators fouling Distorted drums	Distorted drums	Locate and rectify Grind true or install new drums
Anchor plate or pins loose Distorted drums	Shoes picking up Anchor plate or pins loose Distorted drums	Weight linings or renew weak springs Locate and secure True or install new drums
Seized compensators Pull-off springs broken	Shoes seized on pins Piston cups swollen by use of spurious fluid No free pedal movement	Locate, free and lubricate Locate and fit new parts True shoes or reline Adjust correctly
	Air in system Faulty master check valve Shortage of fluid	Bleed system Fit new valve and bleed system Check level in supply tank and examine for leaks
Expander at limit of travel	Broken conduit	Renew broken parts Adjust shoes for wear

Of the older types of mechanical brake, replacement shoes may not be available. Sets of linings, ready-drilled, countersunk and die-pressed to the correct radius, can, however, be obtained in boxed sets, complete with rivets, in most cases. Thus riveting them to the shoes is rendered as simple as possible. The old linings must be removed by drilling out the rivets or cutting them with a cold chisel, taking care not to damage the shoe, see Fig. 14.

The new lining should then be securely clamped to the shoe, and riveting commenced at one end, or at the centre, working outwards. The heads of the rivets must be supported on a bar of suitable diameter, gripped in the vice, and the ends securely burred over on the underside of the flange of the shoe. Make sure that the rivets are really tight, and that their heads are countersunk well below the surface of the lining. The lining must be in perfect contact with the shoe throughout its length, and free from buckling. The ends will need chamfering with a coarse file if this has not already been done.

THE STEERING GEAR

Good steering depends on a combination of factors. Beginning at the steering gearbox, the operating gear must be free from backlash, yet easy in action. Next, the steering connexions on the drop arm, drag link and track rod must be free from slackness; the wheel bearings and king pins must not be worn; the steering geometry must be correct; and finally the wheels and tyres must be in good condition and correctly balanced.

A Systematic Check. When the steering becomes unstable, or excessive free movement of the steering wheel takes place before the wheels are moved, the best plan is to check over the various items in the order given, so that slackness at any point can be detected and recti-

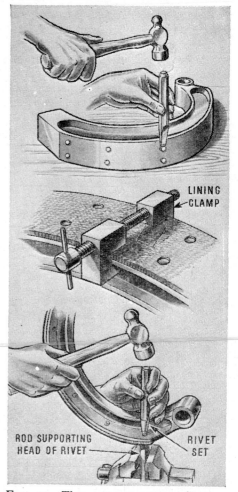

FIG. 14. *Three operations in relining a brake shoe. Details of these operations are given in the adjacent text.*

fied. The services of an assistant will be needed for most of the checks, and the front axle should be jacked up and preferably supported on a substantial block with both front wheels clear of the ground.

Begin by grasping the hub of the steering wheel and attempting to move it up and down. No appreciable vertical movement should be detected. Next, have your assistant rotate the steering

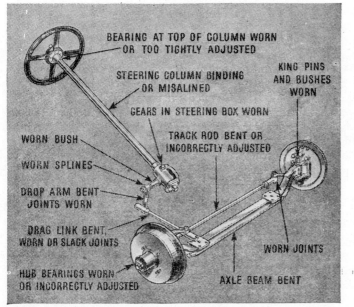

BEARING AT TOP OF COLUMN WORN OR TOO TIGHTLY ADJUSTED

STEERING COLUMN BINDING OR MISALINED

KING PINS AND BUSHES WORN

GEARS IN STEERING BOX WORN

WORN BUSH

TRACK ROD BENT OR INCORRECTLY ADJUSTED

WORN SPLINES

DROP ARM BENT JOINTS WORN

DRAG LINK BENT, WORN OR SLACK JOINTS

WORN JOINTS

HUB BEARINGS WORN OR INCORRECTLY ADJUSTED

AXLE BEAM BENT

FIG. 15. *Steering gear layout showing the location of some faults which may develop during normal running and may cause erratic steering. Methods of rectifying these are dealt with in the text.*

points if the car has covered a moderately large mileage. Before concerning ourselves with the steering angles and geometry, therefore, which are not easy to check accurately, rectification of the existing wear should be put in hand.

Bishop Steering Gear. As will be seen from Fig. 45, Chapter 1, this type of steering gear consists of a worm with a wide, tapered thread, which is attached to the lower end of the steering column. A conical roller engages with this worm, and is carried on a peg attached to a rocking arm which rotates the drop-arm spindle.

wheel backwards and forwards through a small arc while you grasp the drop arm and prevent it from moving. This will reveal any play in the steering gearbox itself.

Detecting Looseness. The drag link and track rod joints can next be tested for slackness by attempting to move each rod lengthwise in turn while the drop arm is held stationary. Finally, grasp a wheel at the top and bottom of a tyre, and try to rock it vertically about its hub. It is not easy to differentiate between wear in the hub bearings and wear of the king pins and bushes, but by watching for movement of the brake drum relative to the backplate, bearing looseness can be identified, while wear of the king pin will be revealed by relative movement between the steering head and the end of the axle.

At this stage it is likely that slackness will have been detected at one or more

To allow end-play on the worm to be taken up, thin metal shims are fitted between the end cover of the steering gearbox and the box itself. Similarly, shims are provided between the side cover and the box so that the roller can be moved closer into mesh with the worm in order to compensate for wear on these parts. When making either adjustment, remove only one shim at a time, replace the cover plate, and check the effect.

On the high-efficiency design of Bishop steering gear, adjustment may be carried out quickly and accurately by slackening the locknut on the ball-ended setscrew which locates the rocker arm and turning the screw in a clockwise direction, thus moving the roller more closely into mesh with the worm.

Burman-Douglas Gear. This type of gear is of the worm-and-nut design, rotation of the steering column causing a cylindrical bronze nut to move up or down the worm thread in a similar manner to a nut moving along a bolt. The rocker arm which moves the drop arm is fitted with a hardened steel ball which fits into a bush in the nut.

The only adjustment normally provided is that which compensates for the end-float. This is effected by screwing down a nut at the top of the steering column, after slackening the lock-nut above it. Sometimes the two nuts are readily accessible, but often the steering wheel must be lifted so that the nuts, which are enclosed in the boss, are revealed. As this generally means that the central control assembly must be disconnected, and a special puller used to raise the steering wheel on its splines. The adjustment in any case is a delicate one, as overtightening of the adjusting nut will render the steering stiff and will damage the ball race.

When wear develops between the bronze steering nut and the worm, it is usual to renew the two parts, as they are lapped together during manufacture. On recent designs of gear an adjustment for end-play on the rocker shaft is incorporated, in the form of a screw, locked by a nut, which bears on the end of the shaft. This should be screwed in until all end-play disappears, but the rocker shaft must be quite free to rotate.

Marles Steering Gear. On the Marles steering gear a worm of "hourglass" shape is used, being wider at each end than at the centre. A roller, carried between two ball races on a forked arm, engages with the worm, and thus transmits a rocking movement to the drop arm. In an alternative design a double roller is used. Since no sliding contact takes place, very little wear develops, and adjustment should not normally be required. It is normally carried out when the steering gear is assembled

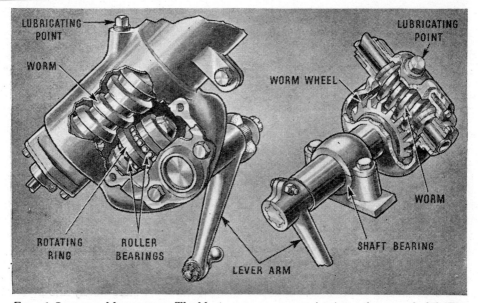

FIG. 16. STEERING MECHANISM. *The Marles type steering mechanism is shown on the left. This consists of a worm attached to the end of the steering column which, when turned, transmits a rocking movement to the lever arm. On the right is a worm wheel type steering mechanism*

during manufacture, or after a complete overhaul, and can only be done with the parts dismantled, so that the average owner need not concern himself with it.

Adjusting the Marles-Weller Gear. In this gear a helical groove is formed at the base of the steering column, into which fits a follower that swivels in a bush in the rocker arm and moves the drop arm shaft. Recessed into each face of the follower are two hemispheres which make contact with the sides of the helical groove. These are self-alining, and may be easily removed when wear develops.

The side cover of the gearbox must be removed, allowing the follower to be withdrawn from its bearing in the rocker arm. Fit new hemispheres to one side of the follower, and test its fit at the centre of the spiral groove, without replacing it in the rocker shaft. If slackness still exists, renew the pair of hemispheres on the other side. Replacing the follower in the rocker arm and, at the same time, persuading the hemispheres to enter the groove is somewhat tricky, but thick grease on the hemispheres will prevent them from falling out of their sockets. The follower is most easily replaced with the rocker arm at one end of its travel, since a larger clearance between the follower and the groove is purposely allowed at each end of the thread. By moving the steering wheel to and fro, and tilting the hemispheres slightly so that they enter the groove, the follower can then be pushed into its bush.

An adjustment is also provided to enable end-play on the column to be taken up, in the form of shims between the bottom cover plate and the steering gearbox. Shims will also be found between the side cover plate and the box, but these control the end-float on the rocker arm, which is correctly adjusted on assembly by the manufacturer, and should not be altered subsequently.

Worm-and-wheel Steering Gear. Various forms of worm-and-wheel steering gear have been widely used in which a worm thread on the steering column rotates a worm wheel attached to the drop arm shaft The type illustrated in Fig. 16 incorporates a complete worm wheel, but in some designs only a sector is used. If a complete worm wheel is used, a wide range of adjustment is available.

End-play on the worm can be eliminated either by slackening the setscrews in a flange which surrounds the steering column at the top of the box, and screwing up a milled adjusting ring about half-a-turn, afterwards relocking the setscrews, or by removing one or more shims from between the end cover and the base of the box. The method depends on the design of the gearbox.

The mesh of the worm and worm wheel is adjusted by rotating the eccentric boss which carries the worm wheel, or by moving the boss or side plate slightly in the direction of the worm. This is done by slackening the bolts which secure the boss or side plate, and rotating an adjusting bolt which gives the desired movement.

Steering Stiffness. If it is found that after this adjustment the steering becomes stiff when the wheels are turned towards full lock, the indication is that the worm wheel is worn. A new section can be brought into use by removing the drop arm from its splines—a special puller may be needed, as it is a tight fit—and rotating the spindle through half-a-revolution before refitting the drop arm.

In a number of cases, however, only a sector of a worm wheel is used instead of a complete wheel, and this last adjustment cannot be carried out. The extreme ends of this sector are generally machined to provide a greater clearance when the wheels are turned to full lock so that trouble is seldom experienced if the mesh of the worm and sector is adjusted with the wheels in the straight ahead position.

Rack-and-pinion Steering Gear. At one time it appeared likely that this type of steering gear would be very popular, and certainly its efficiency, as applied to the Morris Minor Series MM, has proved to be very high indeed. The continued trend on the part of designers to move engines further forward in the chassis, however, has rendered it difficult, if not impossible, to incorporate this design of gear on modern cars; it is not easy, alternatively, to mount the steering gear and linkage behind the engine, as is now done in some instances when other types of steering gearbox are employed.

The maintenance and adjustment of rack-and-pinion gear is quite straightforward and the following notes, which refer to the Morris Minor design, should enable the principles to be understood (see Fig. 17).

It will be evident that in order to take up wear which may develop between the pinion and teeth of the rack, the rack must be moved closer to the pinion. Provision is made for this adjustment by the fitting of shims to the rack damper and plunger which presses the rack into contact with the pinion. To adjust the rack damper, the plunger cap should be unscrewed and the shims and spring removed. The cap and plunger should then be reassembled without the spring or shims and tightened down until it is just possible to rotate the pinion shaft by moving the rack lengthways. A feeler gauge should then be used to measure the clearance between the hexagon of the plunger gap and its seating on the rack housing. To this measurement add 0·002—0·005 in. to obtain the correct shim thickness which must be fitted under the damper cap.

The damper cap and plunger should again be removed and the spring inserted beneath the plunger. The cap should then be replaced with the correct number of 0·003-in. shims.

The ball joints at the ends of the rack can be adjusted by removing shims from beneath each ball seat. The ball housing must be locked in two places by bending over the flange of the locking washer.

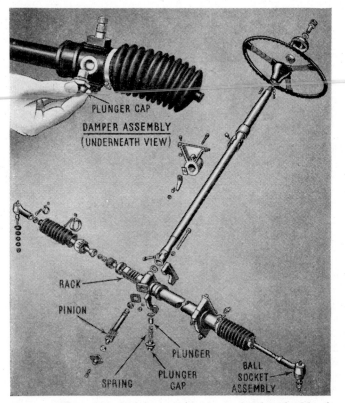

PLUNGER CAP

DAMPER ASSEMBLY
(UNDERNEATH VIEW)

RACK

PINION

SPRING

PLUNGER
CAP

PLUNGER

BALL
SOCKET
ASSEMBLY

FIG. 17. *The rack-and-pinion steering system fitted to the Morris Minor, series MM. Cowley and Oxford lay-outs are similar. The rack is moved from side to side by the rotation of the pinion.*

When the steering gearbox is in satisfactory condition, attention can be turned to the steering connexions. Most modern examples are self-adjusting, so that wear is automatically taken up while the lengths of the coupling rods remain unaltered. In addition, there is the oil-less rubber-bushed type of joint, which is not adjustable, and seldom needs attention. After a considerable mileage the bushes may need renewal; they are not expensive, and dismantling and reassembling is not difficult. Fig. 19 shows a typical example.

THE STEERING CONNEXIONS

Two types of non-adjustable ball joint are shown in Fig. 19; these are not externally adjustable as are those illustrated in Fig. 18, and renewal of the parts is the only cure for slackness when a very large mileage has been covered.

Spring-loaded Joints. Examples of two types of adjustable spring-loaded joints are shown in Fig. 18, Wear is taken up by screwing in the adjusting screw until the cups grip the ball, and then

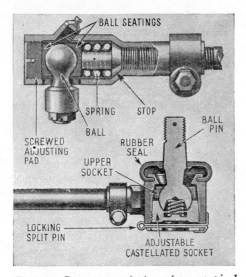

FIG. 18. *Part-sectional view of two typical examples of adjustable steering connexions.*

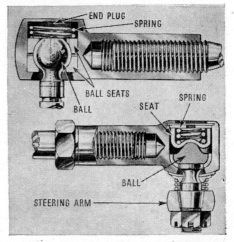

FIG. 19. *Part-sectional view showing the construction of two typical examples of non-adjustable steering connexions.*

slackening it back until the ball is just free to rotate. The adjuster must then be locked in position. Unfortunately, when the ball becomes worn, the wear does not take place equally around its circumference, since most of the steering movements take place over a small arc. The result is that when the joints are adjusted to remove the slackness with the wheels pointing straight ahead, the unworn section of the ball may jam in the cups when the wheels are turned towards full lock. The only remedy for this state of affairs is to renew the ball, and preferably the cups and the spring also. A badly-worn ball in any case is a danger as it may be possible for it to drop out of its socket, with disastrous results if this happens when the car is travelling at speed or in traffic.

HUB BEARINGS AND PIVOT PINS

If, as the result of the test described earlier, appreciable slackness is apparent in the front-wheel hub bearings, adjustment is required. In practice, this slackness does not affect the steering to any appreciable extent, and the hubs should

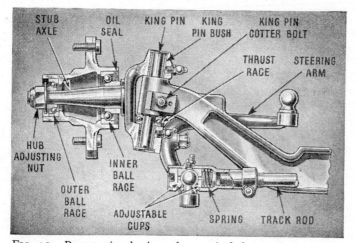

STUB AXLE | OIL SEAL | KING PIN | KING PIN BUSH | KING PIN COTTER BOLT | THRUST RACE | STEERING ARM | HUB ADJUSTING NUT | INNER BALL RACE | OUTER BALL RACE | ADJUSTABLE CUPS | SPRING | TRACK ROD

FIG. 20. *Part-sectional view of a typical front wheel steering layout. Note the adjustable type steering connexions fitted to the end of the track rod; details of these are shown in* FIG. 18.

steering head in which they work. Again this is a job which, while not beyond the scope of an amateur, is best left to a service station. Removal of the old bushes often calls for some form of extractor, while the new bushes are compressed when driven or pulled into place, so that a king pin will be too tight a fit in them, if it can be persuaded to enter at all.

Consequently, it is usual to supply undersize bushes which must be accurately reamed to size after being fitted. The manufacturers of the car usually supply a special reamer which has a pilot section which ensures that the bores of both bushes are reamed in line. In other cases, as with Ford cars, the bushes are brought to the correct diameter and burnished at the same time by using a tool known as a broach.

not be adjusted unnecessarily. A small amount of end-play in the bearings is essential; if they are too tightly adjusted, the ball or roller races will wear rapidly. Generally the correct amount of end-float is between five and fifteen thousandths of an inch, and this should preferably be measured accurately with a dial indicator. Discretion suggests, therefore, that the work should be left to a service station.

The adjustment itself is easily carried out after removing the wheel. Either taper-roller bearings or ball-bearings with tapered cones may be fitted. In either case, the split pin must be removed from the large castellated hub nut, which should then be screwed up fully. This will cause the bearings to bind, and the nut must be slackened back by approximately one castellation to give the correct clearance when the split pin should be replaced.

PIVOT PINS AND BUSHES

Worn pivot pins or king pins, as they are often termed, will affect both steering and braking adversely. The only cure is to renew the pins and the bushes in the

STEERING ANGLES AND GEOMETRY

Wear of the king pins and bushes will alter the angle at which the front wheels meet the ground. It will be noticed that the front wheels lean outwards slightly at the top, while the king pin is not parallel to the wheel, but is inclined inwards at its upper end. The result is that a line through the centre of the king pin should meet a line passing downwards through the wheel at the point of contact of the tyre with the road. The tilt or inclination of the wheel is termed the camber angle, and that of the king pin is known as king pin inclination. Both are measured in degrees. The method of measuring these angles together with the "toe-in" and "toe-out" measurement are shown in Fig. 23.

While it is possible to check the camber by using a plumbline and protractor as shown in Fig. 22, measurement of these angles is best left to a garage which has the specialized gauges required and the hydraulic power or other tools used for cold-straightening or bending the axle or steering arms to restore the correct angles. This advice applies with equal force to the checking and adjustment of any of the measurements referred to below, although it is possible for an owner to check the various points roughly, as an aid to diagnosing steering troubles.

Correct Wheel Alinement. Due to the outward inclination of the wheels, it is necessary for them to point slightly inwards at the front in order to prevent rapid tyre wear; the wheels would otherwise tend to splay apart when the car is in motion. This is by no means a universal rule with all suspension systems, however, as the particular castor angle used may necessitate the wheels being set exactly parallel when stationary, or it may even be necessary for them to toe-out slightly when independent front suspension is fitted.

The one fact that can be taken for granted is that the alinement of the

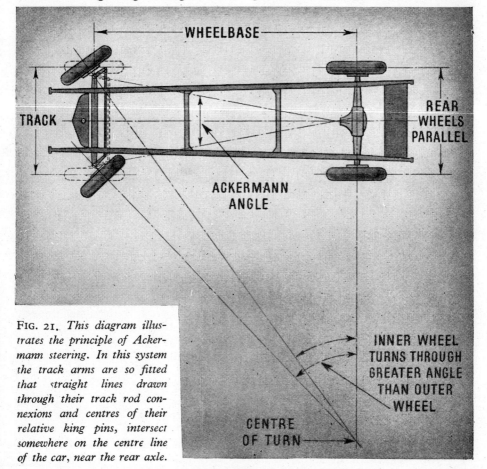

FIG. 21. *This diagram illustrates the principle of Ackermann steering. In this system the track arms are so fitted that straight lines drawn through their track rod connexions and centres of their relative king pins, intersect somewhere on the centre line of the car, near the rear axle.*

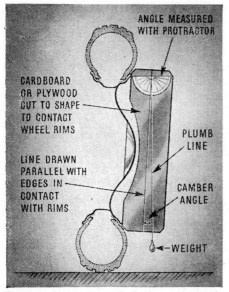

ANGLE MEASURED
WITH PROTRACTOR

CARDBOARD
OR PLYWOOD
CUT TO SHAPE
TO CONTACT
WHEEL RIMS

PLUMB
LINE

LINE DRAWN
PARALLEL WITH
EDGES IN
CONTACT
WITH RIMS

CAMBER
ANGLE

◀—WEIGHT

FIG. 22. *A simple method of measuring the camber angle of a front wheel, see upper view in* FIG. 23.

front wheels exercises a very real influence on tyre wear. No owner would willingly set one front wheel at right-angles to the car, and drive with it spinning in that position for eleven yards in every mile: yet that is the effect of an error in alinement of only ⅛ inch!

Measuring and Adjusting Wheel Alinement. Having ascertained the correct amount of toe-in or toe-out from the manufacturer or his agent, the front wheels should be checked with the aid of a gauge made from a length of rod, a wooden lath, or similar material, on the lines shown in Fig. 23. It should not be difficult to improvise a suitable gauge from any materials which may be available. By taking the measurement as nearly as possible on the centre-line of the tyre, such faults as a slightly buckled wheel will not affect the measurement appreciably. Nevertheless a bent wheel will upset the steering, and should be rectified as soon as possible, as described later in this chapter.

Chalk a small area at the centre of the tyre tread and at the same height on each wheel, and push the car back until the spots are on a level with the hubs at the rear of the wheel. With the gauge suitably adjusted for height, make a mark on each chalk spot with the pointers. Then push the car forward again until the chalk spots are at the height of the pointers, aline one pointer with a mark, and make a fresh mark with the other pointer alongside the original mark. The difference between these two marks will indicate the amount of toe-in or toe-out.

The track rod usually has a screwed adjustment at one or both ends, so that its length may be altered by slackening off locknuts or clamping nuts at each ball joint and rotating the rod. Sometimes a ball joint must be disconnected and screwed further inwards or outwards on the end of the rod. When a divided track rod is used, both halves must be adjusted equally.

Castor Angle. A fourth important factor is castor angle. Most of us are familiar with the self-alining action of the wheels used on chairs and dinner wagons, in which the wheel swivels on a vertical pivot which is in advance of its point of contact with the floor. The result is that the wheel tends to swing into correct alinement behind the pivot, whatever the direction in which the chair or trolley may be moved.

The same effect is obtained on a car by inclining the king pin backwards, see Fig. 44, Chapter 1, so that a line through it would meet the road ahead of the point at which the tyre make contact. The result is that the wheels attempt to maintain a straight-ahead position, and to return to it if the steering wheel is released after turning a corner.

Measuring the Castor Angle. Two methods of measuring the castor angle will serve as rough checks. In the first, a fairly long straightedge is laid across the spring pads and the distance of each end from the ground is measured. The car manufacturer may be able to quote the appropriate measurement for a straightedge of given length. Another scheme is to measure the angle at which a front wheel leans from the vertical when turned through 20 deg. in each direction. In other words, the camber angle is measured with the wheel 20 deg. from the straight-ahead position on either lock. Add the two measurements together, and multiply by $1\frac{1}{2}$ to obtain the castor angle. The camber can be measured as shown in Fig. 23, while various methods of measuring the 20 deg. through which the front wheels are turned can be devised, using a protractor and a sheet of cardboard cut to fit against the wheel rim, and resting on a box or similar support at hub height.

Increasing Castoring Effect. The castor angle will be reduced when semi-elliptic front springs are fitted, if the springs become flattened. The best plan is to have the springs re-tempered and set-up as described in Chapter 9. Some-times the castor angle is determined by a wedge fitted between the axle and the spring. If these wedges are omitted on reassembling the axle, the steering may be almost uncontrollable. The same scheme can be adopted when the springs have flattened by fitting metal or hard fibre wedges, with the tapered end point-ing forwards, or by increasing the angle of the wedges if these are already fitted. The correct thickness of the wedge must be determined largely by trial and error; too great a degree of castor will cause unstable steering, as will too little.

In independent suspension systems the castor angle may be adjustable, as de-scribed in Chapter 9, or it may be necessary to bend or twist the axle or wheel carrier with an hydraulic power tool to alter it. Adjustment of the latter type should be carried out by a mechanic.

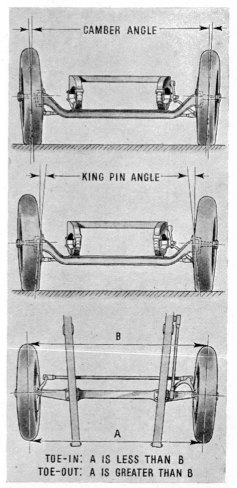

FIG. 23. *The principal wheel angles and measurements. The checking of these is fully described in the text*

Steering Geometry. Finally, the question of steering geometry has a bearing on the ease of controlling the car. As was explained in Chapter 1, the inner front wheel must turn through a greater angle than the outer when rounding a corner, and this is achieved by arranging the steering arms so that they converge; lines passing through each arm would meet at the centre of the rear axle, or, in some cases, at a point about two-thirds of the way back on the centre-line of the car as illustrated in Fig. 21.

These angles are difficult to check accurately without specialized equipment, although any accidental bending of a steering arm will be revealed by an alteration of the alinement in the front wheels. Unfortunately, although the alinement can be corrected by adjusting the length of the track rod, this does not restore the correct angle to the bent steering arm, so that the job is one for a service station possessing the necessary special tools and equipment.

WHEELS AND TYRES

The wheels normally give so little trouble that they are taken for granted by the average motorist. Certainly the modern type of pressed-steel wheel does not need maintenance. It can, however, be slightly buckled by a minor accident or kerb collision, so that it pays to check the truth of the wheels from time to time. When wire wheels are fitted, this periodical check is essential.

Jack up the wheel, and rest a piece of chalk on a suitable support at the height of the hub, so that it is just clear of the outer edges of the rim. On spinning the wheel the chalk will mark the rim at any point which is buckled. Next, hold the chalk close to the inside edge of the rim and check the wheel for any eccentricity.

Buckled Wheels. If a pressed steel wheel is faulty it must be handed over to a specialist for repair. Similarly, a wire wheel can be trued up by an expert in a few minutes, whereas an amateur might spend a day in tightening and loosening various spokes, only to find that the wheel is further out of truth than originally. A loose spoke can, however, be tightened up by screwing up the nipple at the point at which it enters the rim; a spoke nipple key may be used, or the head of the nipple may be turned with a screwdriver when the tyre has been taken off. Replacing a broken spoke is generally a fairly simple matter, although difficulty is sometimes experienced in threading it into place. Some wire wheels have spokes which are welded or riveted in place, and these obviously require a specialist's attention.

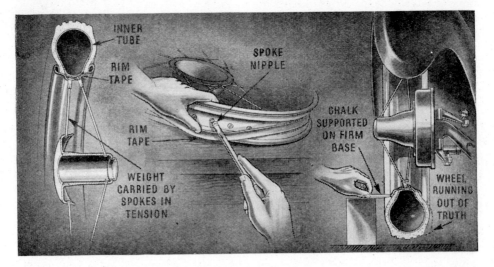

FIG. 24. WIRE WHEEL. *This illustration shows the construction of a wire wheel (left), simple way of checking the true running of a wheel (right), and method of tightening a loose spoke (centre).*

FIG. 25. TYRE WEAR. (a) *shows a tyre wearing on the shoulders of the tread, and reveals that the tyre is under-inflated.* (b) *shows the formation of thin fins or lips of rubber, and a sharp edge on the tread of a tyre. These are the first signs of wear due to the misalinement of the front wheels. If the alinement of the wheels is not corrected, the tyre wear will rapidly increase until it reaches the stage shown in* (c) *when it will have to be replaced.*

Wheel Nuts. The wheel nuts repay occasional inspection. If any grit is present between the coned end of the nut and its seating in the wheel hub, the foreign matter will disintegrate in time, leaving the nut loose. Nuts should be tightened fully, using the leverage available with the ordinary wheel brace. Sometimes garages use a special type of brace, however, and fit the nuts so tightly that they cannot be unscrewed with the normal tool. A lever can be used to apply additional leverage to unscrew the hub nut. The hub nuts on centre-lock wheels must be firmly tightened with a copper hammer in the direction of the arrow on each nut, as any slackness will result in rapid wear of the splines in the wheel and on the hub. The coned contact faces must also be scrupulously clean before the wheel is fitted. The hub nuts have right-hand and left-hand threads, as do the wheel nuts on some cars, to provide a self-tightening effect, as more fully explained in Chapter 1.

Tyre Maintenance. The tyres have other functions than merely to act as cushions between the wheels and the road. The rear tyres are the last link in the transmission system; the front tyres play an important part in steering the car, and all four tyres are the link between the braking system and the road. Tyre maintenance, therefore, affects performance, fuel consumption and braking efficiency, apart from reducing the bill for tyre replacements.

The tyre pressures should be checked at least once a week, before a run; if the pressures are checked when the tyres are warm after a run, they will be found to be higher than normal. In summer it may be advisable to make some allowance for this rise in pressure if the harder tyres render the suspension uncomfortable. A higher pressure than normal, however, is always preferable to too low a pressure. The tyres should be maintained at the same pressure. Unequal pressure will effect tyre wear and steering.

M.M.—K

Worthwhile Routine. Even sound inner tubes slowly lose pressure due to a process known as diffusion, in which the oxygen from the air in the tube is absorbed by the tube. This raises the oxygen content of the rubber, so that oxygen is given off from its outer surface. Thus the process is different from the loss of air from a porous tube; the loss of pressure, though small, necessitates topping-up at weekly intervals.

It is also a wise precaution to examine the tread of each tyre at the same time for embedded flints, nails, and other sharp particles which will slowly work their way into the rubber and cause a puncture. Preventive maintenance on these lines will generally result in freedom from punctures for long periods. At the same time each tyre valve should be checked by holding a moistened finger to the open end. The formation of bubbles will indicate a leaking valve. Try screwing down the valve core; the valve cap may be extended and slotted to form a key, or a key may be incorporated in the tyre gauge. If this does not cure the trouble, the valve must be renewed. These are inexpensive items and a supply of spare cores and valve caps should be kept in reserve.

To equalize tyre wear it is a good plan to change the wheels round every thousand miles or so; the spare should go on the near-side rear wheel, which will replace the near-side front, and so on round the car, the off-side rear becoming the spare.

Repairing a Puncture. When a puncture does occur, some owners find difficulty in removing the tyre. Since inextensible wires are fitted in the rims of the tyre, one side of the cover cannot be pulled over the rim until the opposite edge has been pushed right down into the well of the rim. The tyre valve core should be removed to deflate the tube completely, and the valve should be pushed into the rim. Both edges of the cover should then be pushed or trodden into the rim opposite the tyre valve. The edge of the cover next to the valve should now be levered over the rim. If the cover has been correctly positioned very little leverage will be required; if force is necessary, the bead of the tyre is not fully home in the rim. By using two tyre levers in succession, the edge of the cover can be brought clear of the rim, until it is possible to pull the remainder off by hand.

The tube can now be drawn out of the cover. It should be partly inflated to detect the point at which it is punctured. It is not always easy to find a small puncture, and a bucket or trough of water in which the tube can be immersed is not always available. By holding the tube close to the face while it is slowly rotated, however, it is generally possible to detect the puncture by the jet of air which escapes from it.

The area round the puncture should be cleaned with petrol and roughened with sandpaper, and given a coat of rubber solution which should extend at least half-an-inch beyond the actual damage, and which should be allowed to dry. A patch of corresponding size should be selected, or cut from a sheet of patching material. The self-vulcanizing type of patch should be used, as it becomes bonded to the tube under the influence of warmth and pressure when the tyre is in use. Immediately the protective backing has been stripped off the patch should be pressed firmly on to the prepared surface of the tube. If the rubber band which protects the inner tube from being chafed by the spokes is perished, it should be renewed at this stage.

Synthetic Tyres and Tubes. Tubes made from synthetic rubber do not take kindly to the normal type of patch, and the repair seldom lasts very long. The patch should be vulcanized to the tube,

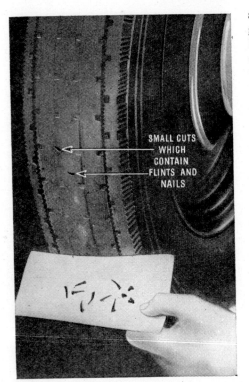

SMALL CUTS
WHICH
CONTAIN
FLINTS AND
NAILS

FIG. 26. *Small cuts in a tyre which contain flints and nails. It is a wise precaution to examine periodically the tread of each tyre and remove any embedded flints, nails, etc., which, if allowed to stay, will slowly work their way into the tyre and cause a puncture.*

and this can be done cheaply by most garages. Small vulcanizers which are heated by pellets of solid fuel are, however, available at a modest price, so that the owner can carry out his own vulcanizing quite successfully, provided that the instructions furnished with the outfit are followed.

Synthetic rubber tubes are identified either by a red spot near the valve, or by a red ring round the inside diameter. Sometimes some other distinctive colour is used. Synthetic tyres are identified by a red disk at some point on the diameter. Do not confuse this, however, with the small red dot which indicates the lightest part of the tyre, and which should be adjacent to the valve when the tyre is fitted to the rim, in order to obtain the best balance.

Synthetic tubes require care in fitting if the best results are to be obtained. The following instructions can also be followed with advantage when ordinary rubber tubes are being fitted, as they ensure the minimum risk of damaging the tube.

Fitting the Tube and Tyre. Dust the inside of the tyre with French chalk. Inflate the tube until it begins to round out, and insert it in the tyre, tucking it well into place, and lining up the valve

FIG. 27. *Checking the tyre pressure with a tyre gauge. This check should be carried out regularly to ensure that the correct tyre pressure is maintained. The inset shows a double-check valve cap which may be screwed on to the valve to enable the pressure to be checked without removing the cap.*

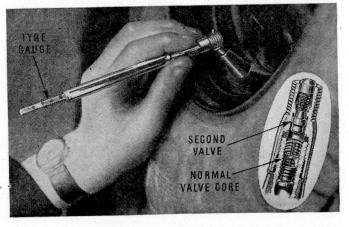

TYRE
GAUGE

SECOND
VALVE

NORMAL
VALVE CORE

with the hole in the rim so that it can be pressed through the hole. A frothy soap-and-water solution is the next requirement. This should be painted around the inside diameter of the tube, and between the tube and the walls of the tyre to a height of about two inches; avoid allowing water to run into the crown of the tyre, however. Apply the solution to the beads of the tyre, and mount the tyre on the rim while the solution is still wet.

Start by pushing the edge of the tyre right down into the base of the rim at a point opposite the valve. Then, working on either side of this point, press the bead into the rim. The simplest method is to tread it in with a heel-and-toe action. The last few inches of the inner tube i.e., adjacent to the valve, may require the use of two small tyre levers to persuade it over the edge of the rim, but every possible care must be taken not to trap the tube, for if this is inadvertently done, the tube may get torn.

Now inflate the tube slowly, and bounce the tyre evenly around its circumference so that the indicating line or

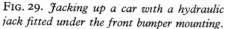

FIG. 29. *Jacking up a car with a hydraulic jack fitted under the front bumper mounting.*

ridge just inside the bead is level with or parallel to the rim all the way round, showing that the tyre is correctly seated. Then remove the valve core and deflate the tube completely, but do not disturb the beads of the cover. This will allow any stretched portions of the tube to readjust themselves in the cover and will relieve any strains. The tube may now be inflated to the correct pressure.

Fitting Oversize Tyres. When purchasing new tyres it is often an advantage to fit tyres of a slightly larger section than standard. This means that the tyres can operate at a lower pressure, giving greater comfort, while due to the greater area of contact with the road adhesion is improved and wear is reduced. The speedometer will read slightly slower, due to the greater overall diameter of the tyre, but the difference is too small to be of any practical significance. The oversize which can be fitted depends on the size of the rim. If 4·50 in. × 17 in. tyres are fitted as standard, for instance, 4·75 in. × 17 in. tyres can be adopted as an oversize. Any tyre dealer will be able to advise on a suitable oversize to replace a given standard size. If only two oversize tyres are fitted they should, of course, be kept to the same axle.

FIG. 28. *Jacking up a car with a screw type jack fitted under the rear bumper mounting.*

Fig. 30. Renewing a Tyre. Removing. (a) *pressing the wire bead off its seating with two levers. Work round the bead in small steps.* (b) *Inserting the lever at the valve position. Press the bead into the well of the rim diametrically opposite the valve.* (c) *levering off the bead. Continue until the bead is completely off the rim.* (d) *pulling the cover back over the flange.* Fitting. (e) *placing the cover eccentrically over the rim. The lower bead should be pressed as much as possible into the well.* (f) *levering the lower bead over the rim. This should be continued until the bead is completely over the rim.* (g) *levering the upper bead into position. Push the bead into the well diametrically opposite the valve.*

293

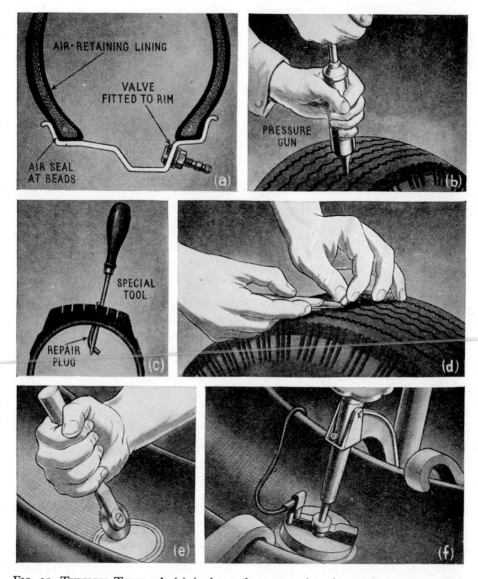

Fig. 31. TUBELESS TYRES. *At (a) is shown the construction of a tubeless tyre. It will be seen that the tyre valve is fitted directly into the well of the rim of the wheel and that an air seal is obtained between the beads of the tyre and rim flanges. At (b) is illustrated the garage method of filling small punctures with tread compound. At (c) and (d) is shown the plug-repair method used by most owners. A short length of rubber plug is inserted with a special tool and then cut off flush with the outside of the tread. At (e) and (f) are illustrated methods of cold patching and vulcanizing patches to the interior surfaces of the tyre to repair fairly extensive damage.*

Tubeless Tyres. Tubeless tyres, fitted as standard by many car manufacturers, may be fitted either singly or as complete sets as replacements for conventional tyres, provided that the wheel rims are in good condition; but the owner who contemplates changing over to tubeless tyres may benefit from a brief assessment of the pros and cons of such a conversion.

In the first place, he will find tubeless tyres are much less liable to puncture than the conventional variety. The special construction of the lining of the tyre ensures that the puncturing object is firmly gripped, and the hole sealed against leakage.

Proof of this lies in the fact that a tubeless tyre can safely be driven for 2,000 to 3,000 miles with a nail embedded in it without loss of pressure, whereas an embedded object in a conventional tyre will quickly fray the edges of the inner tube around the puncture and cause rapid deflation.

Secondly, because tubeless tyres are not porous, there is no need for periodical pressure checks and reinflation. An ordinary inner tube, of course, loses from 2 to 5 lb. per week. It must be admitted, however, that inner tubes made of butyl are also immune to pressure loss, so that in this respect the tubeless tyre is not unique.

Servicing Tubeless Tyres. The main disadvantage of a tubeless tyre from the point of view of the practically-minded owner is that it cannot be fitted to the rim without the use of a garage airline, since it is very difficult to obtain the initial seal between the beads of the tyre and the rim unless a rush of air is available to "jump" the beads against the rim.

This is done at the service station by removing the inner portion from the tyre valve, applying the airline, obtaining a satisfactory seal and then removing the airline and refitting the tyre valve. The tyre is inflated to about 40 lb./sq. in. and checked for air leaks by submerging the wheel-and-tyre assembly in a water tank.

On the other hand, normal punctures can be repaired without removing the tyre from the rim—a very distinct advantage from the owner's point of view! Under normal circumstances, in fact, the pressure should not be reduced below 5 lb./sq. in. in order to avoid disturbing the seal between the tyre beads and the rim.

There are two methods of sealing normal punctures caused by nails and similar objects. In the plug method, the object causing the puncture must be removed— it may be necessary to probe for it with a sharp implement and then to grip the tip of it between a pair of pointed-nosed pliers—and any road grit cleaned from the hole. A special needle, supplied in the puncture-repair kit, should then be dipped in rubber solution and passed through the hole so that the inner surfaces are moistened by the solution. Next, a short length of rubber sealing plug is cut off and one end is threaded through the eye of the needle, as shown in Fig. 31. The plug is then dipped in rubber solution and forced through the tread of the tyre with the needle, which must be disengaged from the inner end of the plug and withdrawn. The outer end of the plug should then be trimmed off flush with the tyre tread. Plugs are supplied in large, medium and small sizes to suit different types of puncture.

In the sealing-gun method, a pressure gun charged with special tread filler is used to inject rubber compound into holes caused by small nails and similar objects, after cleaning the hole as previously described. Normally, this equipment is used only by service stations.

Punctures caused by irregularly shaped cuts cannot be repaired by either of the above methods. It is necessary to remove the tyre from the wheel and apply either the conventional type of patch, using rubber solution, or a vulcanized patch. These must both be applied, of course, on the inside surface of the tyre.

CHAPTER 11

BODYWORK AND FITTINGS

REGULAR cleaning and polishing of the car is half the battle in preserving the finish of the coachwork. Nor should the chassis be neglected. Fairly frequent hosing down of the underside of the car renders routine maintenance such as chassis lubrication and brake adjusting easier, while it also has the advantage of showing up any oil leaks or breakages without delay. This presupposes a supply of water under pressure, either from a tap, or from a bucket aided by an efficient hand pump. Otherwise, the car should be taken to a service station occasionally to have the chassis thoroughly hosed down. The bodywork, however, will respond to sponging down, using a liberal supply of water in a bucket; a high-pressure jet, in fact, is liable to do more harm than good.

Cleaning the Car. The first step in cleaning the car should be to remove the floor mats, if detachable, and brush the carpets or floorboards. The upholstery should be brushed with a clean brush; if a vacuum cleaner with a flexible hose adaptor can be brought to the car, so much the better. By completing the cleaning of the interior of the body first, the risk of dust and grit marring the final polish on the body is avoided.

For washing down we require two sponges and two chamois leathers. One sponge and leather are kept for the bodywork, and the remaining pair for the wheels and mudguards, which are apt to be greasy. A bucket, or preferably two, will also be required. Various types of brush are also available for dealing expeditiously with the underside of the mudguards and the wheels and chassis.

Using Hose and Sponge. Start by hosing down these parts, using full pressure. Then reduce the pressure to a gentle flow, and holding the bodywork sponge in the right hand and the hose in the left so that water flows under the sponge, go over the bonnet and body panels with long sweeping strokes. Squeeze the sponge nearly dry, and remove the surplus water from the panels. Follow with the leather, wrung out until it is practically dry. This should leave an excellent finish on the paintwork if it is in good condition, and the application of a polish should not be necessary. Much the same procedure should now be followed with the wings and wheels, using the sponge and leather kept for these parts.

It is worth repeating that the mud and grit should be carried off the panels by the gentle flow of water, rather than rubbed off by the sponge. Deposits should, therefore, be thoroughly softened by using plenty of water. Do not wash the car in direct sunlight if this can be avoided, as the panels will dry too quickly to enable a good finish to be obtained. A further tip is to spread a sheet of brown paper or cloth over the engine before hosing down to prevent water reaching the ignition system and causing difficult starting.

Choice of Polishes. Although a chauffeur can obtain and maintain a gleaming finish on the body panels by expert leathering down alone, most owners resort to a polish to provide the final gloss. Most of the proprietary polishes are excellent, provided the instructions issued with them are followed.

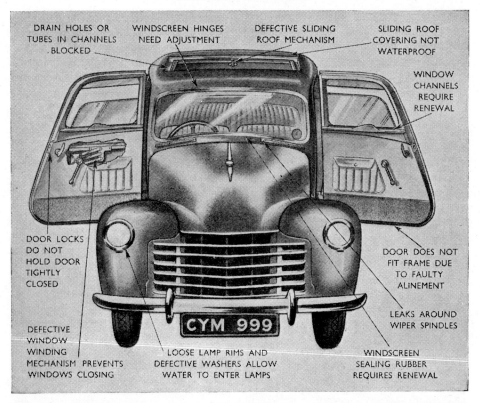

DRAIN HOLES OR TUBES IN CHANNELS BLOCKED

WINDSCREEN HINGES NEED ADJUSTMENT

DEFECTIVE SLIDING ROOF MECHANISM

SLIDING ROOF COVERING NOT WATERPROOF

WINDOW CHANNELS REQUIRE RENEWAL

DOOR LOCKS DO NOT HOLD DOOR TIGHTLY CLOSED

DOOR DOES NOT FIT FRAME DUE TO FAULTY ALINEMENT

LEAKS AROUND WIPER SPINDLES

DEFECTIVE WINDOW WINDING MECHANISM PREVENTS WINDOWS CLOSING

LOOSE LAMP RIMS AND DEFECTIVE WASHERS ALLOW WATER TO ENTER LAMPS

WINDSCREEN SEALING RUBBER REQUIRES RENEWAL

CYM 999

FIG. 1. BODY FAULTS. *This front view of a saloon model car fitted with a sunshine roof, shows the location of faults that develop as a result of normal wear and tear, but which should be repaired at the earliest opportunity. Most, if not all, repairs resulting from normal wear and tear are simple, and can be carried out by the owner.*

A golden rule is never to use a fresh brand of polish without first cleaning off all traces of previous preparations. It is also worth remembering that some polishes are available in two different grades: one is suitable for cellulose finishes, and the other is intended for the synthetic enamels which are baked onto the parts. Most body panels are finished in cellulose, although baked enamels are used in some cases. If the mudguards are finished in black, enamel is generally used; if they are coloured, cellulose is the most likely finish unless the rest of the body is enamelled. This distinction however, is not important where the general range of wax polishes are concerned, as these give good results on cellulose, enamel, varnish, and plastics as well as being excellent for plated parts and the windscreen and window glasses.

It is an advantage to use a special cleaner on the bodywork occasionally to remove the oxidized film which slowly develops. These polishes expose a fresh surface, which should be protected by a normal polish; as they are necessarily more drastic in action, they should not be used too frequently. Once every three or four months will suffice in most cases.

Cleaning Chromium Plating. It is usually recommended that chromium

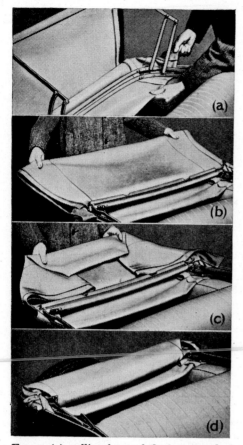

FIG. 2. (a) *pulling forward the rear panel of the hood to prevent it getting trapped between the hoodsticks.* (b) *pulling hood material out, after the hoodsticks have been folded, and* (c) *folding the two corners at right-angle before finally folding as shown in* (d), *ready for the cover to be fitted.*

plating should be cleaned by washing only. Certainly ordinary metal polishes should never be used on chromium. As the surface slowly becomes tarnished, however, it will benefit from an occasional clean with one of the special chromium polishes which are available. Such items as bonnet clips and other awkwardly-shaped components can be brightened up with the aid of a soft tooth-brush

dipped in this polish, but a brush should never be used on larger areas such as the headlamps, which would show any scratches. Chromium plating can also be cleaned effectively by rubbing it with a cloth damped with water to which a little household ammonia has been added.

Care of Folding Hoods. On open cars and drop-head coupés the hood material will benefit from brushing with a good stiff brush when dry; this will remove mud and dust in most cases. The hood may then be washed down with clean cold water. Coloured fabrics tend to show up dirt and grease stains more quickly than black, of course, and the use of a proprietary cleaning fluid may be necessary to remove oil or grease marks. Do not use petrol, as it dissolves the rubber in the fabric, and impairs its waterproof properties. A gentle scrub with soap and water, from time to time, followed by thorough rinsing will help to maintain the original appearance of coloured hood fabrics.

An important point to be observed with a folding hood is that it is not left folded away underneath the tonneau cover for long periods, as the creases will eventually ruin the cover fabric. It should be cleaned and refolded from time to time.

Preserving the Tyres. Finally, it is a good plan to give the tyres a coat of special tyre paint occasionally. Not only does this add appreciably to the appearance of the car as a whole, but the paints sold for this purpose consist of a rubber compound dissolved in a suitable solvent, so that the rubber in the paint becomes bonded to the tyre and gives a definite degree of protection.

RENOVATING THE UPHOLSTERY

While a good brushing or vacuum cleaning will go a long way towards keeping the upholstery in good condition, it will occasionally need more thorough cleaning, including the removal of stains.

When the seats and interior panels are covered with leather cloth, such as Rexine, instead of real leather, they may be scrubbed with warm water and a non-alkaline soap if they are grimy. Use the minimum amount of water, so that it does not penetrate the stitching and render the wadding sodden. This type of upholstery will also respond to rubbing with a paraffin-moistened cloth, but all traces of paraffin should be washed off before the surface dries.

Real leather upholstery is not so easy to clean, as the stain may spread. Petrol or proprietary cleaning solvents should never be used on leather. Careful use of soapy lather may improve matters, but on no account wash brown furniture hide, which is stained by an aniline dye. The best plan is to use a special saddle soap or hide food. The effect can be tried out on some inconspicuous part of the upholstery before venturing on large areas.

Cleaning Fabric and Mohair. Fabric upholstery, including cloth and mohair, will respond to the usual domestic cleaning methods. Oil and grease stains may be removed by carbon tetrachloride or a proprietary solvent, although petrol will do as a stop-gap. Start operations well outside the spot, and work inwards to prevent a ring forming. A good plan with small spots is to pour a few drops of solvent directly on the stain, and immediately press a sheet of clean white blotting paper against it; repeat the operation, using a fresh section of blotting paper until the stain has disappeared. If a mark remains due to dirt which was present in the grease, this can be sponged out with soapy water.

Soap and water should be used with discretion on other stains. Soap will "set" a fruit stain, for instance, while hot water will have a similar effect on bloodstains. Cold water is the best antidote, any discoloration which remains being removed

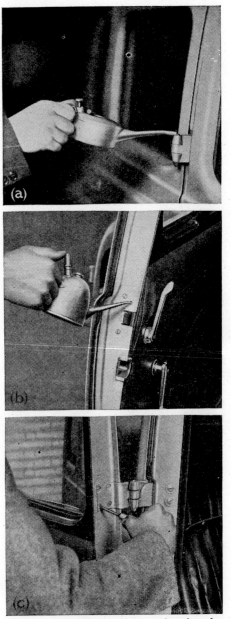

FIG. 3. (a) *oiling the pivot pin of a door hinge.* (b) *oiling the door-lock bolt through the lubrication hole.* (c) *tightening the door hinge screws. The screws attaching the hinge to the door pillar are accessible by removing the timber or plastic moulding.*

by a dilute solution of household ammonia. This also freshens up the colours of the upholstery and carpets generally, while it will prevent battery acid burning the upholstery if it is applied in a strong solution as quickly as possible after the acid has been spilt.

Ink spots can be removed by an ink eradicator as sold by stationers; the only drawback is that the eradicator may bleach the upholstery. It is often possible, however, to touch-in the bleached spot with dye applied with a camel-hair brush. Paint spots must be dissolved by the thinner sold for the brand of paint or cellulose which caused the spot. Tar stains should be tackled with a proprietary tar solvent, which usually works wonders, both on the upholstery and on the paintwork. Lipstick stains may be dissolved by carbon tetrachloride, but often require the use of chloroform.

Removing Hairs from Upholstery. When a dog is carried in the car the hairs shed on the upholstery are somewhat of a nuisance, especially if cloth is used. The hairs appear to adhere tenaciously to the fabric, and vigorous brushing only seems to drive them further in. A vacuum cleaner simplifies their removal, but the

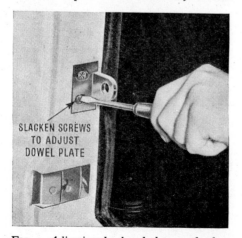

SLACKEN SCREWS
TO ADJUST
DOWEL PLATE

FIG. 4. *Adjusting the dowel plate on the door pillar to make it a close fit on the dowel peg.*

quickest method is to rub a damp wash-leather gently over the cushions and carpets. This picks up the hairs very quickly and they can then be allowed to float off the leather by moving it around in a bucket of water.

PREVENTING BODYWORK SQUEAKS AND RATTLES

The wise owner will forestall the development of door rattles by lubricating the hinges and locks at 2,000-mile intervals with a mixture of engine oil and penetrating oil, wiping off any surplus after allowing the oil to soak in. Wear is thus reduced, but the time will come when some adjustment is required; most modern bodies, therefore, provide adjustment at several points so that rattles may be eliminated.

Attention to Door Hinges. Whenever the hinges are lubricated, test the tightness of the screws which secure them to the door and frame with a good-sized screwdriver, meanwhile lifting the door to take the weight off the hinge. It will probably be found that each screw can be tightened up by half-a-turn or more. If the retaining screws have become loose in a wooden door frame, they can often be persuaded to grip by inserting Rawlplugs of suitable diameter into their holes. Pressing plastic wood into the holes before the screws are inserted and supporting the door until the plastic wood has had time to dry will also cure the trouble in many cases.

When the hinge itself is worn, the simplest plan is to replace it. If a replacement is not available, a practical owner can often remove the hinge, drive out the old pin, and fit a slightly oversize pin, drilling or reamering the bushings to suit. On some American cars removable bronze bushes are fitted to the hinge so that new bushings can be pressed into place and reamered to take a standard hinge pin. The local agent or the service

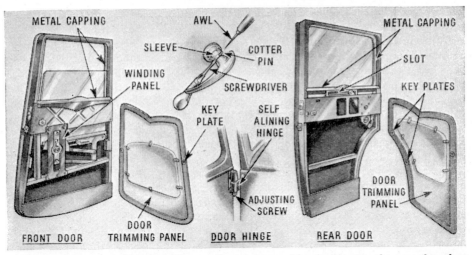

FIG. 5. WOODEN FRAME DOORS. *Front and rear doors with trimming panel removed to show the location and arrangement of the window-winding mechanisms. Before the trimming panel can be removed, the inside door handle must be removed. In some designs it is secured with a screw and must be removed with a screwdriver, and in others with a pin which can be pushed out with an awl (upper centre view). The usual trouble with window-winding mechanisms is stripped teeth on the gears that operate the system of levers which raise and lower the window.*

department of the car in question will possess the necessary tools to carry out the work quickly and efficiently.

When new hinges or bushes have been fitted it is usually necessary to readjust the door so that it fits properly in the door frame. Sometimes the hinge plates have slotted holes to allow the door to be positioned correctly. In other cases the arms of the hinges must be bent. If a metal rod is inserted between the hinge plates, and the door gently forced towards the closed position, it will be set further from the frame. A steel link placed over the hinge while the door is forced open will bring about the opposite effect. These adjustments are best left to a service station. When properly carried out they will prevent annoying rattles due to the door fouling the frame at some point.

Door Anti-rattle Devices. The locating devices on the doors play a major part in preventing rattles. One arrangement is a wedge-shaped locating tongue which fits into a tapered socket formed by two flanges on a backplate attached to the door pillar; sometimes the socket is combined with the striking plate of the door lock. By tapping the flanges lightly with a hammer they can be closed up slightly to take up any looseness. If a wedge-rubber buffer is used, it should be renewed if worn. Spring loaded dovetails are sometimes fitted to register the door with the pillar. The spring-loaded portion can be removed and the springs replaced; a specially ground tool to suit the contour of the dovetails is necessary. Another scheme is a tapered pin carried on a plate attached to the door frame, which fits into a hole in an angle plate on the pillar. The screw holes in this plate are usually slotted so that it can be moved outwards to obtain a closer fit on the pin. In addition to these main locating devices, several rubber buffers may be fitted to cushion the flange of the door.

These again can usually be adjusted when they become worn.

Adjusting the Door Locks. Adjustment of the various locating devices must be linked with attention to the door locks. Most modern cars are fitted with locks which have an adjustable striker plate with a serrated back which engages with similar serrations on a plate attached to the door pillar. By slackening the screws which attach the striker plate to the pillar plate it can be moved inwards by one or more serrations, thus ensuring that the door closes more firmly. It is the inner flange on the striker plate with which the tongue of the lock must engage; the outer flange is a safety measure. If the inner flange of the striker plate is worn it should be filed to restore the correct contour, although it is better to fit a new plate.

It is also worth mentioning that when the lock in the door handle fails to do its duty, it can be removed quite simply in most cases by taking out the screws which secure its flange to the door, so that a replacement may be fitted. Sometimes the handle is secured from the inside, in which case it will generally be necessary to remove the trimming panel from the door. This will also have to be done if a rattle develops in the window-winding mechanism. While the job is best left to a service station familiar with the particular car, a few hints may assist the owner who wishes to tackle the job himself.

Removing Trimming Panels. The first step is to remove the inside door handle and the window-winding handle. Various methods of fixing these may be found. A countersunk screw may attach the handle to the end of the spindle. More usually, the handle is attached by a pin passing through the spindle. This can be pushed out with a bradawl when the escutcheon plate at the base of the handle has been pushed back. Yet another arrangement is a spring clip which grips the spindle through slots in the base of the handle; this must be pressed back by passing a bradawl

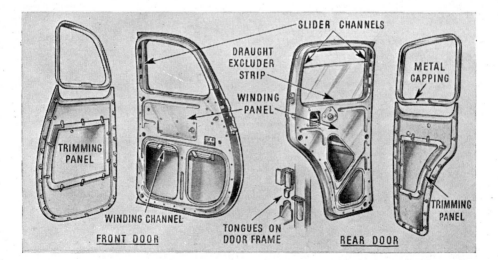

FIG. 6. METAL FRAMED DOORS. *Front and rear doors with trimming panels removed to show the location of the window-winding mechanism. As will be observed, access to the mechanism is by no means simple and it is recommended that repairs to it are left to a specialist.*

through the base of the handle. Other fixing devices include a magnetized key, or a spring-loaded disk incorporated in the escutcheon plate. The latter is put out of action by rotating a tag on the underside of the handle.

Next it will generally be necessary to remove the capping around the base of the window frame. This may be held in place by plated screws. If no visible method of fixing can be detected, try levering it gently upwards, but be careful not to crack a plastic moulding. The trimming panel itself may be held in place by a series of screws or small nails concealed by a tape around the edge. On all-steel bodies, however, the panel is generally secured by spring clips, and can be sprung off by levering with a screwdriver at intervals around its edge.

Window-winding Mechanism. The door locks and window-winding mechanism will now be exposed. Both should be serviced by a specialist if faulty. The most usual trouble with the window-winding mechanism, for instance, is stripped teeth on the gears which operate the system of levers which raise and lower the glass, or a broken coil spring which normally compensates for the weight of the glass.

On the front doors wooden blocks usually limit the downward movement of the glass, and once these have been unscrewed the glass can be wound down until the lifting buttons are clear of the winding-channel. The glass can then be lifted outwards and upwards. On the rear doors it is generally necessary to remove the channels in which the glass slides, the method varying on different cars. In some cases both front and rear glasses are raised by cables passing over pulleys. After removing the rubber stop which limits the downward travel of the glass, the outer draught strip, and the front guide channel, the glass can be swung clear of the door opening, when the clamps securing the cables can be undone.

At this stage it will be possible to renew the felt in the guide channels; worn felt is a frequent source of rattles. Fresh felt can be obtained from the manufacturer or from an accessory dealer and should be cemented into the channels with a waterproof adhesive.

Miscellaneous Noises. There are a number of other points at which squeaks and rattles can arise in the body and fittings. Starting at the front of the car and working backwards, we have loose bumper mountings, or a bumper bar which is bent so that it strikes some part of the front valance or a fog-lamp mounting as it flexes due to road vibration. A loose number plate should not be overlooked, while the mudguard stay bolts may have slackened off. The radiator grille is another possible source of noise.

Check the headlamp rims and glasses, and the front bonnet tape. If the latter is worn it can be packed out by inserting strips of rubber under it until it can be renewed. The bonnet catches may also need attention. Next check the wheel centre plates, which can set up an annoying tinkle if loose. The packing between the rear-side of the front mudguard and the running board may be worn. The bolts which hold the two flanges together, and the mudguard stays themselves will also repay inspection.

Under-chassis Checks. By now the first of the bolts securing the body to the chassis, when separate body construction is used, will have been reached. The manufacturers' agent can generally advise where to look for the bolts, as it is sometimes difficult to obtain access to some of them. The packing between the body members and the chassis can be checked at the same time. While working beneath the car, the brake rods should be examined if this form of operation is used. Persistent brake rod rattles can be cured

FIG. 7. BODY MAINTENANCE. *Side view of a saloon car with both doors open showing the points that should be given special and regular attention. Of particular importance are loose fittings which not only cause rattle, but can lead to expensive repairs if they are not given early attention. Such points as cleaning and lubrication should be carried out at regular intervals to preserve the bodywork and prevent squeaks. A good plan is to give the tyres a coat of special tyre paint occasionally which, because it becomes bonded to the tyre, gives a definite degree of protection.*

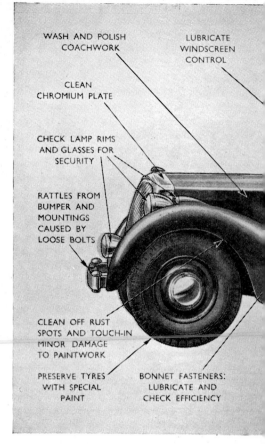

WASH AND POLISH COACHWORK

LUBRICATE WINDSCREEN CONTROL

CLEAN CHROMIUM PLATE

CHECK LAMP RIMS AND GLASSES FOR SECURITY

RATTLES FROM BUMPER AND MOUNTINGS CAUSED BY LOOSE BOLTS

CLEAN OFF RUST SPOTS AND TOUCH-IN MINOR DAMAGE TO PAINTWORK

PRESERVE TYRES WITH SPECIAL PAINT

BONNET FASTENERS: LUBRICATE AND CHECK EFFICIENCY

by linking rods together with tension springs; for cars on which the trouble is prevalent, in fact, a set of silencing springs is often available from the agents or accessory dealers. Loose exhaust pipe and silencer mountings can be rectified at the same time.

Noises at Rear of Body. At the rear of the car rattles and squeaks can be traced to loose rear wings, bumper fittings and the luggage grid. On recent models the lid of the luggage compartment may be slightly loose, but an adjustment is often provided at the hinges. The spare wheel may also be a culprit. Make sure, too, that the jack and any other tools carried in the luggage compartment are properly secured.

Interior Fittings. Inside the car, such items as the doors and window glasses are the most usual offenders, and should be dealt with as already described. Floorboards may cause rattles or drumming. A loose gear lever knob will vibrate at certain engine speeds, while the runners of the passenger's seat can also cause an elusive rattle when the seat is not occupied. Other possible sources of trouble are a loose steering column clip, a control assembly at the centre of the column which is not properly secured, and a rattle inside the assembly caused by a screw or nut which has come adrift. The dashboard fittings may not be above

suspicion, while such items as the speedometer driving cable or the oil-pressure gauge pipe may chatter if they vibrate in contact with the scuttle or dashboard support.

BODYWORK WATER LEAKS

Attention to the doors and windows on the lines already indicated will enable water leaks and draughts to be cured as well as preventing rattles. There are one or two other points at which water leaks are commonly experienced, however, chiefly around the windscreen and the sliding roof.

Leakage at Windscreen. Many owners, and some garages, fail to realize

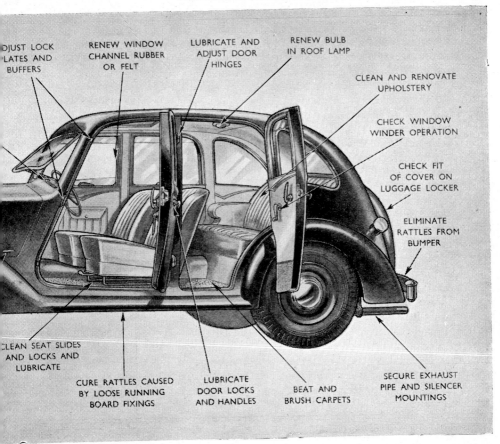

ADJUST LOCK PLATES AND BUFFERS

RENEW WINDOW CHANNEL RUBBER OR FELT

LUBRICATE AND ADJUST DOOR HINGES

RENEW BULB IN ROOF LAMP

CLEAN AND RENOVATE UPHOLSTERY

CHECK WINDOW WINDER OPERATION

CHECK FIT OF COVER ON LUGGAGE LOCKER

ELIMINATE RATTLES FROM BUMPER

CLEAN SEAT SLIDES AND LOCKS AND LUBRICATE

CURE RATTLES CAUSED BY LOOSE RUNNING BOARD FIXINGS

LUBRICATE DOOR LOCKS AND HANDLES

BEAT AND BRUSH CARPETS

SECURE EXHAUST PIPE AND SILENCER MOUNTINGS

that most opening windscreens have an adjustment at the hinges which permits the frame to be drawn into closer contact with the rubber sealing strip. Examine the hinge plates from inside the car. If a hexagon-headed screw and a countersunk slotted screw are seen, the former should be slackened off, as it is a locking screw. The slotted screw can then be turned clockwise to draw the screen closer to the frame, although this adjustment should not be overdone. Retighten the locking screw.

Sometimes the capping above the screen must be removed to reveal slotted hinge plates by means of which the screen can be moved inwards after the retaining nuts have been slackened. The top edge of the screen can be tapped inwards with the base of the hand. If the rubber surround is perished, it is not difficult to fit a replacement when either form of adjustment has been slackened off as far as possible; begin by inserting the rubber at the bottom corners, working it inwards towards the centre of each side of the screen. Repeat the procedure at the top corners. When the screen is of the fixed type, water leaks can be cured by re-cementing the sealing rubber to the bodywork, using a cement, and lifting the edge of the rubber with a blunt knife.

Miscellaneous Leaks. Other points at which water may enter are around the

wiper spindles and at the scuttle ventilator. The first trouble can be overcome
by fitting new sealing rubbers to the
spindles: the type varies on different cars.
The second, by fitting a new rubber
gasket on which the ventilator closes, or,
when it is mounted on top of the scuttle,
by causing it to close more tightly by
shortening the link behind the dashboard. Minor water leaks at such points
as the rubber sealing strips on fixed
window glasses can be sealed by using a
glazing compound, or by pressing modelling clay into the cracks.

Sliding Roof Leaks. When sunshine
roofs leak the trouble is usually due to
the drainage pipes which lead the water
away below chassis level; these may be
choked. If it is necessary to remove the
sliding roof, the work should be left to a
garage, since the operation of removing
and refitting it is somewhat tricky.

It is a good plan to repaint the fabric-
covered type of sliding roof with cellulose
or synthetic enamel before it begins to
show signs of cracking; not only is the
appearance improved, but it will be
rendered weatherproof.

DAMAGED BODYWORK

When a mudguard or body panel
suffers minor damage it is seldom worth
while attempting to beat out the dent
without proper equipment. The hammer
blows inevitably stretch the metal, and
the final result is seldom satisfactory. A
skilled panel beater, using specially-
shaped hammers and blocks known as
dollies, can restore the original shape of
a part in a surprisingly short time. The
art lies in controlling the "flow" of the
metal as it is hammered. It is possible to
shrink a stretched portion by thickening
up the metal with carefully graduated and
directed hammer blows.

Less expert operators obtain similar
results by heating a localized area with an
oxyacetylene flame, and then quenching

it suddenly with damp asbestos pulp.
Dents which are difficult to tap out
without extensive stripping of the internal
upholstery are often pulled out by
welding a steel wire to the centre of the
depression; those which will not respond
to this treatment may be filled with solder,
which is sprayed on the previously-
tinned surface from a special gun. An
experienced spray-painter can then restore the finish so effectively that it is
difficult to detect the retouched area.

Touching-in Minor Damage. Tins
of brushing cellulose or synthetic enamel
of the same colour as the wings and bodywork should, however, find a place in
the owner's garage. A point to remember
is that cellulose retouching enamels are
quite unsuitable for use on the synthetic
finishes used on the wings or bodywork
of many modern cars; the two materials
will not knit together properly.

Any such damaged areas should be
rubbed down with a medium grade of
sandpaper, using the type known as
"wet-or-dry" if it is available, as a
better result is obtained if plenty of water
is used. When the bare metal is bright,
dry it thoroughly, and give it a coat of
enamel or cellulose. Next, apply a small
quantity of plastic "stopping," which
can be obtained from most garages which
do any recellulosing, or which is obtainable in tubes or tins from accessory
dealers. Build up the stopping in layers,
allowing each to dry before applying the
next, until the surface is slightly above
the surrounding paintwork. Then rub
it down until it is level with a fine grade
of wet-or-dry paper. Patience at this
stage will make all the difference to the
finished job.

When the surface is thoroughly dry,
wipe it over with petrol, and apply the
cellulose with a soft brush, spreading a
full coat quickly; do not be tempted to
go over it again until it is thoroughly dry,
or the surface will be spoilt. Synthetic

enamels require rather different treatment, as too heavy a coat will cause "runs"; the surface can, therefore, be worked out with several strokes, but this should not be overdone. More than one coat of cellulose or enamel may be necessary, and each should overlap that beneath it so that the surface merges into the surrounding paintwork as smoothly as possible.

Using a Spray Gun. Very effective results can be obtained with a spray gun if a little practice is first carried out on scrap metal. The correct degree of dilution of the paint with thinner is half the battle. Too thick a paint will give an "orange peel" effect, while too much thinner will cause runs. Even the hand-operated type of gun, similar to an insecticide spray, is quite efficient when

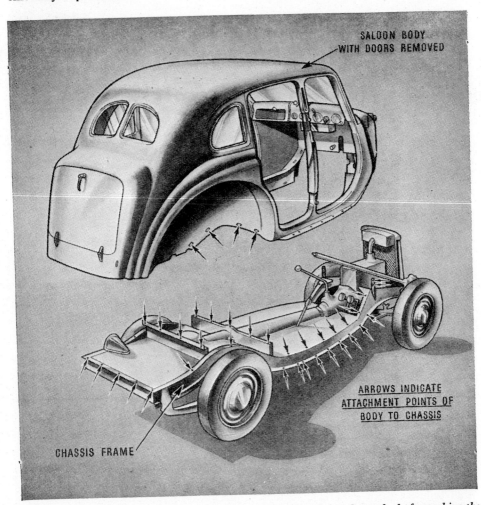

FIG. 8. ATTACHMENT OF BODY TO CHASSIS. *This view shows the method of attaching the body to the chassis on a modern saloon model. Setscrews are used to secure the body, and are screwed into either tapped holes or caged nuts in the chassis.*

FIG. 9. STOWING TOOLS. *Two methods of stowing tools in modern makes of cars. The tools supplied by the manufacturer are usually adequate for any job that is likely to be tackled by the roadside. The owner can add to the tools supplied, but it is advisable to house them so that they will not rattle when the car is moving; a tool roll is useful for this purpose.*

dealing with small areas, although spray painting of this type obviously cannot be compared with professional work, where the degree of thinning, control of air pressure, and degree of atomization all contribute to a perfect finish.

Ensuring a Good Gloss. Neverthe-less, if the surface obtained by brushing or spraying is not quite up to expec-tations, it can be considerably improved by light sandpapering when perfectly dry, using plenty of water, and a little soap as a lubricant. Follow this by rubbing down with a fairly coarse metal polish, to blend the edges into the sur-rounding surface, and to provide a good gloss. Finish off with a polish of the "cleaner" type referred to earlier in this chapter, and finally wax-polish.

Two practical tips will be found useful. The first is to mask the area around the damage by means of a sheet of paper in which a suitably shaped hole has been cut, so that drops of paint will not mark undamaged finish. Remember that if fresh cellulose drips on to the cellulose finish it will soften the paint very quickly, and leave a mark which is difficult to eradicate. When spraying, a mask is, of

course, essential to protect the sur-rounding paintwork. The second pre-caution is to damp the garage floor before beginning work, so that as little dust as possible is disturbed.

TOOLS AND SPARES

Mention earlier of the rattle caused by an insecurely fastened jack, starting handle, or wheel brace suggests that an improved method of stowing the tools can often be devised. On many modern cars, it is true, excellent stowage is pro-vided for these important items, and attention will probably be concentrated on disposing of such additional tools as the owner considers desirable.

The number of tools carried will naturally depend on the inclinations and mechanical ability of the owner. The tools furnished by the manufacturer are generally adequate for any job that is likely to be tackled by the roadside, and these are usually fitted in a tool roll which prevents them from rattling. The practically-minded owner can often im-prove on this arrangement, however, by carrying a selection of the most generally-used tools in a drawer fitted beneath one of the front seats, or in the luggage compartment, so that when it is slid out each tool is ready to hand. One scheme is to fit the tools in spring clips screwed to the base and sides of the drawer. Alternatively, an owner who is handy with a fretsaw can cut out a series of openings in a sheet of plywood to accommodate the tools snugly. This is fitted at a suitable height above the bottom of the drawer, and the openings are lined with baize or felt. The result is a form of tool stowage which is both effective and pleasing to the eye.

Some Useful Items. In addition to a comprehensive range of tools, one or two other items should find a place in the tool box or in suitable stowage on the car. These include a roll of insulating tape, preferably the pure rubber variety; a stick of modelling clay, invaluable for sealing water leaks and a host of other stop-gap uses; an inspection lamp with sufficient cable to reach any part of the car so that wheel-changing or repairs at night can be carried out at least with adequate illumination, if not in comfort; a coil of copper wire for temporarily securing loose or broken items; a box of assorted nuts, bolts, split pins and steel, fibre and spring washers covering the most commonly-used sizes on the car; and last, but by no means least, a fire extinguisher.

Rather a mixed bag perhaps but each item is likely to be needed by the roadside sooner or later. Such spares as sparking plugs, lamp bulbs, and fuses are not included, as they should find a place on any well-equipped car; on the other hand there is no object in carrying a large variety of spares or materials which can only be effectively used in the garage.

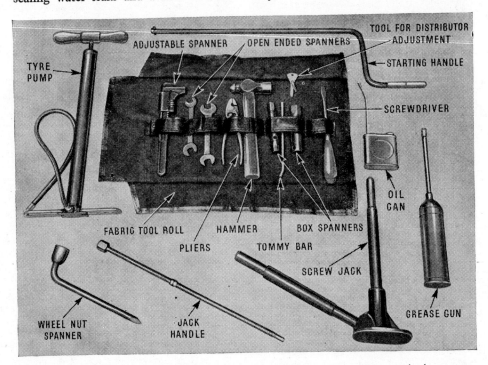

FIG. 10. TOOL KIT. *This representative tool kit is sufficient to carry out repairs in an emergency. They are wrapped in a fabric tool roll to prevent them rattling when the car is moving.*

CHAPTER 12

STORING THE CAR—GETTING IT READY FOR THE ROAD

IF it is decided not to licence the car for a period of three months or longer, it is essential to take certain precautions in order to avoid deterioration by corrosion and otherwise. The following action should be taken, therefore, when the car is laid up

LAYING-UP THE CAR

The car should be raised off the ground. Obtain four wooden blocks of the correct height, jack up the front axle, and place one block under each end of the axle beam to raise the tyres 2 in. above the ground. Keep the handbrake "on" when doing this. Next, jack up one rear corner of the car, place another block under the rear spring pad and lower on to the block. Before raising the fourth wheel place two chocks, one on either side of one of the front

wheels, then jack up the other rear corner of the car and place the fourth block in position. The chocks can then be removed and the handbrake released. Care should be taken to ensure that the car is stored in a dry and convenient position so that any parts needing attention as outlined later are easily accessible.

Radiator and Cooling System. First drain all the water off, then flush out the system to thoroughly clean it. Make sure that the cylinder drain tap is not choked, so that no water is left in the cooling system.

Anti-Freeze Fluid. Unless the anti-freeze has been recently added to the cooling water, it is not worth saving. If the cooling fluid in the radiator is dirty, it is far better to throw it away.

Engine. One of the most important

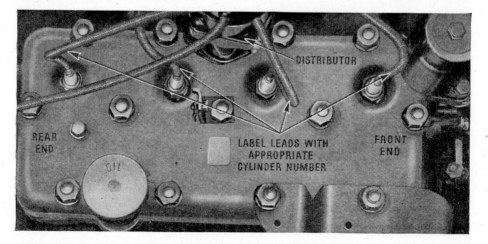

FIG. 1. MARKING THE LEADS. *Before removing the sparking plugs, tie a label on each lead bearing the cylinder number. The engine cylinders are always numbered from front to rear.*

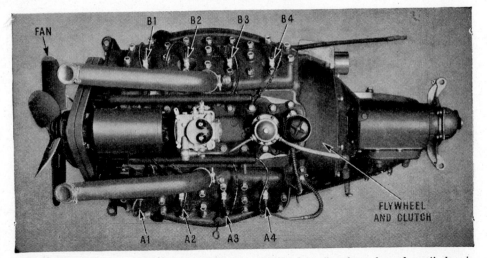

FIG. 2. MARKING THE LEADS OF A V-8 ENGINE. *This plan view shows how the cylinders in a V-8 engine should be marked before disconnecting the leads and removing the sparking plugs; the leads should be similarly marked before the plugs are removed.*

points is to protect the cylinder bores and it is recommended that the following steps should be taken:

Tie a small label to each of the high tension leads (the wires connected to the sparking plugs), each label bearing the cylinder number. The engine cylinders are always numbered from front to back. Thus, starting at the radiator end the first cylinder will be No. 1, the second No. 2 and so on. (Cylinder numbering for a V-8 is shown in Fig. 2). Disconnect the leads and remove the sparking plugs (clean the plugs and put them away in a dry place). Insert a tablespoonful of fresh lubricating oil into each cylinder, and turn the engine by hand a few times quite slowly so that the oil will be well smeared over the cylinder walls. Put a cork in the sparking plug holes to keep out dust and dirt when this operation has been completed. Drain off the lubricating oil in the sump; flush out and refill with fresh oil. The custom adopted by some people of running the engine at intervals during the storage of the car is strongly deprecated and does nothing but harm.

In explanation, it is well known that cylinder wear takes place most rapidly when the engine is started up from cold, this being due to the fact that a rich mixture must be used, and liquid fuel is introduced into the cylinders which washes away the oil on the cylinder walls. Again, when the engine has been "warmed-up" in this way and is stopped, condensation takes place inside the cylinder and this moisture sets up corrosion.

When the car is laid up, therefore, give the cylinder walls a coating of oil as recommended, and do not run the engine while the car is out of use.

Fuel System. Any fuel remaining after the last run should be removed and stored in airtight cans, petrol left in the car tank while the vehicle is not being used will deteriorate as the lighter fractions will evaporate (the petrol tank in a car is not airtight), and difficulty may be experienced when restarting the engine after storage. The carburettor float chamber should also be emptied and all fuel filters removed, cleaned and replaced, renewing any defective joints during the process.

The clutch, gearbox, and rear axle need no special treatment.

Tyres. As the car has been raised off the ground and the handbrake released, the wheels can be turned and the tyres examined.

All stones, nails, etc., should be removed from the treads.

The tyres should then be deflated and the outer covers eased away from the rim sides.

Examine the tyre valves and replace any defective valves. It is a good plan to introduce a little French chalk between the sides of the outer covers and the wheel rim. Do not inflate the tyres until the car is replaced in service.

Batteries. It should be realized that a battery deteriorates rapidly when not in use unless steps are taken to prevent it.

The following courses are open to the car owner:

A. Remove the battery from the car and send it to a garage or battery maintenance depot. They will keep the battery in good condition by regular charging and topping-up of the electrolyte (the liquid in

FIG. 3. *Refilling the sump with fresh oil after draining and flushing the old oil away.*

the battery). The cost of this service is quite small, but a reputable battery agent or repairer should be selected. Only firms specializing in this class of business should be employed.

B. The car owner can keep his battery in order himself. If this course is adopted, the electrolyte should be maintained at the correct level by the addition of distilled water (on no account use ordinary tap water). The electrolyte should always cover the lead plates inside the battery which can be seen if the filling plugs are removed, see Fig. 2, Chapter 7.

Once in every five to seven weeks charge up the battery by using a battery charger or "trickle" charger as it is often known. As its name implies, a "trickle" charger is a portable electric transformer which may be connected to the standard A.C. house circuit and provides a suitable direct current (D.C.) to recharge the battery. "Trickle" chargers are normally provided with three tappings: 2, 6, and 12 volt as required.

It is usually more convenient to remove the battery from the laid-up car and fix it up on a bench with the charger near a suitable point in the house circuit.

In addition to the regular charging of the battery, it should be discharged for an hour or so between charges by switching on the headlights or if it has been removed from the car, it should be connected to a couple of headlamp bulbs.

"Trickle" chargers can be obtained through any garage and full instructions are supplied with every charger. If in doubt, the vendors will usually advise as to the best method of using the "trickle" charger, and most of them will install it if they are asked to do so.

NOTE. Batteries do not last for ever; their life seldom exceeds between two and three years, and if the battery is nearly worn out when the car is laid up, it is not worth trying to preserve it as it will only fail shortly after the car has been re-

SHAKE OUT CARPETS
AND MATS
AND APPLY D.D.T.

LUBRICATE DOOR HINGES
AND LOCKS

CLEAN AND POLISH
BODYWORK

DEFLATE TYRES AND
EASE OUTER COVERS
AWAY FROM RIM SIDES

RAISE CAR AND SUPPORT ON
WOODEN BLOCKS PLACED UNDER
EACH END OF AXLE BEAM

POLISH CHROMIUM PLATED
FITTINGS AND COVER WITH
THIN FILM OF LIGHT OIL

FIG. 4. PREPARATIONS FOR STORAGE. *The procedures detailed above and described in the text should be carried out by the owner-driver to ensure the efficient performance of the car when it is subsequently put into service. All the procedures detailed on the drawing are simple to carry out and require no special tools or equipment.*

placed in service. Better to scrap it and buy a new one.

C. There is a third course which is only applicable to new batteries or those which are in practically new condition. This is the dismantling and drying-off process. It involves charging the battery, completely dismantling it, and taking the components apart. The positive plate groups are then allowed to dry. The negative plate groups are allowed to dry after first being soaked in water for 24 hours. The wood separators and the acid are discarded. The container, lids, vent plugs, etc., are washed in clean water, dried, and then stored, along with the plate groups, in a cool dry place.

When putting into commission again, the battery requires reassembling with new wood separators. It must then be filled with fresh acid and given a pro-longed first charge, just as though it were a new battery.

The cost and complication of this process would not be warranted for an old battery.

Where there are any electrical units permanently connected to the electrical circuit of the car, such as an electric clock, it is advisable to disconnect the battery when the car is laid up.

Wherever practicable course B is recommended, and the battery should be removed from the car as referred to previously.

Body. The coachwork should be thoroughly cleaned and polished before the car is laid up, in addition it is wise to cover it over with a dustsheet.

Chromium Plating. This type of metal finish deteriorates quickly when the car is not in use unless precautions are

DISTRIBUTOR

TOMMY
BAR

BOX
SPANNER

FIG. 5. REPLACING SPARKING PLUGS. *This view shows a sparking plug being tightened down with a box spanner and tommy bar. When carrying out this operation do not tilt the spanner or you may break the porcelain insulator.*

taken. First polish and then cover the plating with a thin film of light running oil (sewing machine oil is good).

Mats and Carpets. Beware of moths, this warning also applies to any upholstery other than leather or Rexine.

Shake out carpets and mats and apply D.D.T. powder to discourage moths and other insects.

Door Fittings. Take the opportunity of checking over latches and hinges and lubricate these parts—they are often neglected—the absence of squeaks will be appreciated when the car is replaced on the road.

Spare Wheel. Inspect the spare wheel and tyre and make sure that the wheel can be readily removed from its housing in the car. Nothing is more annoying after replacing the car in service than to discover that the spare wheel fastenings have corroded or seized up, and the spare

wheel is not quickly available in the case of an unexpected puncture. Deflate tyre on spare wheel and inspect valve as in the case of the other tyres. The procedures and tools for relining brakes are detailed and illustrated in Chapter 10.

Brakes. It is not necessary to take any special action as regards the brakes when laying up the car, but it is as well to confirm the condition of the brake linings and drums if there is any suspicion that the linings are approaching the end of their useful life.

Some manufacturers provide a small opening in the brake drum enclosed by a cover. The thickness of the brake linings can be observed through this opening when the cover is removed.

REPLACING THE CAR IN SERVICE

The first step will be to inflate the tyres to the correct pressure. Do not for-

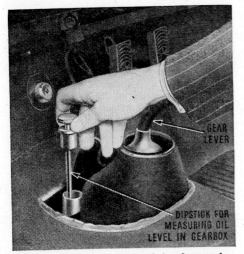

FIG. 6. *Checking the level in the gearbox with the dipstick. If the level is too low, the gearbox should be topped up with fresh oil of the grade recommended by the manufacturer. The filler plug is usually located on the top of the gearbox.*

get to inflate the tyre on the spare wheel.

Apply the handbrake, then jack up the car and remove the wood blocks. If the car is stored in a confined space, it can then be pushed out of the garage which affords greater freedom of movement when proceeding with the other preparations for replacing the car in service.

Sparking Plugs. Check the gap between the firing points, this should be about ·020 in.; the instruction book will specify the exact figure. Make sure all sparking plug points have the same gap. Warm the sparking plugs, leave them on the hot-plate of the kitchen boiler until ready to start up the engine. Check the lubricating oil level in the engine by means of the dipstick, adding oil if necessary.

Gearbox and Rear Axle. Check the level of gear oil in these units and add more lubricant of the type recommended by the manufacturers in the instruction book if necessary. The gearbox usually

has a dipstick to indicate the gear oil level, see Fig. 6. The rear axle gear oil level can be ascertained by removing the filler plug when the lubricant should be visible. The position of the filler is usually arranged in line with the gear oil level so that it cannot be over-filled.

Air-Filter. Clean the air-filter on the intake to the carburettor and refill with oil; the principles of most air-filters are the same, but their construction varies, so consult the instruction book supplied with the car, where specific instructions will be found for the cleaning and treatment of such equipment. The point is that after cleaning an air filter and preparing it for use there is usually an excess of lubricating oil, which is very beneficial when running the engine for the first time after the car has been laid up.

Fill the fuel tank with petrol and to ensure quick starting, fill the carburettor float chamber with petrol as well.

Remove corks from the sparking plug holes and give the engine a few turns by

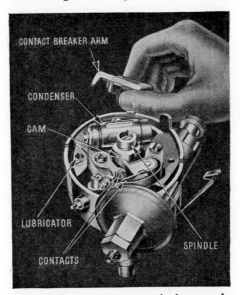

FIG. 7. *Rotor arm removed showing the spindle which should be polished with a strip of fine emery cloth and oiled if the arm sticks.*

hand to ensure that the moving parts are free. Fill the radiator with hot water and leave for a few minutes while you replace the battery, should this have been removed as recommended. Lastly, place the warm sparking plugs in position, using a little graphite grease on the threads and tighten down hard with a box spanner, see Fig. 5.

Attach the high tension leads to the sparking plugs, the labels on them will indicate their correct allocation.

The engine is then ready for starting up, and the hot water introduced into the radiator will have ensured that the power unit is effectively warmed up.

Before starting the engine, make sure that the handbrake is "on" and the gear lever in its neutral position.

Check the clutch by depressing the clutch pedal to make sure that there is no undue resistance to the freeing of the clutch. Switch on, and before using the starter switch, look at the ammeter on the instrument panel to verify that the ammeter is working. Use the carburettor choke with discretion, do not overchoke because if the induction system gets flooded with unvaporized fuel, starting will be delayed and may prove very difficult.

If by chance overchoking has occurred, switch off the ignition, open the throttle wide by depressing the accelerator pedal to its fullest extent, put the choke out of action and use the starter for five or six seconds to clear the system. Then switch on and start again.

Overchoking is the most frequent cause of difficulty in starting after a car has been laid up and provided the foregoing suggestions have been rigidly adhered to, the engine will fire at the first attempt. If the engine still refuses to start, test the ignition. A simple method is to disconnect one sparking plug, take it out, reconnect the lead and lay the plug on the cylinder-block. If the ignition system is in order, a fat spark should occur at the plug points when the engine is turned. If there is no spark, the most likely cause of the trouble will probably be found in the distributor. After being immobilized it is possible that the contact breaker arm as shown in Fig. 7 is sticking on its pivot pin; if this is found to be so, remove the arm, polish the pivot pin, if necessary using a strip of fine emery cloth, and apply a smear of light oil when replacing the arm.

Chromium Plating. Wipe off film of oil applied when the car was laid up and polish.

Door Fittings. Remove any excess of oil from latches so that clothes will not be soiled when entering or leaving the car.

Direction Indicators. Check their operation and if inclined to stick, lubricate the bearing at the base of the arm.

Before taking the car on the road, check the following:

Lighting. Switch on the various lamps and make sure that they are in working order and properly adjusted.

Number Plates. Check the attachment of the number plates to the vehicle to ensure that they are not loose. Also, note that the rear plate is illuminated.

Warning Device. Try the electric horn. After storage the press button sometimes sticks and requires easing. It is embarrassing to be caught out on the road with a hooter which won't be silenced.

Driving Licence and Insurance Policy. Make sure that your Driving Licence has not expired and that your Insurance Policy is in force. It is an offence to drive a car without third party cover.

Finally, take the car for a preliminary run of a few miles, and try out the brakes and steering. At the same time verify that the instruments in the dashboard panel are functioning correctly, particularly the oil pressure gauge.

INDEX

Figures in italics refer to illustrations

ACKNOWLEDGEMENTS

The publishers wish to thank the following for their co-operation and permission to make use of copyright drawings, photographs, and other material: A.C.-Sphinx Spark Plug Co.; Alvis, Ltd.; Andre (Components), Ltd.; Armstrong Siddeley Motors, Ltd.; The Austin Motor Co., Ltd.; Automotive Products Co., Ltd.; E. P. Barrus, Ltd.; Bentley Motors (1931), Ltd.; Black & Decker, Ltd.; Borg & Beck Co., Ltd.; Champion Sparking Plug Co., Ltd.; Citroen Cars, Ltd.; The Daimler Co., Ltd.; Delaney Gallay, Ltd.; Dunlop Rubber Co., Ltd.; Ford Motor Co., Ltd.; Girling, Ltd.; Hardy Spicer & Co., Ltd.; H. M. Hobson, Ltd.; Humber, Ltd.; Jaguar Cars, Ltd.; Jowett Cars, Ltd.; Lagonda, Ltd.; Lanchester Motor Co., Ltd.; Lockheed Brake Co., Ltd.; Joseph Lucas, Ltd.; The M.G. Car Company, Ltd.; Morgan Motor Co., Ltd.; Morris Motors, Ltd.; Riley (Coventry), Ltd.; Rolls-Royce, Ltd.; The Rover Co., Ltd.; Self-Changing Gear Co., Ltd.; Shell-Mex and B.P., Ltd.; Simms Motor Units, Ltd.; Solex, Ltd.; The Standard Motor Co., Ltd.; The S.U. Carburettor Co., Ltd.; Tecalemit, Ltd.; Triumph Motor Co. (1945), Ltd.; Vauxhall Motors, Ltd.; C. C. Wakefield & Co., Ltd.; Wolseley Motors, Ltd.; The Zenith Carburettor Co., Ltd.